NEUTRINOS
IN PHYSICS AND
ASTROPHYSICS

Recommended Titles in Related Topics

Massive Neutrinos in Physics and Astrophysics
Third Edition
by Rabindra N Mohapatra and Palash B Pal
ISBN: 978-981-238-070-8
ISBN: 978-981-238-071-5 (pbk)

Chasing the Ghost: Nobelist Fred Reines and the Neutrino
by Leonard A Cole
ISBN: 978-981-126-093-3

NEUTRINOS
IN PHYSICS AND
ASTROPHYSICS

Esteban Roulet
CONICET, Argentina

Francesco Vissani
INFN, Italy

NEW JERSEY · LONDON · SINGAPORE · BEIJING · SHANGHAI · HONG KONG · TAIPEI · CHENNAI · TOKYO

Published by

World Scientific Publishing Co. Pte. Ltd.
5 Toh Tuck Link, Singapore 596224
USA office: 27 Warren Street, Suite 401-402, Hackensack, NJ 07601
UK office: 57 Shelton Street, Covent Garden, London WC2H 9HE

Library of Congress Control Number: 2022946217

British Library Cataloguing-in-Publication Data
A catalogue record for this book is available from the British Library.

NEUTRINOS IN PHYSICS AND ASTROPHYSICS

ISBN 978-981-126-093-3 (hardcover)
ISBN 978-981-126-094-0 (ebook for institutions)
ISBN 978-981-126-095-7 (ebook for individuals)

For any available supplementary material, please visit
https://www.worldscientific.com/worldscibooks/10.1142/12982#t=suppl

Typeset by Stallion Press
Email: enquiries@stallionpress.com

To our families

Preface

This book aims to be a pedagogical approach to the field of neutrino physics and astrophysics. It should be useful to both graduate students and researchers in the field, and it may as well be useful as material for a course about the topics covered. It has indeed evolved from several lectures and courses that we gave at Universities and research institutions over the years, as well as from the review articles we have written in the past on these subjects.

The neutrino research is in continuous progress and covers a very broad range of topics. We have tried to discuss those that are well established and to describe also the main developments which are expected in the near future in the different areas at the frontier of the field. Besides describing the main laboratory studies of neutrinos from reactors and accelerators, which allowed to learn about neutrino interactions and oscillations, as well as the direct searches of neutrino masses using beta (and double-beta) decays of radioactive nuclei, we gave special emphasis to the natural sources of neutrinos in the cosmos. In particular, we considered the geoneutrinos from the radioactivity of the Earth, those from fusion reactions in the Sun, those from supernova explosions as well as those produced by cosmic rays when they interact in our atmosphere or with gas or photon targets they traverse in their sources or during their propagation. The high-energy astrophysical neutrinos have been detected in recent years and they have opened a new window to observe the Universe, which has strong connections with cosmic ray and gamma ray astronomies. We have also briefly considered the neutrino background left over from the hot early Universe and its impact on big bang nucleosynthesis and on the large scale structure formation. Finally, we discussed the basics of baryogenesis through leptogenesis, which provides a very attractive connection between the neutrinos and the origin of the observed matter-antimatter asymmetry of the Universe.

We have included at the end of the different chapters a few recommended readings as a guidance to some of the many books and specialised review articles that could be useful to deepen the study of the different topics. We have in general made reference in the text to the more historical works as well as to the articles more directly related with the exposition followed but, given the huge amount of works written on the subjects covered, which can be counted by the thousands, we have not been able to be exhaustive in the citations included. We hence apologize in advance for the possible omissions of relevant works. We have also included at the end of the chapters a few suggested exercises that may be useful to follow some of the derivations of the expressions discussed in the text and also to consolidate the knowledge gained about the topics discussed.

We want to thank our many collaborators, students and colleagues which helped us to learn and develop the field, including G. Battistoni, J. Candia, L. Covi, A. Capone, E. Cappellaro, S.R. Dugad, A. Esmaili, W. Fulgione, A. Gallo Rosso, G. Gelmini, G. Giudice, P. Gondolo, A. Ianni, P. Lipari, C. Mascaretti, S. Mollerach, E. Nardi, Y. Nir, A. Palladino, J. Racker, C. Righi, N. Rius, K. Rozwadowska, G. Sigl, A.Yu. Smirnov, M. Spurio, O. Straniero, A. Strumia, F. Tavecchio, D. Tommasini, D. Vescovi, C. Volpe and V. Zema.

Esteban Roulet and Francesco Vissani, April 2022

Acknowledgments

We are grateful to the institutions that financed our research. In particular E.R. thanks CONICET (Consejo Nacional de Investigaciones Científicas y Tecnológicas) for the grants PIP 015-0369 and PIP 2021-0565 and AN-PCyT (Agencia Nacional de Promoción Científica y Tecnológica) for the grant PICT 2016-0660. F.V. is grateful to INFN (Istituto Nazionale per la Fisica Nucleare) and LNGS (Laboratori Nazionali del Gran Sasso); and is thankful to MIUR (Ministero dell'Istruzione, dellUniversità e della Ricerca) for the support grant 017W4HA7S "NAT-NET: Neutrino and Astroparticle Theory Network", PRIN 2017.

We are also very grateful to the Editors of World-Scientific for their enormous patience with this project, which took several years more than initially foreseen.

Contents

Chapter 1

The Neutrino Story

1.1 The hypothetical particle

One may trace back the appearance of neutrinos in physics to the discovery of radioactivity by Becquerel in 1896. When the energy of the electrons (beta rays) emitted in a radioactive decay was measured by Chadwick in 1914, it turned out to his surprise to be continuously distributed. This was not to be expected if the underlying process in the beta decay was the transmutation of an element X into another one X' with the emission of an electron, i.e. $X \to X' + e$, since in that case the electron should be monochromatic. The situation was so puzzling that Bohr even suggested that the conservation of energy may not hold in the weak decays. Another serious problem with the nuclear models of the time was the belief that nuclei consisted of protons and electrons, the only known particles by then. To explain the mass and the charge of a nucleus with mass number A and atomic number Z it was then necessary that it had A protons and $A - Z$ electrons in it. For instance, a ^{4}He nucleus would have 4 protons and 2 electrons. Notice that having a total of six fermions the ^{4}He nucleus should be a boson, which is correct. However, a problem arose when this theory was applied for instance to ^{14}N, since if it were to consist of 14 protons and 7 electrons it should be a fermion, but the measured angular momentum of the nitrogen nucleus was $I = 1$.

The solution to these two puzzles was suggested by Pauli only in 1930, in a famous letter addressed to the *Radioactive Ladies and Gentlemen* gathered in a meeting in Tübingen, where he wrote: *I have hit upon a desperate remedy to save the exchange theorem of statistics and the law of conservation of energy. Namely, the possibility that there could exist in nuclei electrically neutral particles, that I wish to call neutrons, which have spin*

1/2 .... These particles had to be not heavier than electrons and should interact not more strongly than the gamma rays.

With this new paradigm, the nitrogen nucleus became $^{14}\text{N} = 14p + 7e + 7'n'$, which is a boson, and a beta decay now involved the emission of two particles through the process $X \rightarrow X' + e + 'n'$, in which case the electron spectrum turns out indeed to be continuous. Note that no particles were created in a weak decay, both the electron and Pauli's neutron 'n' were believed to be already present in the nucleus of the element X, and they just came out from it in the decay. However, in 1932 Chadwick discovered the particle referred today as neutron, having a mass similar to that of the proton and being the missing building block of nuclei. In this new context a nitrogen nucleus finally became just $^{14}\text{N} = 7p + 7n$, which also had the correct bosonic statistics.

In order to account now for the beta spectrum of weak decays, Fermi re-named Pauli's hypothesized particle as the neutrino (small neutron), which is denoted with the greek letter ν. He furthermore suggested that the fundamental process underlying beta decay was $n \rightarrow p + e + \bar{\nu}$, so that the e and the ν are created in the decay, rather than being already present in the nucleus. He wrote [Fe34] the basic interaction among these four fermions by analogy with the interaction known at the time, i.e. the QED, as a product of two vector currents ($V \times V$), with a Hamiltonian density

$$\mathcal{H}_{\text{F}} = G_{\text{F}} \left[\overline{\Psi}_p \gamma_\mu \Psi_n \right] \left[\overline{\Psi}_e \gamma^\mu \Psi_\nu \right] + \text{h.c.} \qquad (1.1)$$

Note that each of the currents involves fermions with different charges, and hence they are called charged currents (CC). This interaction accounted for the continuous beta spectrum and, moreover, from the measured shape at the endpoint Fermi concluded that m_ν was consistent with zero and it had to be small. The Fermi coupling G_{F} was then determined to be $G_{\text{F}} \simeq 10^{-5}\,\text{GeV}^{-2}$ from the observed lifetimes of radioactive elements. Bethe and Peierls [Be34] estimated the cross section for the inverse beta process $\bar{\nu} + p \rightarrow n + e^+$, which was the relevant reaction to attempt the direct detection of a neutrino, and the value obtained was so tiny that they wrote that ... *one can conclude that there is no practically possible way of observing the neutrino.* Indeed, the actual value for this cross section is $\sigma \simeq 4(G_{\text{F}}^2/\pi)p_e E_e \simeq 2.3 \times 10^{-44}(p_e E_e/m_e^2)\,\text{cm}^2$, and if one computes the mean-free path in water (with a hydrogen density $n \simeq 10^{23}\,\text{cm}^{-3}$) of a neutrino with energy $E_\nu = 2.5\,\text{MeV}$, typical of a weak decay, the result is $\lambda \equiv (n\sigma)^{-1} \simeq 10^{20}$ cm, which is eleven orders of magnitude bigger than the diameter of the Earth, and comparable to the thickness of the Galactic disk.

It was only in 1956 that Reines and Cowan were able to prove that Bethe and Peierls had been too pessimistic, by measuring for the first time the interaction of a neutrino through the inverse beta process [Co56]. Their strategy was essentially that, given that 10^{20} cm of water are required for a neutrino to have a significant chance to interact, just one cm should be enough to observe the interaction of one neutrino provided that 10^{20} neutrinos were available. The feasibility of achieving such high neutrino fluxes became possible after the second World War, when powerful reactors started to become operational. Indeed, taking into account that in every fission of an uranium nucleus the neutron-rich fragments beta decay producing typically 6 $\bar{\nu}$ and liberating ~ 200 MeV, it is easy to show that the (isotropic) neutrino flux at a reactor is[1]

$$\frac{\mathrm{d}\Phi_\nu}{\mathrm{d}\Omega} \simeq \frac{2 \times 10^{20}}{4\pi} \left(\frac{\text{Power}}{\text{GWatt}} \right) \frac{\bar{\nu}}{\text{s sr}}. \qquad (1.2)$$

Hence, placing near the Savannah-River reactor a few hundred liters of water with some cadmium in it, sandwiched between liquid scintillator detectors viewed with photo-multiplier tubes, they were able to see the production of positrons (through the observation of the two γ rays produced in their annihilation with electrons) and neutrons (through the few delayed γ rays from the neutron capture in Cd, totaling an energy of about 9 MeV). The observed rate turned out to be consistent with the expectations from the weak interactions of the neutrinos.

One should mention that Ray Davis had attempted some years before to detect reactor neutrinos using the process

$$\nu + {}^{37}\text{Cl} \rightarrow {}^{37}\text{Ar} + e, \qquad (1.3)$$

which had been suggested by Pontecorvo [Po46]. He first built a 4 tonne detector of $C\,Cl_4$ and exposed it to the neutrino flux from the Brookhaven reactor [Da55]. The main difficulty was to extract the produced Ar atoms and count them by observing the 2.8 keV Auger electrons emitted, with a lifetime of 35 d, when an electron capture took place. The negative results of this pioneering search is now easy to understand because reactors produce antineutrinos, which cannot induce the reaction in Eq. (1.3), rather than neutrinos, but this distinction was not completely clear at the time.[2]

---

[1] Note that 1 TeV = 1.602 erg. Throughout this book we generally use natural units, with $\hbar = c = 1$. A useful relation to convert them is that 197 MeV = fm^{-1}, which relates the QCD scale ($\Lambda_{\text{QCD}} \simeq 200$ MeV) to the inverse of the proton size (1 fm = 10^{-15} m).

[2] An interesting outcome of this experiment was that, prompted by an initial rumor of a positive detection, and probably inspired by the recent observation of $K_0 \bar{K}_0$ oscillations, Pontecorvo was led to suggest the possibility of neutrino–antineutrino oscillations [Po57].

A byproduct of this experiment was that it allowed to set an upper bound on the flux of neutrinos produced in the Sun. The existence of this neutrino flux had been predicted when it was understood that the solar energy source was the fusion of four protons to produce ^{4}He. In this process also two neutrinos and two positrons get produced (or electrons get absorbed). With the aim of positively measuring this solar neutrino flux, Davis then constructed a much bigger chlorine detector (615 tonne of the less toxic $C_2 Cl_4$) that was run for almost thirty years deep underground at the Homestake mine in South Dakota. The results of this experiment were fundamental in establishing the presence of a deficit of solar neutrinos, a fact that became known as the solar neutrino problem.

1.2   The vampire

Going back in time again to follow the evolution of the theory of the weak interactions of neutrinos, in 1936 Gamow and Teller [Ga36] noted that the $V \times V$ Hamiltonian of Fermi was probably too restrictive, and they suggested the generalization

$$\mathcal{H}_{GT} = \sum_i G_i[\bar{\Psi}_p O_i \Psi_n][\bar{\Psi}_e O^i \Psi_\nu] + \text{h.c.}, \qquad (1.4)$$

involving the operators $O_i = 1$, γ_μ, $\gamma_\mu\gamma_5$, γ_5, $\sigma_{\mu\nu}$, that correspond respectively to scalar (S), vector (V), axial vector (A), pseudoscalar (P) and tensor (T) currents. Note that since A and P only appeared here as $A \times A$ or $P \times P$, the interaction was still parity conserving. The situation became unpleasant since there were now five different coupling constants G_i to fit with experiments. This step was however required because some observed nuclear decays involving the so-called Gamow-Teller transitions, in which the nuclear spin changes, were not allowed in the $V \times V$ Fermi theory but turned out to be allowed with the proposed generalization.

The story became more involved when, in 1956, Lee and Yang suggested that parity could be violated in weak interactions [Le56]. This could explain why the particles named theta and tau had exactly the same mass, charge and lifetime, but differed only in that the first one was decaying to two pions while the second one to three pions (which are states having different parity). The explanation of the puzzle was that the Θ and τ were just the same particle, now known as the charged kaon, but that the weak interaction leading to its decay violated parity.

Parity violation was confirmed the same year by Wu and collaborators [Wu57], studying the direction of emission of the electrons produced in the beta decay of polarized ^{60}Co. The decay rate of this process is proportional to $1 + \alpha \cos\theta$, where θ is the angle between the Co polarization vector $\vec{P}$, which is an axial vector, and the electron momentum $\vec{p}_e$, which is a vector. Since $\cos\theta \equiv \hat{P} \cdot \hat{p}_e$ is a pseudoscalar quantity, the measurement of a non–vanishing coefficient α would be a clear signature of parity violation. The measured value was $\alpha \simeq -0.4$, reflecting the fact that the electrons are preferentially emitted in the direction opposite to $\vec{P}$. Note that if one were to look to this experiment in a mirror, the direction of the Co polarization vector would be reversed and, as a consequence, the electrons would be instead seen as being emitted preferentially along the direction of $\vec{P}$. This indicates that the reflected image behaves differently from the real world or, in other words, the parity symmetry has to be violated in weak interactions. Besides the asymmetry in polarized nuclear decays, another evidence for parity violation was obtained soon afterwards, by Garwin, Lederman and Weinrich [Ga57] and by Friedman and Telegdi [Fr57], from the asymmetry of the electron emission in polarized muon decays. All these findings turned out to have very profound implications for the physics of the weak interactions.

The generalization proposed by Lee and Yang of the Gamow-Teller Hamiltonian was

$$\mathcal{H}_{LY} = \sum_i [\bar{\Psi}_p O_i \Psi_n][\bar{\Psi}_e O^i (G_i + G'_i \gamma_5)\Psi_\nu] + \text{h.c.} \tag{1.5}$$

Here the presence of terms such as $V \times A$ or $P \times S$ allows for parity violation. The situation became hence even more unpleasant, because there were in this case 10 couplings to determine, G_i and G'_i, so that some new simplifying principle was really called for.

It was soon realized by Lee and Yang [Le57], Landau [La57] and Salam [Sa57] that there could be a simple reason explaining why parity was violated in weak interactions, but not in the electromagnetic or strong interactions. Since the weak interaction is the only one involving neutrinos, the explanation could ultimately be related to the intrinsic nature of these neutral particles. They noticed that if the neutrinos happened to be massless, there was actually no need to have both left and right neutrino chirality states in the theory. The existence of just a unique handedness of the neutrino could then be the reason behind the observed parity violation.

To see this, consider the chiral projections of a fermion

$$\Psi_{L,R} \equiv \frac{1 \mp \gamma_5}{2}\Psi. \tag{1.6}$$

We note that in the relativistic limit the two chiral projections describe left-handed (negative) and right-handed (positive) helicity states, where the helicity is the spin projection in the direction of motion, which is a conserved quantity for a free particle. For massive particles, an helicity eigenstate is in general a mixture of the two chiralities. For instance, the probability that a left-handed helicity state be into a left-chiral state is just $(1 + v/c)/2$, while that to be into a right-chiral state is $(1 - v/c)/2)$, with v/c the particle velocity normalized to the speed of light. Moreover, since massive particles move with a velocity smaller than the speed of light, it is always possible to make a boost to a system moving faster than the particle. In this new reference frame the helicity would be reversed, and hence we see that the helicity is clearly not a Lorentz invariant. On the other hand, the currents connecting different chiral states are Lorentz covariant quantities, what makes them suitable building blocks to write down the interactions between particles, as is indeed exploited in the electroweak theory.

Let us then consider the equation of motion for a free Dirac fermion of mass m, like the one used to describe charged massive particles such as the electrons. This equation is

$$(i\slashed{\partial} - m)\Psi = 0, \tag{1.7}$$

where $\slashed{\partial} \equiv \gamma^\mu \partial_\mu$, with a sum being understood over the repeated indices. In terms of the chiral projections, the Dirac equation can be decomposed as

$$i\slashed{\partial}\Psi_\mathsf{L} = m\Psi_\mathsf{R}$$
$$i\slashed{\partial}\Psi_\mathsf{R} = m\Psi_\mathsf{L}. \tag{1.8}$$

It is clear then that a mass term has the effect of mixing the two chiralities. On the other hand, we see that for $m = 0$, as could have been the case for the neutrinos if they were massless, the two equations above would actually be decoupled from each other. This means that one can write a consistent theory for massless fermions using only one of the two chiralities (which moreover would coincide in this case with the helicity). It is interesting to note that, back in 1929, Weyl had written a wave equation equivalent to that for massless fermions that would presumably apply to the neutrinos. His equation was however considered at that time of little interest compared to Dirac's one, which was useful for atomic physics studies.

If the Lee-Yang Hamiltonian were just to depend on a single neutrino chirality, one would have then $G_i = \pm G_i'$ and the parity violation would indeed be maximal. This situation has been described by saying that neutrinos are like vampires in Dracula's stories, because if they were to look to themselves into a mirror they would just see nothing, because their parity reflected images are absent in the theory.

The actual helicity of the neutrino emitted in a radioactive decay was measured by Goldhaber et al. [Go58]. The experiment consisted in observing the K-electron capture in

$$^{152}\text{Eu}(J = 0) \rightarrow^{152} \text{Sm}^*(J = 1) + \nu. \tag{1.9}$$

The excited samarium nucleus then decayed into ^{152}Sm ($J = 0$)$+\gamma$, and the measurement of the circular polarization of the photon gave the required information on the helicity of the neutrino emitted initially. The conclusion reached in this work was summarized in the sentence: ...*Our results seem compatible with ... 100% negative helicity for the neutrinos.* This meant that the neutrinos should be left-handed particles (and the antineutrinos should be right-handed particles).

This paved the road for the $V - A$ theory of weak interactions advanced by Feynman and Gell-Mann [Fe58], and Sudarshan and Marshak [Su58], which stated that weak interactions just involve vector and axial vector currents, essentially in the combination $V - A$ which allows only the coupling to left-handed fields (note that $V - A = \overline{\Psi}\gamma_\mu\Psi - \overline{\Psi}\gamma_\mu\gamma_5\Psi = 2\overline{\Psi}_\mathsf{L}\gamma_\mu\Psi_\mathsf{L}$). The Hamiltonian associated to the $V - A$ theory responsible for beta decays is

$$\mathcal{H} = \frac{G_\mathrm{F}}{\sqrt{2}} J_\mu^\dagger J^\mu, \tag{1.10}$$

where the weak current describing the interaction of leptons and nucleons is

$$J_\mu = \bar{e}\gamma_\mu(1 - \gamma_5)\nu + \cos\theta_\mathrm{C}\bar{n}\gamma_\mu(g_V - g_A\gamma_5)p, \tag{1.11}$$

where for simplicity we have denoted the different spinors fields just with the symbols of the corresponding particles, such as $\Psi_e = e$, $\Psi_p = p$, etc. The current between the leptons in Eq. (1.11) only involves the left-handed fields. On the other hand, the current between the nucleons is actually not exactly proportional to $\gamma_\mu(1 - \gamma_5)$, only the interaction at the quark level turns out to have this form, but it instead involves $\gamma_\mu(g_V - g_A\gamma_5)$.

The vector coupling in this current remains however equal to unity, $g_V = 1$, not being renormalized by the strong interactions thanks to the so-called conserved vector current hypothesis (CVC). To formulate the CVC hypothesis one should consider the strong isospin space in which the proton and the neutron form a doublet, $\Psi = (p, n)^\mathsf{T}$. This space was introduced by Heisenberg to exploit the fact that the strong interactions are very similar for protons and neutrons, and hence they should be essentially invariant under $SU(2)$ rotations in the strong isospin space. The vector currents between the isospin doublet states include both the electromagnetic current, $J_\mu^{em} \propto e\bar{\Psi}\gamma_\mu(1 + \sigma_3)\Psi$, and the vector part of the weak hadronic charged currents, $J_\mu^\pm \propto g_V \bar{\Psi}\gamma_\mu\sigma^\pm\Psi$, where the raising and lowering operators in the isospin space are $\sigma^\pm \equiv (\sigma_1 \pm i\sigma_2)/2$, in terms of the Pauli matrices

$$\sigma_1 = \begin{pmatrix} 0 & 1 \\ 1 & 0 \end{pmatrix} \quad , \quad \sigma_2 = \begin{pmatrix} 0 & -i \\ i & 0 \end{pmatrix} \quad , \quad \sigma_3 = \begin{pmatrix} 1 & 0 \\ 0 & -1 \end{pmatrix}. \tag{1.12}$$

The CVC hypothesis combines the isospin invariance of the strong interactions with the conservation of the electromagnetic current to state that the vector part of the weak current, together with the isovector part of the electromagnetic current (i.e. the term proportional to σ_3 in J_μ^{em}), actually constitute an isospin triplet of conserved currents ($J_\mu^i \propto \bar{\Psi}\gamma_\mu\sigma^i\Psi$). Hence, the conservation of the triplet of vector currents guarantees that the associated charges, g_V and e, remain unaffected by strong interactions. This enforces the relation $g_V = 1$ to remain valid, in the same way as the charge e is not affected by strong interactions.

On the other hand, the axial vector hadronic current is not protected from strong-interaction renormalization effects and, as a consequence, g_A does not remain equal to unity. The value of g_A can be inferred for instance from the observed lifetime of the neutron, and it is $g_A \simeq 1.27$. This implies that at the nucleonic level the charged-current weak interactions are actually '$V - 1.27A$'.

The expression in Eq. (1.11) also accounts for the fact that the strength of the coupling in the neutron decay is $G_F \cos\theta_C$, with θ_C being the Cabibbo angle [Ca64]. To understand this reduction of the coupling strength in the neutron to proton transition, it is actually useful to consider the CC interaction at the level of quarks, which within each flavor generation involves a coupling with the lepton current with the full strength G_F. Note that, by the very same definition of weak eigenstates, the charged current couples directly the (left-handed) weak quark eigenstates of the same generation, i.e. they couple u to d (i.e. up quarks with down quarks for the first generation), s to c (strange quarks to charm quarks for the second generation) or b to t (bottom quarks to top quarks for the third generation). However, the charged currents are not diagonal between mass eigenstates, hereafter denoted with a prime, which are the states that actually constitute the different mesons and baryons. Ignoring the much heavier third quark family and choosing the flavor basis such that the up-type quark flavor and mass eigenstates coincide, the down-type quark weak flavor eigenstates (d, s) are related to the mass eigenstates (d', s') by a rotation involving the Cabibbo angle θ_C. The unitary rotation between these states is $d = \cos\theta_C d' + \sin\theta_C s'$ and $s = -\sin\theta_C d' + \cos\theta_C s'$. In particular, for strangeness conserving processes involving a d' to u' transition, such as in the neutron decay, the strength of the coupling is then $G_F \cos\theta_C$. For strangeness changing weak processes involving instead an s' to u' transition, such as in the kaon or hyperon decays, the strength of the coupling is $G_F \sin\theta_C$. The comparison of the rates of these different types of processes leads to a measured value $\sin\theta_C \simeq 0.23$, corresponding to $\theta_C \simeq 13°$ (see Chapter 3 for more details). One can also conclude from this discussion that in order to obtain a clean measurement of the Fermi coupling it is convenient to avoid the uncertainties related to the hadronic physics, obtaining G_F directly from the rate of the muon decay, $\mu \to e\bar{\nu}_e\nu_\mu$, which is a purely leptonic process.

A curious fact was that the new $V - A$ theory predicted a cross section for the inverse beta decay that was a factor of two larger than the result obtained initially considering the case of a four component neutrino, which had already been found to be within 5% of the central value obtained in 1956 by Reines and Cowan (with an uncertainty of about 25%). However, with an improved experiment they found in 1958 a more precise value for this cross section, that was well consistent with the new prediction [Re59].

Note that the interaction in Eq. (1.10) accounts for the β^- decays $(A, Z) \to (A, Z + 1) + e^- + \bar{\nu}_e$ of neutron rich isotopes, as well as for the β^+ decays $(A, Z) \to (A, Z - 1) + e^+ + \nu_e$ or the electron capture (EC) processes $(A, Z) + e \to (A, Z - 1) + \nu_e$ in proton rich isotopes. It also accounts for low-energy weak scattering processes, and in particular it predicted the existence of the purely leptonic weak charged currents $\nu + e \to \nu + e$, to be experimentally observed only much later. Note that the idea that there is some sort of correspondence between hadrons and leptons was a principle that guided the construction of the theory of weak interactions since Fermi's time, and still maintains heuristic value.

Let us remark that with the present understanding of weak interactions, we know now that the clever idea proposed to explain parity violation as due to the non-existence of the right-handed neutrino chirality was completely wrong, although it led to major advances in the theory and ultimately to finding the correct interaction. As we understand today, the parity violation is not a consequence of the absence of right-handed fields but is instead due to the fact that the W boson responsible for the gauge interaction only couples to the left-handed fields. For instance, in the quark sector both left and right chiralities exist, but parity is violated because the right-handed fields, being singlets for the weak charged currents, do not couple to the W boson. The question of whether right-handed neutrinos exist or not will be discussed later on.

1.3 The trilogy

In 1937 the muon was discovered in cosmic rays by Neddermeyer and Anderson [Ne37]. It then became apparent [Co47] that it had no strong interactions and hence, contrary to the initial guesses, it could not be the meson introduced by Yukawa as a mediator of the nuclear forces [Yu35]. It was suggested by Pontecorvo [Po47] that the muon was just a heavier copy of the electron and that it participated in weak processes with the same universal strength G_F (see also [Ti49]). This hypothesis should then lead to processes such as $\mu + p \rightarrow n + \nu$ with a computable rate. By studying the spectrum of the electrons emitted in muon decays, Steinberger [St49] showed that the muon was decaying into three particles, $\mu \rightarrow e + \nu + \nu$. It was however not clear whether the two neutrinos emitted in the muon decay were similar or not. In an interesting work, Feinberg [Fe58b] found that assuming that the neutrinos were indeed similar, one should conclude that the weak interactions could not be mediated by gauge bosons. His reasoning was that if the two neutrinos were indeed of the same kind, it should be possible to join the line of the neutrino produced in the emission of the intermediate boson with that of the neutrino associated to the reabsorption of the boson and, attaching a photon to the exchanged virtual charged gauge boson (W) or to the external charged lepton legs, one would generate a diagram for the radiative decay $\mu \rightarrow e + \gamma$. The resulting branching ratio for this decay would turn out to be larger than 10^{-5}, a value that was already excluded at that time. This was probably the first use of rare decays to constrain the properties of new particles.

The correct explanation for the absence of the radiative decay $\mu \rightarrow e + \gamma$ was put forward by Lee and Yang [Le60], who suggested that the two neutrinos emitted in the muon decay had actually different flavors, such that $\mu \rightarrow e + \bar{\nu}_e + \nu_\mu$. The postulated conservation of the respective leptonic flavors made then impossible to join the two neutrino lines to draw the radiative decay diagram.

The two neutrino hypothesis was later confirmed at Brookhaven, in the first accelerator neutrino experiment [Da62]. The accelerator neutrino beams were obtained from the decays of negatively charged pions, that give rise to an almost pure $\bar{\nu}_\mu$ beam. This can be understood because[3] $\Gamma(\pi^- \to \ell + \bar{\nu}_\ell) \propto m_\ell^2$, so that the decay $\pi \to e + \bar{\nu}_e$ is strongly suppressed with respect to the $\pi \to \mu + \bar{\nu}_\mu$ one by the factor $(m_e/m_\mu)^2 \simeq (1/200)^2$. Putting a detector in front of this antineutrino beam they were able to observe the process $\bar{\nu} + p \to n + \mu^+$, but no production of positrons resulted. This proved that the neutrinos produced in a weak decay in association with a muon are not the same as those produced in a beta decay in association with an electron. Note that although the neutrino fluxes are much smaller at accelerators than at reactors, their higher energies make their detection feasible due to the increase of the cross sections with energy. In particular, one expects that $\sigma(\nu N) \propto E_\nu^2$ for $E_\nu \ll m_p$ and that $\sigma(\nu N) \propto E_\nu$ for $E_\nu \gtrsim m_p$. Moreover, accelerator neutrinos are beamed towards the detector while those from reactors get emitted isotropically.

The third charged lepton, the tau, was discovered in 1975 by Perl and collaborators at SLAC [Pe77]. Being just a heavier copy of the electron and the muon, it was concluded that also a third neutrino flavor had to exist. The direct detection of the tau neutrino was achieved in 2000 by the DONUT experiment at Fermilab [Ko08]. This experiment looked for the short τ tracks produced by the interaction of a ν_τ, emitted in the decay of a D_s meson containing a charm and strange quark-antiquark pair, that was produced in a beam dump. As discussed further below, we know today that the number of light weakly interacting neutrinos is precisely three, so that the proliferation of neutrino species seems to be now under control.

1.4 The gauge theory

As was already mentioned, the short-range charged-current weak interaction is actually due to the exchange of a heavy charged vector boson, the $W^\pm$. The associated CC gauge interaction is described by the Lagrangian

$$\mathcal{L} = -g J_\mu^+ W^{+\mu} + \text{h.c.}, \tag{1.13}$$

where for instance the leptonic part of the weak current is $J_\mu^+ = (\bar{\nu}_L \gamma_\mu e_L)/\sqrt{2}$. At small momentum transfers the W boson exchange between two leptonic currents looks like the non-renormalizable four fermion interaction of the $V - A$ theory discussed before (see Fig. 1.1). Indeed, in

---

[3]The proportionality of the amplitude of $\pi^- \to \ell + \bar{\nu}_\ell$ to the lepton mass m_ℓ arises because, to preserve the angular momentum in the decay of the spin zero pion, it is required that the outgoing charged lepton of left-handed chirality be in a right-handed helicity state, what is achieved through a chirality flip involving the lepton mass m_ℓ.

Fig. 1.1   Low-energy limit of the W exchange diagram as an effective four fermion interaction.

the low-energy limit one has for the amplitude of the associated diagram

$$\left(\frac{ig}{\sqrt{2}}\bar{e}\gamma^\mu P_L \nu\right)\frac{ig_{\mu\rho}}{M_W^2}\left(\frac{ig}{\sqrt{2}}\bar{\nu}\gamma^\rho P_L e\right) \simeq -i\frac{g^2}{8M_W^2}\bar{e}\gamma^\mu(1-\gamma_5)\nu\,\bar{\nu}\gamma_\mu(1-\gamma_5)e. \tag{1.14}$$

This corresponds to the matrix element of the effective Hamiltonian density $-i\mathcal{H}$. One can hence identify the Fermi coupling as

$$G_F = \frac{\sqrt{2}g^2}{8M_W^2}. \tag{1.15}$$

Note that this relation will actually also receive some small corrections at higher order in perturbation theory.

In the sixties, Glashow [Gl61], Salam [Sa68] and Weinberg [We67] showed that it was possible to write down a unified description of electromagnetic and weak interactions. This is achieved considering a gauge theory based on the group $SU(2)_L \times U(1)_Y$, corresponding to the weak isospin $\times$ hypercharge symmetries. The resulting model, which became known as the Standard Model of electroweak interactions, involves the three gauge bosons V_i^μ (with $i = 1, 2, 3$) in the adjoint of $SU(2)$, and the hypercharge gauge field B^μ. The starting Lagrangian for the coupling of the gauge bosons with the fermionic currents is

$$\mathcal{L} = -g\sum_{i=1}^{3} J_\mu^i V_i^\mu - g' J_\mu^Y B^\mu + \text{h.c.} \tag{1.16}$$

The $SU(2)_L$ current is $J_\mu^i \equiv \sum_a \bar{\Psi}_{aL}\gamma_\mu(\sigma_i/2)\Psi_{aL}$. The left-handed leptonic and quark isospin doublets are $\Psi = (\nu_{eL}, e_L)^\mathsf{T}$ and $(u_L, d_L)^\mathsf{T}$ for the first generation, and similar components are present for the other two heavier generations. The right-handed fields are instead $SU(2)_L$ singlets. The hypercharge current is obtained by summing over both left and right-handed fermion chiralities and is $J_\mu^Y \equiv \sum_a Y_a \bar{\Psi}_a \gamma_\mu \Psi_a$, with Y_a being the hypercharge of the field Ψ_a. Note that the upper components of the doublets, such as ν_L or u_L, have the third component of isospin $T_3 = 1/2$, while the lower ones, such as e_L or d_L, have $T_3 = -1/2$. The right-handed $SU(2)_L$ singlet fields have instead $T_3 = 0$, and they couple only to the hypercharge field B^μ.

The hypercharge turns out to be related to the electromagnetic charge and the weak isospin through $Y = q_{em} - T_3$. Hence, since for a given isospin multiplet the average T_3 vanishes, its hypercharge is just equal to the average charge in the multiplet. For instance, for the lepton doublet $L = (\nu_L, \ell_L)^T$ one has that $Y(L) = -1/2$, while for the quark doublet $Q = (u_L, d_L)^T$ on has that $Y(Q) = 1/6$. For the isospin singlet fields the hypercharge Y coincides with the electromagnetic charge q_{em}, so that $Y(e_R) = -1$, $Y(u_R) = 2/3$ and $Y(d_R) = -1/3$. The quantum numbers of the different fermions of the first generation are summarized in Table 1.1, with similar assignments holding also for the corresponding fermions of the other two generations.

Table 1.1   Electric charge q_{em} and hypercharge Y of the fermions of the first generation.

	ν_L	e_L	u_L	d_L	e_R	u_R	d_R
q_{em}	0	-1	$2/3$	$-1/3$	-1	$2/3$	$-1/3$
Y	$-1/2$	$-1/2$	$1/6$	$1/6$	-1	$2/3$	$-1/3$

The weak charged currents are given by $J_\mu^\pm = (\bar{\Psi}\gamma_\mu \sigma^\pm \Psi)/\sqrt{2}$. These charged currents couple to the W boson $W^{\pm\mu} = (V_1^\mu \mp iV_2^\mu)/\sqrt{2}$, and it is indeed easy to see that from Eq. (1.16) one can recover the term

$$\mathcal{L}_{CC} = -gJ_\mu^+ W^{+\mu} + \text{h.c.} \qquad (1.17)$$

This $SU(2)_L \times U(1)_Y$ symmetry has to be spontaneously broken at the weak scale down to the electromagnetic symmetry $U(1)_{em}$. The breaking of the electroweak symmetry is produced through the Higgs mechanism when the neutral component of the Higgs doublet acquires a vacuum expectation value. After the electroweak breaking, the two neutral vector bosons V_3^μ and B^μ will mix into the photon and Z boson fields through a rotation by the weak mixing angle θ_W,

$$\begin{pmatrix} A^\mu \\ Z^\mu \end{pmatrix} = \begin{pmatrix} \cos\theta_W & \sin\theta_W \\ -\sin\theta_W & \cos\theta_W \end{pmatrix} \begin{pmatrix} B^\mu \\ V_3^\mu \end{pmatrix}. \qquad (1.18)$$

In the broken theory, electromagnetism should remain unbroken, with the photon field A^μ remaining massless, what requires that $\tan\theta_W = g'/g$, with the identification of the electromagnetic charge as $q_{em} = T_3 + Y$ and with the electromagnetic coupling being $e = g \sin \theta_W$. The additional neutral vector boson Z^μ acquires a mass, which turns out to be related to the W boson mass through $M_W = M_Z \cos \theta_W$. The measured values of these masses are $M_W = 80.4\,\text{GeV}$ and $M_Z = 91.2\,\text{GeV}$, and actually their heaviness explains why the weak interactions mediated by them are so feeble (see Eq. (1.15)).

The electromagnetic and the weak neutral currents are given by

$$J_\mu^{em} = J_\mu^Y + J_\mu^3 \tag{1.19}$$

and

$$J_\mu^0 = J_\mu^3 - \sin^2 \theta_W J_\mu^{em}. \tag{1.20}$$

The neutral Z boson couples to the neutral currents (NC) through the term

$$\mathcal{L}_{\text{NC}} = -\frac{g}{\cos \theta_W} J_\mu^0 Z^\mu. \tag{1.21}$$

The validity of this model was proven in 1973 with the experimental observation of the predicted weak neutral currents. This was achieved by means of the elastic process $\nu_\mu + e \to \nu_\mu + e$, using muon neutrino beams at CERN and the Gargamelle bubble chamber detector [Ha73].

The neutrino neutral current interactions with nuclei, $\nu + N \to \nu + X$, were also studied, and the comparison of neutral and charged-current rates provided a measurement of the weak mixing angle, leading to $\sin^2 \theta_W \simeq 0.23$. From the formal side, 't Hooft and Veltman proved that the theory was renormalizable [tH72], and in this way the computation of electroweak radiative corrections became meaningful.

The most important test of the Standard Model came with the direct production of the $W^\pm$ and Z gauge bosons at the proton-antiproton collider at CERN in 1984, and with the precision measurements achieved after 1989 with the Z factories LEP (at CERN) and SLC (at Stanford). These e^+e^- colliders worked at squared center of mass energies $s \simeq M_Z^2$, i.e. around the Z resonance, and turned out to be also crucial for neutrino physics. Studying the shape of the $e^+ + e^- \to f + \bar{f}$ cross section near the resonance, which has the Breit–Wigner form

$$\sigma \simeq \frac{12\pi \Gamma_{Z \to e\bar{e}} \Gamma_{Z \to f\bar{f}}}{M_Z^2} \frac{s}{(s - M_Z^2)^2 + M_Z^2 \Gamma_Z^2}, \tag{1.22}$$

it becomes possible to determine the total Z width Γ_Z (see Fig. 1.2). Note that in particular the value of the cross section at the peak of the resonance,

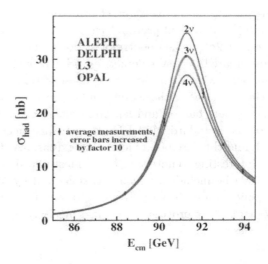

Fig. 1.2   Shape of the Z-resonance peak measured combining the results from the four detectors at LEP, and Standard Model predictions for different numbers of neutrino families (from [PDG]).

$\sigma^{\text{peak}} \propto \Gamma_Z^{-2}$, is quite sensitive to Γ_Z. This total width is just the sum of all possible partial widths, i.e.

$$\Gamma_Z = \sum_f \Gamma_{Z \to f\bar{f}} = \Gamma_{\text{vis}} + \Gamma_{\text{inv}}. \tag{1.23}$$

The visible width, Γ_{vis}, can be measured directly from the rate of production of charged leptons and quarks, and this allows to infer the value of the invisible width as $\Gamma_{\text{inv}} \equiv \Gamma_Z - \Gamma_{\text{vis}}$. Since in the Standard Model the invisible width arises from the decays $Z \to \nu_i + \bar{\nu}_i$, whose theoretically expected rate for decays into a given neutrino flavor is $\Gamma^{\text{th}}_{Z \to \nu\bar{\nu}} = 167\,\text{MeV}$, one can finally obtain the number of neutrino flavors coupling to the Z as $N_\nu = \Gamma_{\text{inv}}/\Gamma^{\text{th}}_{Z \to \nu\bar{\nu}}$. The present best value for this quantity is $N_\nu = 2.994 \pm 0.012$, what gives then a strong support to the Standard Model with three generations of light neutrinos coupled to the Z boson.

Let us add here a couple of remarks regarding the neutrino masses, which will be discussed at length in Chapter 3. The theory of Glashow, Salam and Weinberg predicts that neutrinos have no mass, but by now we have however experimental evidence that they are massive. Therefore, this theory cannot be complete. Another issue which arose in the early days of particle physics had to do with the fact that the conservation laws known at that time (energy, angular momentum, charge) did not forbid disintegrations such as $p \rightarrow e^+ + \pi^0$ (called proton decay) or the hypothetical process $(A, Z) \rightarrow (A, Z+2) + 2e^-$ (called neutrinoless double beta decay, in which two electrons are created). New symmetries, which involve the baryonic and leptonic numbers, with their associated conservation laws, were then postulated to keep the rates of these and similar processes under theoretical control. These global baryon and lepton numbers actually turn out to be symmetries of the Standard Model Lagrangian just accidentally (they are not imposed), and they are often violated in extensions of the Standard Model. It is also interesting to note that in the most plausible way in which neutrino masses can be included, which was suggested by Majorana back in 1937, the leptonic number is actually violated, and the rate for the neutrinoless double-beta decay process is governed precisely by the magnitude of the neutrino masses.

1.5   Neutrinos in astrophysics and cosmology

As we have seen, neutrinos made their shy appearance in physics by just taking away part of the energy in the radioactive decays of nuclei. It later became feasible to artificially produce neutrinos in reactors and accelerators and, in this way, their experimental study was possible. But neutrinos are actually overwhelmingly present in the Universe, and this book will mostly focus on the study of the different natural sources of neutrinos.

There are neutrinos with energies below few MeV that are produced by the radioactivity of the nuclei present inside the Earth. The overall power associated to these geoneutrinos, which is of the order of tens of Terawatts, is actually comparable to the total human power consumption.

The interactions of the cosmic-ray nuclei with the air nuclei at the top of the atmosphere produce pions and heavier hadrons that eventually decay, producing neutrinos. These atmospheric neutrinos have a spectrum that peaks at GeV energies and then falls steeply, reaching up to beyond PeV energies.[4] Their integrated flux at the surface of the Earth is about $1 \, \mathrm{cm}^{-2} \, \mathrm{s}^{-1} \, \mathrm{sr}^{-1}$.

The Sun, which gets its power from nuclear fusion reactions, emits about 3% of its energy in neutrinos, with the total flux reaching the Earth being about $6 \times 10^{10} \, \mathrm{cm}^{-2} \, \mathrm{s}^{-1}$. Most of these neutrinos have energies below $0.4 \, \mathrm{MeV}$, although some can reach energies up to $19 \, \mathrm{MeV}$. Both atmospheric

---

[4]The different energy units employed are, increasing by a factor of 10^3 in each step: meV, eV, keV, MeV, GeV, TeV, PeV and EeV.

and solar neutrinos were of paramount importance to establish the phenomenon of neutrino oscillations, which gave the first indications that neutrino masses are non-vanishing and that the mass eigenstates involve mixing between different neutrino flavors.

Besides the production of neutrinos in fusion reactions, there are several processes taking place in the central parts of the stars that produce neutrinos with typical thermal energies. These processes involve the production of neutrino pairs in Compton-like interactions ($\gamma e \to e\nu\bar{\nu}$), bremsstrahlung from nuclei ($Ae \to Ae\nu\bar{\nu}$), plasmon decay ($\gamma^* \to \nu\bar{\nu}$) and pair annihilation ($e^+e^- \to \nu\bar{\nu}$). In the case of the Sun, which has a central temperature $T_c \simeq 1.3\,\text{keV}$, the luminosity associated to these thermal neutrinos is negligible. However, these processes become increasingly important in later stages of the evolution of stars, i.e., those beyond the H burning main sequence. For instance, carbon burning stars, in which the main energy source involves reactions such as $C + C \to Ne + He$, the central temperature reaches about $50\,\text{keV}$ and the luminosity of the star in thermal neutrinos becomes comparable to the one in electromagnetic radiation. For Si burning stars the central temperature typically reaches $270\,\text{keV}$, and the resulting thermal neutrino luminosity is a million times larger than the electromagnetic one, so that the star evolution in these later stages is mostly determined by the neutrino losses.

When a star with mass larger than about $8\,M_\odot$ ends its life in a supernova explosion, a huge amount of energy, of the order of 3×10^{53} erg, is emitted when the core of the star collapses. Almost 99% of this is emitted as neutrinos that escape in a burst lasting several seconds and with typical energies of about 10 to 30 MeV. In these spectacular processes neutrinos really have a predominant role. Besides attempting to observe neutrinos from the rare explosions of nearby Supernovae, such as one that could take place in our Galaxy or the one seen in 1987 that took place in the nearby Large Magellanic Cloud galaxy, one may also try to detect the cumulative neutrino background resulting from all the past supernovae that exploded in the Universe. This flux is small but may be observable at energies just above the maximum solar neutrino energies or, when searching for antineutrinos, at energies above those of the background from nuclear reactors.

Neutrinos of much higher energies might originate from interactions of energetic cosmic rays accelerated in special astrophysical sites, such as in active galaxies (in which relativistic jets can be produced due to the accretion into the supermassive black holes located at their centers) or in extreme stellar objects such as the gamma ray burst associated to hypernova explosions or neutron star mergers. Since cosmic rays have been observed with energies extending up to about 100 EeV, their interactions with the radiation or with the gas that they encounter while they exit from the sources, or with the background radiations of the Universe that they travel through when they propagate from the sources up to us, may lead to the production of neutrinos with energies extending up to several EeV.

Neutrinos of non-atmospheric origin, with energies in the 100 TeV to few PeV range, were indeed observed in recent years with the IceCube observatory located at the South Pole. This was a major breakthrough that opened the field of high-energy neutrino astronomy. Note that astrophysical neutrinos would arrive straight and unattenuated from their sources, unlike the charged cosmic rays that get deflected by the intervening magnetic fields, or the very-high energy photons whose flux is strongly suppressed by their interactions with the radiation backgrounds that they encounter while traveling from distant sources. This makes the neutrinos an ideal messenger to do astronomy at energies above a few tens of TeV. The identification of their origin should allow to learn about the sources of ultra-high energy cosmic rays, and should also allow to better understand the processes responsible for the acceleration of the cosmic rays up to the highest energies observed in nature.

High-energy neutrinos may also be produced in more exotic scenarios, such as in the annihilation of hypotetical dark matter particles. These annihilations can take place in the halos of galaxies or also inside astrophysical objects, such as the Sun or the Earth, since when the heavy dark matter particles get trapped and accumulate in these objects their rate of annihilation can be strongly enhanced. In particular, the weakly interacting massive particle (WIMP) paradigm is that in which particles with masses typically in the range of GeV to TeV get thermally produced in the early universe and, due to their weak couplings their interactions freeze-out and the surviving particles remain around us as dark matter. This scenario is being actively scrutinized by searching for the neutrinos that get produced upon their annihilation, having energies extending in principle up to the dark matter mass. The most appealing WIMP candidate is the supersymmetric neutralino [Ju96], which is the lightest combination of the fermionic superpartners of the neutral bosons of the supersymmetric standard model, i.e. the partners of the Higgs, the photon and the Z boson. The eventual observation of such energetic neutrinos could hence be considered as an *indirect detection* of the dark matter particles, and it could help to understand their nature, which is a long standing open problem in astrophysics.

Neutrinos were also important in the early universe. In the very hot plasma produced after the Big Bang they were in equilibrium with the other particles, such as electrons or photons, until the Universe cooled down to temperatures below few MeV. As a result, a relic background of very low energy neutrinos was left, with a present day temperature of 1.9 K. The associated average number density of these cosmic neutrinos and antineutrinos is about 100 cm^{-3} per flavor, which in total is comparable to the density of photons in the cosmic microwave background (CMB). These neutrinos were relevant to determine the expansion rate of the Universe during the primordial nucleosynthesis era and hence influenced the final value of the primordial He abundance. By the time of the photon decoupling, they also affected the temperature fluctuations that are observed in the CMB through their effect on the expansion. Being relativistic during the epoch in which matter became dominant and the inhomegeneities started to grow, they partially erased the overdensities on small scales. Through their dynamical effects during the gravitational collapse that gave rise to the large scale structures in the Universe, they also affected the formation of Galaxies, Clusters and Superclusters of Galaxies since, after all, massive neutrinos do contribute slightly to the dark matter. Hence, the analysis of observations related to the matter distribution of galaxies at large scales, in combination with the study of the anisotropies of the CMB, allows to constrain the number of neutrino species and to put strong constraints on the sum of the neutrino masses.

Finally, neutrinos may have heavier neutral partners which can help us to understand the origin of the observed neutrino masses. In particular, via the so-called see-saw mechanism the heavy right-handed neutrinos may explain why the masses of the light neutrinos are so much smaller than the masses of the charged particles. These additional very heavy neutrinos could in turn be fundamental in the process that generates the observed excess of matter over antimatter that exists in the Universe. This baryonic asymmetry could be dynamically explained in the scenario known as lepto-genesis, in which a leptonic asymmetry is generated at very early times in the out of equilibrium decays of the heavy neutrinos, to be then reprocessed into a baryonic asymmetry by non-perturbative Standard Model processes. These heavy neutrinos naturally fit in theories where the different forces of nature get unified, and hence neutrinos may not only have been crucial to understand the Standard Model of particle physics, but they may also end up helping us to understand the way to go beyond it.

Suggested exercises:

- Bethe and Peierls' original argument for estimating the cross section σ of the reaction $\bar{\nu} + p \rightarrow e^+ + n$ considered its ratio to the neutron decay amplitude, Γ_n (with the neutron's lifetime being $\tau_n = 1/\Gamma_n \simeq 15\,\mathrm{min}$).

  (1) Convince yourself that the ratio σ/Γ_n is independent of the Fermi constant G_F.

  (2) Including an energy scale $E \sim 1\,\mathrm{MeV}$ to get a guess of the ratio with the right dimensions, estimate the cross section.

  (3) Discuss the difference with other nuclei subject to beta decay.

The following exercises require some familiarity with particle physics, so you may consult books such as:

   - *Quarks and Leptons: An Introductory Course in Modern Particle Physics*, F. Halzen and A.D. Martin

   - *Introduction to Elementary Particles*, D. Griffiths

- Compute the cross section for the inverse β process: $\bar{\nu}_e + p \rightarrow n + e^+$.
- Compute the width of the pion decay to leptons, $\pi^+ \rightarrow \ell^+ + \nu_\ell$, and kaon leptonic decays $K^+ \rightarrow \ell^+ + \nu_\ell$.
- Compute the decay width of the Z-boson: $Z \rightarrow \bar{f} + f$ for all allowed fermion anti-fermion pairs in the Standard Model.
- Compute the cross section $\sigma(e\bar{e} \rightarrow f\bar{f})$ near the Z resonance.

Recommended reading:

Among the many books about neutrinos which also discuss their connection with astrophysics, we can mention:

- *Massive Neutrinos in Physics and Astrophysics*, R. Mohapatra and P. Pal
- *Physics of Neutrinos and applications to Astrophysics*, M. Fukugita and T. Yanagida
- *Neutrinos in Particle Physics, Astronomy and Cosmology*, Z.-Z. Xing and S. Zhou
- *Fundamentals of Neutrino Physics and Astrophysics*, C. Giunti and Ch.W. Kim

Chapter 2

Neutrino Interactions and Detection Techniques

2.1 Neutrino cross sections

In order to observe the neutrinos it is important to understand how they interact with the different possible targets. At low energies, one can use the corresponding effective Fermi-type four fermion interactions. Besides interacting with atomic electrons, many detectors rely on the interactions of neutrinos with nuclei, in which case nuclear form factors enter into the computation of these processes. As the energy increases above few tens of MeV, the internal structure of the nucleons starts to be probed and, in the deep-inelastic regime taking place at energies above a GeV, the neutrinos directly interact with the quarks present inside the nucleons. When the energies are high enough so that the momentum transfer becomes non-negligible with respect to the masses of the exchanged W or Z bosons, the full propagators of these mediators need to be taken into account.

2.1.1 *Neutrino–lepton interactions*

The Hamiltonian for the leptonic weak interactions, $\nu_{\ell'} + \ell \to \nu_{\ell'} + \ell$, arising from the two diagrams displayed in Fig. 2.1, can be obtained considering the interactions of the Standard Model presented in the previous Chapter. In the low-energy limit, i.e. for momentum exchanges much smaller than the gauge boson masses M_W and M_Z, it is just given by

$$\mathcal{H}_{\nu_{\ell}'\ell} = \sqrt{2}G_{\mathrm{F}}[\bar{\nu}_{\ell'}\gamma_\mu(1 - \gamma_5)\nu_{\ell'}][\bar{\ell}\gamma^\mu(c_{\mathsf{L}}(\ell)P_{\mathsf{L}} + c_{\mathsf{R}}(\ell)P_{\mathsf{R}})\ell]. \qquad (2.1)$$

The left and right couplings are $c_{\mathsf{L}}(\ell) = g_{\mathsf{L}}(\ell) + \delta_{\ell\ell'}$ and $c_{\mathsf{R}}(\ell) = g_{\mathsf{R}}(\ell)$. Here the chiral couplings of a fermion f to the Z boson are $g_{\mathsf{L},\mathsf{R}}(f) \equiv T_3(f_{\mathsf{L},\mathsf{R}}) - q_{em}(f)\sin^2\theta_W$, with T_3 being the third component of the weak isospin and q_{em} the corresponding electromagnetic charge (see Eq. (1.20)).

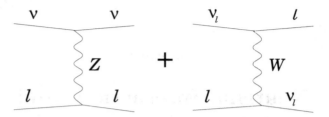

Fig. 2.1 Neutral and charged-current contributions to neutrino lepton scattering. For antineutrino lepton scattering, the W is exchanged in the s-channel.

Table 2.1 Chiral couplings to the Z boson.

	ν	e	u	d
g_L	$\frac{1}{2}$	$-\frac{1}{2}+s_W^2$	$\frac{1}{2}-\frac{2}{3}s_W^2$	$-\frac{1}{2}+\frac{1}{3}s_W^2$
g_R	0	s_W^2	$-\frac{2}{3}s_W^2$	$\frac{1}{3}s_W^2$

The $\delta_{\ell\ell'}$ term in c_L is due to the charged-current diagram that couples the left-handed chiralities for $\ell = \ell'$.[1] On the other hand, due to the hypercharge gauge field component present in the Z boson, the weak neutral currents also couple to the charged lepton right-handed chiralities (for which $c_R = -q_{em}(f)\sin^2\theta_W$). For convenience, we collect in Table 2.1 the values of the chiral couplings of the different fermions to the Z boson, using the shorthand notation $s_W^2 \equiv \sin^2\theta_W$.

At the tree level, the differential cross section for the interaction of neutrinos with unpolarised leptons ℓ at rest, as a function of the kinetic energy T_ℓ of the final lepton, is

$$\frac{d\sigma}{dT_\ell}(\nu\ell \to \nu\ell) = \frac{2G_F^2 m_\ell}{\pi}\left[c_L^2 + c_R^2\left(1 - \frac{T_\ell}{E_\nu}\right)^2 - c_L c_R \frac{m_\ell T_\ell}{E_\nu^2}\right], \qquad (2.2)$$

where the kinematic range is given by

$$0 \leq T_\ell \leq \frac{E_\nu^2}{E_\nu + m_\ell/2}. \qquad (2.3)$$

One of the most interesting cases is when the charged lepton is an atomic electron, corresponding to the so-called electron scattering (ES) reaction, which is the process exploited in some solar neutrino detectors. For the

---

[1]The product of the two charged currents that couple to the W boson in the second diagram of Fig. 2.1 was rewritten as a product of two neutral currents using the Fierz identity $\bar{\Psi}_1\gamma_\mu P_L\Psi_2\bar{\Psi}_3\gamma^\mu P_L\Psi_4 = \bar{\Psi}_1\gamma_\mu P_L\Psi_4\bar{\Psi}_3\gamma^\mu P_L\Psi_2$.

neutrinos with the lowest detected energies (as in the case of the Borexino detector whose threshold is $T_e^{\text{th}} \simeq 150\,\text{keV}$) the above expression is employed, possibly including also radiative corrections. However, in situations involving energies higher than few MeV it is adequate to just neglect the lepton mass with respect to the neutrino energy, in which case the total cross section becomes

$$\sigma(\nu\ell \to \nu\ell) \simeq \frac{2G_{\text{F}}^2}{\pi} m_\ell E_\nu \left[c_{\text{L}}^2 + \frac{c_{\text{R}}^2}{3} \right]. \tag{2.4}$$

Further insight into this expression can be gained by splitting the contributions to it in the center of mass (CM) system into $J = 0$ and $J = 1$ pieces. In the high-energy limit in which the lepton masses can be neglected and in which the helicity states approximately coincide with the chirality ones, the $J = 0$ piece arises from the left-handed neutrino interacting with the left-handed lepton chirality, giving an isotropic contribution $d\sigma/d\cos\theta(J = 0) \propto c_{\text{L}}^2$. The $J = 1$ piece arises instead from the interaction of the left-handed neutrino with the right-handed lepton chirality, giving a contribution $d\sigma/d\cos\theta(J = 1) \propto c_{\text{R}}^2[(1 + \cos\theta)/2]^2$. The factor $1/3$ in Eq. (2.4) is obtained after the angular integration and can be interpreted as arising from the fact that just one of the three projections of J_z contributes to the process.

A similar expression, but with $c_{\text{L}} \leftrightarrow c_{\text{R}}$, holds for the antineutrino–lepton scattering, in which case the W exchange in Fig. 2.1 would be in the s-channel. The following relations between the different processes involving the neutrino elastic scattering off electrons then hold:

$$\sigma(\nu_e e) \simeq 9 \times 10^{-45}\text{cm}^2 \frac{E_\nu}{\text{MeV}} \simeq 2.5\sigma(\bar{\nu}_e e) \simeq 6\sigma(\nu_{\mu,\tau} e) \simeq 7\sigma(\bar{\nu}_{\mu,\tau} e). \tag{2.5}$$

For the $\nu_e e$ scattering process, and considering the CM system, one has that the angular distribution of the electron momentum with respect to the incident neutrino direction results from $d\sigma(\nu_e e)/d\cos\theta \propto 1 + (c_{\text{R}}/c_{\text{L}})^2[(1 + \cos\theta)/2]^2$. This distribution is almost isotropic because in this case $(c_{\text{R}}/c_{\text{L}})^2 \simeq 0.1$. However, in the laboratory system a significant correlation between the neutrino and electron momenta will result when $E_\nu \gg \text{MeV}$, due to the boost associated to the change of reference frame, and this makes it possible to do astronomy with neutrinos. For instance, a water Cherenkov detector such as Super-Kamiokande detects solar neutrinos with $E_\nu > 5\,\text{MeV}$ using this process, and has been able to reconstruct a picture of the Sun as seen in neutrinos from the observed directions of the recoiling electrons [Ab16]. For the study of neutrino oscillations, it is also relevant that these kind of detectors are six times more sensitive to electron-type neutrinos than to the other two neutrino flavors (see Eq. (2.5)). The scintillator-based detector Borexino used the ES reaction to perform a full spectroscopy of all the different contributions to the solar neutrino fluxes, but one has to keep in mind that the scintillation signal has however no directional information.

2.1.2 *Low energy neutrino interactions with nucleons and nuclei*

Considering now the neutrino interaction with nuclei at low energies, $E_\nu <$ 100 MeV, the simplest case is that of the CC interactions of electron antineutrinos with protons (i.e., H nuclei), through the so-called inverse beta decay (IBD). This process looks like an elastic scattering, except that the nature of the particles is modified due to the charge exchange, and hence it is referred to as quasi-elastic (QE) scattering. The cross section for the process is

$$\sigma(\bar{\nu}_e p \to n e^+) \simeq \frac{G_F^2}{\pi} \cos^2\theta_C (g_V^2 + 3g_A^2) p_e E_e, \qquad (2.6)$$

where θ_C is the Cabibbo mixing angle. This interaction has a threshold neutrino energy $E_\nu^{\text{th}} = m_n - m_p + m_e \simeq 1.8$ MeV, and above this threshold the cross section grows approximately as E_ν^2 (see [Vo99; St03] for more details). A similar cross section is obtained for the interactions of ν_e with neutrons, while there are no quasi-elastic CC interactions between ν_e and protons, nor between $\bar{\nu}_e$ and neutrons. Note however that in the case in which the nucleons are contained inside a nucleus, as is generally the case for neutrons, one needs to account for the binding energies of the initial state, the nuclear structure of the final nucleus, the Coulomb interactions, etc., and all this affects the threshold energies and transition matrix elements involved.

There are several processes relevant for the low energy neutrino detection in which the neutrino interacts with nucleons bound in nuclei. Some examples are (where according to nuclear physicists notation $A(\nu_e, \beta)A'$ denotes $\nu_e + A \to e + A'$):

- The reactions $^{37}\text{Cl}(\nu_e, \beta)^{37}\text{Ar}$, proposed by Pontecorvo [Po46] and having a threshold neutrino energy $E_\nu^{\text{th}} = 814$ keV, or $^{71}\text{Ga}(\nu_e, \beta)^{71}\text{Ge}$, proposed by Kuzmin [Ku66] and having $E_\nu^{\text{th}} = 233$ keV. These processes have been used in radiochemical experiments to detect, respectively, the higher and lower ranges of the solar neutrino spectrum. The cross sections for these processes have been estimated theoretically on the basis of nuclear models and methods such as the random phase approximation.

- An important target that has been used for solar neutrino detection is heavy water, suggested by Chen [Ch85], in which the neutrinos interact with deuterium both through charged currents, in the case of ν_e, and through neutral currents, for all three neutrino flavors. In these cases the deuterium directly breaks into two nucleons, so that no final state nucleus wave function is involved. The relevant processes are

$$\nu_e + d \rightarrow e + p + p \quad \text{(CC)},$$
$$\nu_x + d \rightarrow \nu_x + n + p \quad \text{(NC)}, \tag{2.7}$$

where $x = e$, μ or τ. Even if the kinematical thresholds for the CC reaction is $E_\nu^{\text{th}}(\text{CC}) \simeq 1\,\text{MeV}$, the actual experimental thresholds are determined by background considerations. For the Subdury Neutrino Observatory (SNO), the CC is observable when the electron energy is above $\sim 4\,\text{MeV}$. The observation of the NC reaction, having a threshold $E_\nu^{\text{th}}(\text{NC}) \simeq 2.2\,\text{MeV}$, requires the detection of the neutron, what was achieved in a first stage through its capture by deuterium, in a second stage using its capture on ^{35}Cl added by dissolving a salt into the water, and finally using special ^3He neutron counters. The capture of the neutrons leads to observable gamma rays from the subsequent nuclear de-excitations.

- In water Cherenkov detectors, besides the elastic scattering off electrons and the IBD interactions with hydrogen nuclei, the neutrinos of sufficient energy may also interact through charged currents with oxygen nuclei. The threshold neutrino energy for this interaction is high, $E_\nu^{\text{th}} \simeq 15\,\text{MeV}$, so that this process is not relevant for the detection of solar or reactor neutrinos, but it may contribute to the detection of the high-energy tail of the neutrinos produced in supernova explosions. Similarly, neutrinos can interact via CC with carbon nuclei in organic scintillators.

- Several other detectors are based on nuclear targets, such as those using noble gases like He, Ar, Ne or Xe, or those based on materials such as lead. Liquid argon detectors are particularly useful to detect ν_e via the charged-current reaction $\nu_e + {}^{40}\text{Ar} \rightarrow e + {}^{40}\text{K}^*$. Detectors based on lead (and able to detect neutrons) are sensitive to ν_e via $\nu_e + {}^{208}\text{Pb} \rightarrow e + {}^{208}\text{Bi}^*$, with the associated neutrons from the excited Bi decays, and can also observe all neutrino flavors via the NC process leading to an excited Pb which then emits a neutron.

- One process that has only recently been observed [Ak17; Ak21] is the neutral current coherent interaction with nuclei, in which neutrinos of any flavor interact with the whole nucleus, just transferring momentum but without modifying it, via the process $\nu_x + A \rightarrow \nu_x + A$. For the interaction to be coherent the momentum exchange should be smaller than few tens of MeV, so that the associated Compton wavelength ($\lambda \sim 1/E_\nu$) is larger than the nuclear size ($R \simeq A^{1/3}$ fm). In this case, the NC coupling scales with the so-called nuclear weak charge Q_W, which is just proportional to the vector coupling of the Z boson summed over all nucleons N_i

$$Q_W = 2 \sum_{nucleons} [g_\mathsf{L}(N_i) + g_\mathsf{R}(N_i)] = Z(1 - 4\sin^2\theta_W) - N \simeq -N, \quad (2.8)$$

with N and Z the number of neutrons and protons respectively, and we used that since $\sin^2\theta_W \simeq 0.23$ the term proportional to Z is actually negligible. Note that the axial part of the Z interaction would couple essentially to the nuclear spin, which tends to cancel between different nucleons, and hence it does not lead to a large enhancement factor. Hence, the coherent cross-section will scale approximately as N^2, what can lead to strong enhancements for heavy nuclei. The main difficulty for the detection of this processes is the very slow nuclear recoil, with an associated kinetic energy $\sim E_\nu^2/m_A$ which is typically below tens of keV. Moreover, the fraction of the recoil energy that goes into ionization or scintillation, the so called quenching factor, is usually less than 20%. New detectors, designed to search for dark matter candidates in the form of weakly interacting massive particles (WIMPs), may reach in the near future the sensitivity required to observe the coherent nuclear scattering of solar, supernova and atmospheric neutrinos. These signals could actually represent the ultimate irreducible background for direct WIMP dark matter searches. Note that the coherent scattering of neutrinos is also relevant for the neutrino propagation inside the supernovae [Fr77], where a large fraction of Fe group nuclei are present.

- Also the NC interactions with H nuclei, even if not coherently enhanced as in the case of heavy nuclei, may lead to recoil energies that could be large enough to make their observation feasible in scintillator detectors (in this case both vector and axial couplings would contribute sizeably to the cross sections).

- In water Cherenkov detectors, the detection thresholds of several MeV do not allow the observation of the nuclear recoils. Instead, the NC

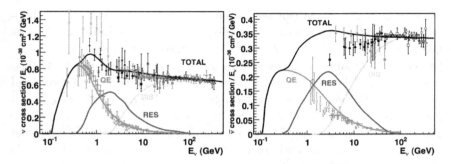

Fig. 2.2 Contributions to the neutrino (left-panel) and antineutrino (right-panel) nucleon charged-current cross section from the quasi-elastic channel (QE), the resonance pion production (RES), and the deep-inelastic regime (DIS). Reprinted figure with permission from [Fo12], Copyright 2022 by the American Physical Society.

inelastic interactions can lead to an excited oxygen nucleus that may be observed through the resulting de-excitation gamma rays. Also the inelastic emission of one nucleon can give rise to an excited daughter nucleus producing observable gamma rays [La96].

- A peculiar process which has been proposed to detect the relic background of extremely low energy neutrinos ($E_\nu \simeq 10^{-3}$ eV) left over from the Big Bang, is to use as targets β-radioactive nuclei, such as tritium [We62; Lo14]. In this case, the capture of ν_e becomes an exothermic process that produces a β ray with an energy larger than that of the beta rays from the ordinary tritium decay. With sufficient energy resolution, large target masses and sufficiently low backgrounds, this may eventually be observable.

2.1.3 *Neutrino interactions with nucleons at high energies*

At $E_\nu \gtrsim 100$ MeV, the nucleons N no longer look like point-like objects for the neutrinos. In particular, if one is still in the quasi-elastic regime in which the final state has just one nucleon, the vector (v_μ) and axial (a_μ) hadronic currents between nucleons are described in this case with momentum dependent form factors. These are the coefficients of the different terms having specific Lorentz structures, i.e.

$$\langle N(p')|v_\mu|N(p)\rangle = \bar{u}(p') \left[\gamma_\mu F_V + \frac{i}{2m_N}\sigma_{\mu\nu}(p'-p)^\nu F_W \right] u(p)$$

$$\langle N(p')|a_\mu|N(p)\rangle = \bar{u}(p') \left[\gamma_\mu\gamma_5 F_A + \frac{\gamma_5}{m_N}(p'-p)_\mu F_P \right] u(p), \qquad (2.9)$$

where $\sigma_{\mu\nu} = i[\gamma_\mu, \gamma_\nu]/2$ (for details on the Dirac matrices see next chapter). The weak vector form factor $F_V(Q^2)$, where the Lorentz invariant quantity $Q^2 \equiv -q^2 = -(p' - p)^2$ parameterizes the momentum transfer, can be measured using electromagnetic processes and the CVC relation $F_V = F_V^{em,p} - F_V^{em,n}$, i.e. as the difference between the proton and neutron electromagnetic vector form factors. Clearly $F_V(0) = g_V = 1$ and $F_A(0) = -g_A \simeq -1.27$. The weak magnetism form factor F_W is similarly related, through CVC, to the difference between the proton and neutron anomalous magnetic moments. The pseudoscalar form factor F_P gives rise to contributions to the cross sections proportional to the lepton mass squared, and is usually neglected for ν_e and occasionally also for ν_μ.[2] The Q^2 dependence of the form factors $F_{V,A}$ is usually parameterized as $F_i = g_i/(1 + Q^2/m_i^2)^2$, with $m_V \simeq 0.84\,\text{GeV}$ and $m_A \simeq 1.05\,\text{GeV}$. These form factors have the effect of significantly flattening the QE cross section above GeV energies.

For neutrino energies above a few hundred MeV, there are other final states that become accessible for the CC interaction, leading to inelastic processes, as illustrated in Fig. 2.2. These include the excitation of hadronic resonances, mainly the $\Delta(1232)$ one, with the associated production of pions ($\bar{\nu}_e p \to e^+ n\pi^0$ or $e^+ p\pi^-$). This resonant contribution has to be computed separately and clearly involves a non-perturbative process. It becomes comparable to the QE cross section for $E_\nu \sim \text{GeV}$, with both contributions saturating above that energy. For larger energies, the production of multi-pions and heavier hadronic resonances becomes also important.

At energies $E_\nu \gg \text{GeV}$, the dominant contribution to the charged-current process $\nu_\ell + N \to \ell + X$ is due to the deep-inelastic scattering of neutrinos directly with the individual (valence or sea) quarks and antiquarks present inside the nucleons. The corresponding differential cross section can be computed perturbatively, and is

$$\frac{\mathrm{d}^2\sigma_{\text{CC}}^{\text{DIS}}}{\mathrm{d}x\mathrm{d}y} = \frac{2}{\pi}G_F^2 m_N E_\nu x \frac{M_W^4}{(Q^2 + M_W^2)^2}\left[q(x,Q^2) + (1-y)^2\bar{q}(x,Q^2)\right].$$

(2.10)

The square of the momentum transfer can be written in terms of the lepton momenta as $Q^2 = -(p_\nu - p_\ell)^2$, while the scaling variables are

$$x \equiv Q^2/[2p_N \cdot (p_\nu - p_\ell)] = Q^2/[2m_N(E_\nu - E_\ell)],$$
$$y \equiv p_N \cdot (p_\nu - p_\ell)/(p_N \cdot p_\nu) = (E_\nu - E_\ell)/E_\nu,$$

(2.11)

---

[2]We also ignore here the so-called second class currents (involving $(p' - p)_\mu$ and $\sigma_{\mu\nu}(p' - p)^\nu\gamma_5$), which are very small in the quark model and are not observed experimentally.

with m_N the nucleon mass. The use of the Lorentz invariant adimensional variables x and y, both positive and smaller than one, proves to be in general more convenient than using just the energy transfer and the scattering angle of the lepton. Another useful parameter is the invariant mass of the hadronic final state, $M_X^2 = p_X^2 = m_N^2 + 2m_N E_\nu x(1 - y)$, which is constrained to be greater than m_Δ^2.

The distributions of quarks and antiquarks inside the nucleons are described by the parton distribution functions q and $\bar{q}$, respectively. Note that, except for the case of hydrogen or of very heavy nuclei, it is usually a good approximation to consider that the target is isoscalar, having an equal number of protons and neutrons. The interaction can be written in this case in terms of an average nucleon, $N = (n + p)/2$. Neglecting the contributions from quarks heavier than the strange quark, one obtains in this case that

$$q = \frac{u_v + d_v}{2} + \frac{u_s + d_s}{2} + s_s,$$
$$\bar{q} = \frac{u_s + d_s}{2}, \tag{2.12}$$

in terms of the valence (v) and sea (s) quark distributions in a proton, all of which depend on x and Q^2. We have used here that neutrinos interact through CC with the down-type quarks or up-type antiquarks and that $u_v \equiv u_v(p) \simeq d_v(n)$ and $d_v \equiv d_v(p) \simeq u_v(n)$. For an isoscalar target one then finds that the valence d quark content is $[d_v(n)+d_v(p)]/2 = (u_v+d_v)/2$. On the other hand, the sea content is equal for quarks and antiquarks.

Note that in the CM system and in the relativistic limit of the neutrino-quark interaction, one has that $1 - y \simeq (1 + \cos\theta)/2$, with θ the scattering angle between the initial neutrino and the final lepton. We see then that the term proportional to $(1 - y)^2$ in Eq. (2.10) is due to the $J = 1$ contribution to the neutrino–antiquark scattering, since in the $\nu + \bar{u} \to \ell + \bar{d}$ process the neutrino is left-handed and the $\bar{u}$ is right-handed. On the other hand, the first term in the square brackets in Eq. (2.10) is due to the $J = 0$ (isotropic in the CM frame) contribution from the neutrino quark interaction, since in the $\nu + d \to \ell + u$ process both the neutrino and the d quark are left-handed.

Given that the $\bar{\nu}q$ cross section is the same as the $\nu\bar{q}$ one, the antineutrino nucleon cross section has the form of Eq. (2.10) with q and $\bar{q}$ interchanged. Hence, at the energies we are discussing the antineutrino nucleon cross section is smaller than the neutrino nucleon cross section because its valence quark contribution, which is the dominant one, is multiplied by the $(1-y)^2$ factor. In order to obtain the total neutrino (or antineutrino) cross

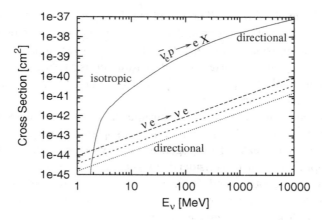

Fig. 2.3   Charged current neutrino electron and neutrino nucleon cross sections vs. energy. The three lines for the neutrino lepton cross sections correspond, from top to bottom, to $\nu_e e$, $\bar{\nu}_e e$ and $\nu_{\mu,\tau} e$ interactions.

section with nucleons one needs to integrate over the variables x and y, adopting some set of quark distribution functions. These functions are in turn determined from fits to experimental results involving different electromagnetic, weak and strong processes.

The behavior of the charged current neutrino electron and the neutrino nucleon cross sections, for energies below 10 GeV, are illustrated in Fig. 2.3.

As long as the Q^2 dependence of the W propagator can be neglected, i.e. for $Q^2 \ll M_W^2$ (which corresponds approximately to $E_\nu \ll M_W^2/(2m_N xy) \simeq 10$ TeV, where we considered as representative value $xy \simeq 1/3$), one has that the deep-inelastic cross section grows linearly with the neutrino energy. The experimental verification of this behavior, displayed in Fig. 2.4, provided an important test of the parton model. The measurements performed for $10\,\mathrm{GeV} < E_\nu < 350\,\mathrm{GeV}$ lead to the approximate values

$$\sigma_{\mathrm{CC}}(\nu N) \simeq 6.67 \times 10^{-39}\mathrm{cm}^2(E_\nu/\mathrm{GeV}),$$
$$\sigma_{\mathrm{CC}}(\bar{\nu} N) \simeq 3.34 \times 10^{-39}\mathrm{cm}^2(E_{\bar{\nu}}/\mathrm{GeV}). \tag{2.13}$$

Regarding the deep-inelastic neutral current cross section, one obtains similarly

$$\frac{\mathrm{d}^2\sigma_{\mathrm{NC}}^{\mathrm{DIS}}}{\mathrm{d}x\mathrm{d}y} = \frac{2}{\pi}G_{\mathrm{F}}^2 m_N E_\nu x \frac{M_Z^4}{(Q^2 + M_Z^2)^2} \left[q_0(x,Q^2) + (1-y)^2 \bar{q}_0(x,Q^2)\right],$$

$$\tag{2.14}$$

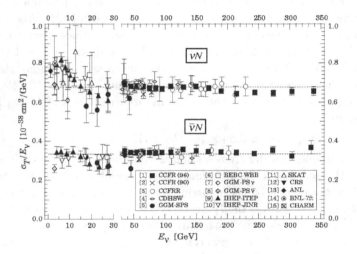

Fig. 2.4 Neutrino (and antineutrino) nucleon charged-current cross section. The plot corresponds to σ/E vs. energy, displaying the linear growth $\sigma \propto E$ in this energy range (form [PDG]).

where

$$q_0 = \left[g_L^2(u) + g_L^2(d)\right]\frac{u_v + d_v}{2} + \sum_{q=u,d,s,\dots}\left[g_L^2(q) + g_R^2(q)\right]q_s,$$

$$\bar{q}_0 = \left[g_R^2(u) + g_R^2(d)\right]\frac{u_v + d_v}{2} + \sum_{q=u,d,s,\dots}\left[g_L^2(q) + g_R^2(q)\right]q_s. \quad (2.15)$$

The total NC cross sections turn out to be smaller than the CC ones by a factor of about 0.3. Approximate expressions for them, valid in the 10 GeV to TeV range, are

$$\sigma_{\mathrm{NC}}(\nu N) \simeq 2.09 \times 10^{-39}\mathrm{cm}^2(E_\nu/\mathrm{GeV}),$$
$$\sigma_{\mathrm{NC}}(\bar{\nu} N) \simeq 1.15 \times 10^{-39}\mathrm{cm}^2(E_{\bar{\nu}}/\mathrm{GeV}). \quad (2.16)$$

Note that the antineutrino nucleon NC cross section is obtained from the neutrino nucleon one by exchanging $g_L \leftrightarrow g_R$ or, equivalently, interchanging q_0 and $\bar{q}_0$.

For energies larger than 10 TeV the gauge boson propagator starts to play a crucial role, suppressing the CC differential cross section when $Q^2 > M_W^2$. In this case, the dominant contribution to the total cross section arises from interactions with quarks having small values of x, typically $x < M_W^2/(2m_N E_\nu) \simeq 3 \times 10^{-3}(\mathrm{PeV}/E_\nu)$. The parton distribution functions have been measured for instance in hadronic machines, which explored values down to $x \sim 10^{-3}$ for certain ranges of Q^2. Also, using the deep inelastic ep processes at the HERA collider values down to about $x \sim 10^{-5}$ have been explored for $Q^2 \simeq \text{GeV}^2$, or down to $x \sim 10^{-3}$ for $Q^2 \simeq 10^2 \text{ GeV}^2$. Using the measured distributions, one finds that the growth of the cross section becomes less pronounced above 10 TeV, and in particular for $E > 10 \text{ PeV}$ the following approximate expression holds [Ga98; Kw99]

$$\sigma_{\text{CC}}(\nu N) \simeq 5.53 \times 10^{-36} \text{cm}^2 \, (E_\nu/\text{GeV})^{0.363} \, . \tag{2.17}$$

Since at these energies the cross section is dominated by the contributions involving the sea quark distributions, the antineutrino cross section becomes almost identical to the neutrino one. For neutrino processes with $E_\nu \gg 1 \text{ PeV}$ it becomes actually necessary to extrapolate, on the basis of theoretical expectations, the parton distribution functions down to values of x smaller than those tested experimentally. The predictions become then sensitive to the particular extrapolation of the distributions adopted, with possible variations within an overall factor of two appearing at the highest relevant energies ($E_\nu \simeq 10^{20} \text{ eV}$).

For the total neutral current cross section, an approximate expression valid at energies beyond 10 PeV is

$$\sigma_{\text{NC}}(\nu N) \simeq \sigma_{\text{NC}}(\bar{\nu} N) \simeq 2.31 \times 10^{-36} \text{cm}^2 \, (E_\nu/\text{GeV})^{0.363} \, . \tag{2.18}$$

The charged and neutral current high-energy neutrino–nucleon cross sections, as well as the total one, are plotted in Fig. 2.5.

The mean free path of neutrinos traveling across a medium with density ρ is (using that $1 \text{ g} = m_p N_A$, with m_p the proton mass and $N_A = 6.02 \times 10^{23}$ being Avogadro's number)

$$\lambda \simeq \frac{m_p}{\rho \sigma} \simeq 1.7 \times 10^6 \text{ km} \left(\frac{\text{g cm}^{-3}}{\rho} \right) \left(\frac{10^{-35} \text{cm}^2}{\sigma} \right) . \tag{2.19}$$

One then finds that the Earth, whose typical average density is 5 g cm^{-3}, can become opaque for neutrinos of sufficiently high energies. Indeed, one has that the neutrino interaction length becomes smaller than the diameter of the Earth ($\lambda < 10^4 \text{ km}$) for $E_\nu \gtrsim 40 \text{ TeV}$. This means that for neutrino energies above 100 TeV the astrophysical neutrino sources have to be searched by looking above or near the horizon, as will be discussed in Chapter 9. On the contrary, for smaller energies it turns out to be convenient to look for neutrinos coming from below the horizon, in order to avoid the cosmic-ray induced background of downgoing muons which is present even at the deepest underground locations.

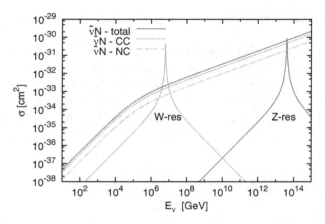

Fig. 2.5   Antineutrino nucleon neutral and charged-current cross sections (as well as their sum) vs. energy. Also shown are the resonant part of the $\bar{\nu}e$ cross section at the W resonance and the $\bar{\nu}\nu$ cross section at the Z resonance (assuming in this case $m_\nu = 0.1\,\text{eV}$ and the target neutrino to be at rest).

2.1.4   *The W and Z resonances*

There are two peculiar situations in which the neutrino interactions can be largely enhanced by the presence of an s-channel resonance, either by a W or a Z-boson exchange.

The first case occurs when an electron anti-neutrino interacts with an electron by the exchange of an on-shell W boson, i.e. when $s = (p_{\bar{\nu}} + p_e)^2 \simeq M_W^2$. Considering that the target electron is at rest, this corresponds to an electron anti-neutrino energy $E_{WR} \simeq M_W^2/(2m_e) \simeq 6.3\,\text{PeV}$. The cross section near this so-called *Glashow resonance* [Gl60] is given, considering for instance the channel into the final state $\bar{\nu}_\mu\mu$, by

$$\sigma(\bar{\nu}_e e \to \bar{\nu}_\mu\mu) = \frac{G_{\rm F}^2 M_W^2}{3\pi} \frac{E_\nu/E_{WR}}{(1 - E_\nu/E_{WR})^2 + (\Gamma_W/M_W)^2}, \qquad (2.20)$$

where $\Gamma_W = 2.1\,\text{GeV}$ is the W boson total width. The other final states have a similar cross section, with the inclusion of a color factor $N_{\rm c} = 3$ for the quarks. Note that the third quark generation is not kinematically allowed as final state. The total contribution of this resonant channel to the cross section is also depicted in Fig. 2.5. One can see that the enhancement occurs only in a narrow energy range around E_{WR}, with a width $\Delta E_\nu \sim (\Gamma_W/M_W)E_{WR} \simeq 0.17\,\text{PeV}$. This process can provide an interesting channel for the detection of PeV electron anti-neutrinos of astrophysical origin, and indeed an event of this type has recently been observed in the IceCube detector.

The other peculiar situation corresponds to the interaction of neutrinos with anti-neutrinos, through the resonant exchange in the s-channel of a Z boson. If the target neutrino (antineutrino) is assumed to have a mass m_ν and to be approximately at rest, the cross section will be strongly enhanced when the incident antineutrino (neutrino) has an energy $E_{ZR} \simeq M_Z^2/(2m_\nu) \simeq 4.1 \times 10^{22}\,\mathrm{eV}(0.1\,\mathrm{eV}/m_\nu)$. The cross section for this process is

$$\sigma(\nu\bar{\nu} \to f\bar{f}) = \frac{2G_{\mathrm{F}}^2 M_Z^2}{3\pi} \frac{E_\nu/E_{ZR}}{(1 - E_\nu/E_{ZR})^2 + (\Gamma_Z/M_Z)^2} \left[g_{\mathrm{L}}^2(f) + g_{\mathrm{R}}^2(f) \right].$$

$$(2.21)$$

It is also depicted in Fig. 2.5, showing the Breit-Wigner resonant behavior characterized by the Z boson width $\Gamma_Z \simeq 2.5\,\mathrm{GeV}$. This process has been suggested [We84; Ro93] as a possible mechanism for the absorption of extremely high energy neutrinos by the background neutrinos left over from the Big Bang, that would be non-relativistic if $m_\nu > 10^{-3}\,\mathrm{eV}$. The resonant annihilation of these neutrinos could produce cosmic rays, mainly gammas but eventually also some protons, at the highest energies observed ($E \sim 10^{20}\,\mathrm{eV}$). However, the neutrino energies and fluxes required for this interaction to be of any relevance are huge.

2.2   Neutrino detection techniques

Once a neutrino interacts, in order to observe it one needs to be able to detect some of the particles that result from the interaction. Different techniques are employed to achieve this, depending on the neutrino energies and the neutrino flavor that one is aiming to detect, on the radioactive purity of the detector elements which is required to reduce the backgrounds, the energy or angular resolution one wants to achieve, and on the neutrino fluxes to be measured, which determine the detector size required.

Some of the most commonly used techniques are:

- Radiochemical detectors: These experiments were used to measure solar neutrinos using the transmutation of $^{37}\mathrm{Cl}$ or $^{71}\mathrm{Ga}$ nuclei in CC interactions of ν_e. Note that chlorine has two stable isotopes, $^{35}\mathrm{Cl}$ with a natural abundance of 76%, and $^{37}\mathrm{Cl}$ with a natural abundance of 24%. Due to its neutron excess, $^{37}\mathrm{Cl}$ has a relatively low threshold for the ν_e CC interaction, producing $^{37}\mathrm{Ar}$ which is prone to decay back into the original ^{37}Cl nucleus by EC, with a half-life of 35 days. A similar thing happens with Ga, whose stable isotopes are ^{69}Ga (60% abundance) and ^{71}Ga (40% abundance), with this last producing ^{71}Ge which then decays with a half-life of 11.4 days. The secondary atoms produced, ^{37}Ar and ^{71}Ge respectively, get extracted typically every few weeks and are counted by observing the Auger electrons produced by their subsequent radioactive decay via electron capture. There is hence no information on the energy (just that it needs to be above threshold) nor on the direction of the original neutrino. The main experiments of this kind were the one using Cl in the Homestake mine in USA and the experiments using Ga: SAGE in the Baksan Laboratory in Russia and Gallex/GNO at the Gran Sasso Laboratory in Italy.

- Water and Ice Cherenkov detectors: a charged particle traveling faster than the speed of light in a medium emits Cherenkov radiation. For this to happen, its velocity v should satisfy $v > c/n$, where n is the index of refraction of the medium. This condition corresponds to the particle having an energy larger than the threshold $E^{\mathrm{th}} = m/\sqrt{1 - 1/n^2}$, where m is the mass of the particle. In particular, the threshold energy for an electron to emit Cherenkov radiation in water, where $n = 1.33$, would be $E_e^{\mathrm{th}} \simeq 0.78\,\mathrm{MeV}$, corresponding to a kinetic energy $T_e \simeq 0.27\,\mathrm{MeV}$. For the more massive muon, the threshold energy would be instead $E_\mu^{\mathrm{th}} \simeq 160\,\mathrm{MeV}$. Particles with energy above their corresponding threshold would produce a trailing cone of blue/UV light with an opening angle $\theta_{\mathrm{Ch}} = \mathrm{acos}(c/(v\,n))$, which in the ultra-relativistic limit would correspond to $\theta_{\mathrm{Ch}} \simeq 41°$. The intersection of these cones with the detector walls leads to Cherenkov rings. Observing the light collected in photomultiplier tubes (PMTs) located around the detector allows to reconstruct the direction of motion of the charged particle and to estimate its energy. Hence, if the particle direction is correlated with the direction of the neutrino that produced it (such as in neutrino-electron elastic scattering but not so much in the case of the inverse beta decay process) one may infer the neutrino arrival direction. One should keep in mind that even if the Cherenkov threshold for electrons is quite low, the actual threshold of an experiment like Super-Kamiokande is about 5 MeV, being determined by the radioactive background at the site (from radon gas that needs to be removed, from gammas produced in the surrounding rocks that need to be vetoed, etc.). The water Cherenkov technique allows to observe electron scattering events, inverse beta decays as well as tracks of muons produced in ν_μ CC interactions. An interesting possibility is to dissolve gadolinium in the water [Be04] so as to be more sensitive to the neutrons produced in IBD processes, something the Super-Kamiokande detector is currently implementing. Gd nuclei capture neutrons more efficiently than the protons present in the water and produce gamma rays with a total energy of about 8 MeV, which is above the detector threshold (unlike the neutron capture by protons which produces deuterium plus 2.2 MeV in gamma rays, and is hence below the typical detector threshold). Also the reaction $\nu_e + O \rightarrow e + F^*$, with a threshold of about 15 MeV, can take place in water. For the electrons to have more than 5 MeV requires the neutrino energy to be above 20 MeV, which may be the case for instance for the high-energy tail of the supernova neutrinos. The Super-Kamiokande detector, which has a mass of 50 kt, has also detected atmospheric neutrinos with energies up to hundreds of GeV. The SNO experiment, using 1 kt of heavy water, has not only detected solar neutrinos via electron scattering but also through the CC and NC interactions with deuterium, this last being equally sensitive to all neutrino flavors.

• Scintillator detectors: scintillating materials produce visible light (or UV light which can then be converted into visible light by wave-shifting elements) when charged particles or radiation interacts in them. Note that positrons would produce a gamma signal when annihilating with electrons in the material. Also neutrons can be captured by protons to form deuteron or by other substances like Cd or Gd that can be added to capture the neutrons more efficiently, and the de-excitation gamma rays produced can be used to tag the neutrons. There are inorganic materials, such as NaI crystals (usually doped with tallium), and organic materials based on hydrocarbon molecules, such as pseudocumene (C_9H_{12}), whose molecular levels can emit in the visible and at the same time they are quite transparent. The emitted light can then be registered with PMTs which look into the detector's volume. These organic scintillators can be immersed in plastics or may stay liquid if added to an appropriate solvent. The liquid scintillators allow to achieve quite large volumes with a very pure material, and they have low threshold energies. This technology was used in the experiments Borexino at the Gran Sasso in Italy (300 t), KamLAND in Japan (1 kt) and SNO+ in Canada (800 t). The achievable threshold for electron scattering processes can be as low as $E_\nu^{th} \simeq 300$ keV, mostly limited by backgrounds from cosmogenic radioactivity and from ^{14}C decays.

Regarding the measurements of proton recoils, due to the smaller photon yield in these recoils (the so-called quenching), only proton energies above an MeV can be detected, but this could be useful for instance to measure the high-energy tail of supernova neutrinos of all flavors using neutral currents. Other experiments using liquid scintillators to study reactor electron anti-neutrinos are Double-Chooz in France and Daya-Bay in China. Examples of scintillator detectors used in long-baseline experiments are the MINOS and NOνA experiments, this last having a mass of 14 kt. Also noble gases are used to make sensitive detectors, since they emit scintillation light and allow to achieve a very high level of purity. Examples of detectors using these elements are HERON (He), CLEAN (Ne), ARGO (Ar), etc.

- Ionization detectors: detectors using Ge or Si semiconductors allow us to observe the ionization produced by charged particles, and can also detect gamma rays if they produce electrons via Compton scattering. They have been used to study for instance the double beta decay processes. Here the charged particles excite the electrons from the valence to the conduction band and an external potential difference generates a measurable current. These detectors are also used for dark matter searches and the increase in size being achieved, that may reach the tonne scale in the near future with experiments such as Genius or Majorana, may also find applications in searches of astrophysical neutrinos. Detectors containing noble gases such as Ar or Xe, both liquid and gaseous, can also detect the ionization signals of the electrons produced by neutrino interactions. They work as time projection chambers (TPC), in which electrons are drifted by strong potential differences, and the signals they produce allow to reconstruct the trajectories of the ionizing charged particles. In some cases, one can combine the ionization signal with the direct signal produced by the scintillation, such as in the XENON1T detector using 3.2 tonnes of Xe in the Gran Sasso Laboratory, or the 40 kt liquid argon detector DUNE which is under construction in the Sanford laboratory near the site of the Homestake experiment, which exploits the reaction $\nu_e + \mathrm{Ar} \rightarrow e + \mathrm{K}$. This will be used in long-baseline experiments to study ν_e appearance using an accelerator ν_μ beam with energies of few GeV, and it will also be useful to study supernova neutrinos with 10–100 MeV energies.

- To detect neutrinos of much higher energies, $E_\nu \gg 1\,\mathrm{TeV}$, very big detectors exploiting the Cherenkov technique have been built using deep sea water (such as the ANTARES Observatory in the Mediterranean), deep lakes (GVD detector in lake Baikal in Siberia) and the Antarctic ice (the IceCube detector in the South Pole). Strings of PMTs are deployed in these sites so as to view a very large volume, which for example reaches $1\,km^3$ in the case of the present IceCube detector. When neutrinos interact through charged-current interactions, different signatures are expected depending on the neutrino flavor considered (the NC interaction with nuclei produces an hadronic cascade in all cases). The electron neutrinos would give rise to an electromagnetic shower initiated by the electron that is produced, in addition to the coincident shower generated by the nuclear recoil. These showers typically extend a few meters inside the detector and their observation provides a good energy reconstruction but they have a poor directionality, with the typical cascade angular resolution for IceCube being about 10° for energies above 100 TeV. Charged current muon neutrino interactions produce muons which can travel very long distances through the water or ice, producing Cherenkov light along their tracks, besides loosing energy by ionization or collisions with nuclei. These muons can even be detected when they are produced outside the detector and then cross it, in which case they are referred to as throughgoing muons. These muon tracks allow to achieve a good angular resolution, even better than 1°, but the energy reconstruction may be poor if only part of the track is observed, in which case just a lower bound on it can be set. A peculiar signature can be obtained with very-high energy tau neutrinos, a phenomenon named double-bang [Le95]. Here the neutrino CC interaction produces a tau lepton and the recoiling nucleus produces a hadronic cascade, leading to the first bang. If the energy is high enough, the tau lepton may travel a significant distance before it decays to produce the second bang, which results from the shower produced by the tau decays into hadrons (or involving an electron). Note that the decay length of a tau lepton is $(E_\tau/\mathrm{PeV})50\,m$, and hence the showers from the two bangs can be distinctly separated in space already for energies above ~ 100 TeV. At electron antineutrino energies $E_{\bar{\nu}_e} \simeq 6.3$ PeV, the resonant W production enhances the interactions of $\bar{\nu}_e$ with electrons, and this signature is exploited in detectors such as IceCube. There are plans to build in the future a new generation of Cherenkov detectors, larger than the existing ones by an order of magnitude. These are the detectors Hyper-Kamiokande ($\sim$300 kt of water) and IceCube-Gen2 ($\sim$10 km^3 volume in the Antarctic ice).

- Extended air shower detectors: at even higher energies, above few hundred PeV and up to 100 EeV, neutrinos can be detected by observing the extended air showers that they produce in the atmosphere. This can be achieved with detectors that sample the air showers at ground level, such as the Pierre Auger Observatory. The main background for these searches comes from the air showers produced by the ordinary cosmic rays, which are protons or heavier nuclei. To get rid of this background one looks for very inclined showers arriving from directions near the horizon. In this case ordinary cosmic-ray showers would be initiated few hundred km away, as the cosmic rays enter into the atmosphere, so that only few surviving energetic muons will arrive to the detectors. On the other hand, inclined showers induced by neutrinos can be produced essentially at any depth in the atmosphere. In particular, horizontal neutrino induced showers can be initiated close to the detector, and these young showers will then have a significant electromagnetic component, looking very different from the cosmic-ray induced background events. The most sensitive search for neutrinos at EeV energies is actually through the detection of tau neutrinos arriving from slightly below the horizon and interacting in the rock or mountains near the detector. At EeV energies, the tau lepton produced in the tau neutrino charged-current interaction can travel several tens of km in the rock without loosing a significant fraction of its energy and its decay length is about 50 km at these energies. If it exits the ground and decays just above the detector, the air shower that it produces could then be observable.

- Radio detection: another technique which is being developed to detect neutrinos with energies above 0.1 EeV, is by means of the radio emission produced by the cascades that they generate. The dominant mechanism producing radio signals is due to the fact that the electrons and positrons of the shower are deflected in opposite directions by the geomagnetic field, and the associated currents generate radio waves. Since the thickness of the front of the air shower is of a few meters, the radio emission is coherent only at frequencies below 100 MHz. This emission can be detected with antennas on the ground, as done in the AERA experiment located at the Auger site in Argentina. Another mechanism producing radio signals is the Askaryan effect [As62], which results from the fact that when a shower is produced in a dense medium, the localized charge excess which is due to the electrons knocked by the shower particles, and also arising from the annihilation of the positrons from the pairs produced in the cascade, will lead to coherent radio

Cherenkov emission. The charge excess is the dominant mechanism for the radio emission in dense media, but it contributes only about 15% of the radio emission for showers produced in the air. In the case of dense media such as the ice, the electromagnetic shower will develop over a few meters but with a lateral extent of only few cm, so that the emission will be coherent at wavelengths larger than few cm, i.e. for frequencies smaller than few GHz. If at these frequencies the medium in which the shower is produced is transparent, as is the case for ice, this radio emission can be detected inserting antennas underground, such as in the ARA array in the Antarctica, or using antennas at the surface, such as in the Antarctic ARIANNA experiment, or looking to these signals from high above ground, such as done by the ANITA experiment, in which arrays of antennas were flown in balloons over the Antarctica.

Suggested exercises:

- Compute the cross section for the neutrino lepton scattering and verify Eq. (2.5)
- Calculate the threshold of the IBD process, i.e. the minimum energy of the electron anti-neutrino required to initiate the reaction. Assuming to know the energy of the final positron and its angle of emission with respect to the direction of the anti-neutrino source, show that the energy of the initial anti-neutrino can be measured. Estimate the energy of the neutron.
- Compute the cross section for the deep-inelastic neutrino nucleon scattering

Recommended reading

- A comprehensive review on neutrino cross sections can be found in J.A. Formaggio and G.P. Zeller, Rev. Mod. Phys. 84 (2012) 1307
- A web page containing links to most neutrino experiments and a comprehensive bibliography, maintained by S. Gariazzo, C. Giunti and M. Laveder, is http://www.nu.to.infn.it

Chapter 3

Neutrino Masses and Mixings

Solid experimental evidence has been obtained in recent years supporting the fact that neutrinos are massive particles. This evidence comes from the observation of flavor oscillations, as will be discussed in the next chapter. Also strong upper bounds on the neutrino masses are obtained from direct searches and from cosmology. A peculiar fact is that the resulting neutrino masses, which are below the eV scale, are much smaller than the masses of the charged fermions. On the other hand, neutrinos are the only Standard Model fermions which do not feel electromagnetic interactions, and it is known that for neutral particles there are qualitatively new ways in which masses can be generated. This fact may indeed be a fundamental clue to understand the origin of the neutrino masses, which is one of the basic open problems in particle physics nowadays. Another peculiar aspect of the neutrinos is that some of the mixing angles describing the contribution of different flavors to the mass eigenstates are quite large, contrary to what happens in the quark sector. Understanding the mechanism responsible for providing a mass to the neutrinos is expected to shed light on the symmetries and interactions of the more fundamental theory underlying the Standard Model of electroweak interactions.

3.1   Charged fermion masses and quark mixing

In the Standard Model the charged fermions get their masses through their Yukawa couplings to the Higgs field. This interaction gives rise to a mass term once the Higgs boson develops a vacuum expectation value (VEV) in the process of electroweak symmetry breaking. The Yukawa couplings have the form

$$\mathcal{L}_Y = -\left(h^\ell_{\alpha\beta} \overline{L^i_\alpha} H^i e_{\beta R} + h^u_{\alpha\beta} \epsilon_{ij} \overline{Q^i_\alpha} H^{j*} u_{\beta R} + h^d_{\alpha\beta} \overline{Q^i_\alpha} H^i d_{\beta R} + \text{h.c.} \right), \quad (3.1)$$

with $\alpha = 1, 2, 3$ being the flavor label and $i = 1, 2$ being the $SU(2)_L$ label. The field $H^\mathsf{T} = (H^+, H^0)$ is the standard $SU(2)_L$ doublet Higgs, $L_\alpha^\mathsf{T} = (\nu_\alpha, e_\alpha)_L$ and $Q_\alpha^\mathsf{T} = (u_\alpha, d_\alpha)_L$ are the lepton and quark left-handed doublets, while $e_{\alpha R}$, $u_{\alpha R}$ and $d_{\alpha R}$ are the $SU(2)_L$ singlet right-handed fields. The fermionic fields considered here are the so-called flavor (or current) eigenstates, which are the states used to write down the terms in the Lagrangian describing the gauge interactions.

When the neutral component of the Higgs field acquires the VEV $\langle H^0 \rangle \equiv v/\sqrt{2} \simeq 174 \, \mathrm{GeV}$, mass matrices of the form $M_{\alpha\beta}^x \equiv h_{\alpha\beta}^x \langle H^0 \rangle$ are induced for the charged fermions ($x = e, u, d$). Before considering the leptonic sector and how neutrino masses can be included, let us first discuss in some detail the situation with quarks, which is well understood theoretically and experimentally and serves as a reference for discussing the case of leptons.

The electroweak interactions of the three quark generations, ignoring here the strong interactions since they are irrelevant for the issue of flavor mixing, are given by Eq. (1.16). In the flavor basis the quark $SU(2)_L$ current is

$$J_\mu^i = \sum_{\alpha=1}^3 \overline{Q_\alpha} \gamma_\mu \frac{\sigma_i}{2} Q_\alpha, \tag{3.2}$$

where $Q_1^\mathsf{T} = (u, d)_L$, $Q_2^\mathsf{T} = (c, s)_L$ and $Q_3^\mathsf{T} = (t, b)_L$, while the hypercharge current is

$$J_\mu^Y = \sum_{\alpha=1}^3 \left[Y_Q \overline{Q_\alpha} \gamma_\mu Q_\alpha + Y_{u_R} \overline{u_{\alpha R}} \gamma_\mu u_{\alpha R} + Y_{d_R} \overline{d_{\alpha R}} \gamma_\mu d_{\alpha R} \right], \tag{3.3}$$

with $Y_Q = 1/6$, $Y_{u_R} = 2/3$ and $Y_{d_R} = -1/3$.

We see that the gauge interaction part of the Lagrangian is invariant under unitary rotations in flavor space of the form

$$Q_\alpha \to U_{\alpha\beta}^Q Q_\beta \ , \quad u_{\alpha R} \to U_{\alpha\beta}^u u_{\beta R} \ , \quad d_{\alpha R} \to U_{\alpha\beta}^d d_{\beta R}. \tag{3.4}$$

These unitary rotations leave invariant also the Lagrangian kinetic terms. On the other hand, the quark mass terms in the Lagrangian are given by

$$-\mathcal{L}_m = M_{\alpha\beta}^u \overline{u_{\alpha L}} u_{\beta R} + M_{\alpha\beta}^d \overline{d_{\alpha L}} d_{\beta R} + \text{h.c.} \tag{3.5}$$

The quark mass eigenstates, distinguished hereafter with a prime, are the states

$$\begin{pmatrix} u' \\ c' \\ t' \end{pmatrix}_{L,R} = U_{L,R}^u \begin{pmatrix} u \\ c \\ t \end{pmatrix}_{L,R} \quad , \quad \begin{pmatrix} d' \\ s' \\ b' \end{pmatrix}_{L,R} = U_{L,R}^d \begin{pmatrix} d \\ s \\ b \end{pmatrix}_{L,R} \quad , \tag{3.6}$$

with the unitary rotations being those that diagonalize the quark mass matrices, i.e. such that

$$U_L^u M^u \left(U_R^u\right)^\dagger = \operatorname{diag}(m_u, m_c, m_t) \quad , \quad U_L^d M^d \left(U_R^d\right)^\dagger = \operatorname{diag}(m_d, m_s, m_b).$$
(3.7)

These rotations have a non-trivial implication for the weak charged currents,

$$\mathcal{L}_{\mathrm{CC}} = -g J_\mu^+ W^{+\mu} + \text{h.c.} \ ,$$
(3.8)

which connect up-type to down-type left-handed quarks of the same doublets, i.e. those in the same flavor generation. Indeed

$$J_\mu^+ = \frac{1}{\sqrt{2}} \sum_\alpha \overline{u_{\alpha L}} \gamma_\mu d_{\alpha L} = \frac{1}{\sqrt{2}} \sum_{\alpha,\beta} \overline{u'_{\alpha L}} \gamma_\mu \left(V_{\mathsf{CKM}}\right)_{\alpha\beta} d'_{L\beta},$$
(3.9)

showing that the unitary Cabibbo-Kobayashi-Maskawa matrix

$$V_{\mathsf{CKM}} \equiv U_L^u U_L^{d\dagger}$$
(3.10)

appears in the charged currents among mass eigenstates.

Note that the quark mass matrices are in general non-diagonal in flavor space. However, given the freedom discussed in Eq. (3.4) it is possible, and convenient, to choose the starting flavor basis by identifying the up-type flavors with the up quark mass eigenstates of the three generations, such that $u_\alpha = u'_\alpha$. In this case, $M^u_{\alpha\beta} = \operatorname{diag}(m_u, m_c, m_t)$ and $U_{L,R}^u = 1$. This choice leaves however the down-type mass matrix non-diagonal[1] and the mixing matrix appearing in the charged currents is related to the mixing in the left-handed down quark sector, $V_{\mathsf{CKM}} = U_L^{d\dagger}$. The left-handed quark doublets, whose up and down components couple to the W boson, can in this case be written in terms of the mass eigenstates as

$$Q_\alpha = \begin{pmatrix} u'_\alpha \\ (V_{\mathsf{CKM}})_{\alpha\beta} d'_\beta \end{pmatrix}_L.$$
(3.11)

This means that a W-exchange will connect a given up-type quark mass eigenstate with the three different down-type mass eigenstates (see diagram in Fig. 3.1).

The unitarity of V_{CKM} implies that this complex matrix depends on 9 independent real parameters (or N^2 in the hypothetical case of N generations). Moreover, since one has the freedom to redefine the quark phases

---

[1]One could have chosen instead $d_\alpha = d'_\alpha$, i.e. define the flavor states such that the down quark flavors coincide with the mass eigenstates. In that case, the quark mixing would have appeared in the up-type sector. The traditional convention is due to the fact that the first mixing ever studied was that among the d and s quarks, what happened before the discovery of the charm quark and of the third generation.

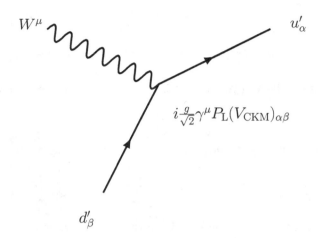

$$i\frac{g}{\sqrt{2}}\gamma^\mu P_{\rm L}(V_{\rm CKM})_{\alpha\beta}$$

Fig. 3.1   Coupling of the W boson to the quark mass eigenstates.

through $d_{\alpha \rm L} \to \exp(i\theta_\alpha)d_{\alpha \rm L}$ and $u_{\alpha \rm L} \to \exp(i\xi_\alpha)u_{\alpha \rm L}$, this allows to re-absorb $6 - 1 = 5$ parameters (or $2N - 1$ for N generations), which are just the number of relative phases among the quark fields. Notice that a common global phase, corresponding to $\theta_1 = \theta_2 = \theta_3 = \xi_1 = \xi_2 = \xi_3$, is nothing but the baryon number symmetry, which leaves $V_{\rm CKM}$ invariant. This means that $V_{\rm CKM}$ can in general be parameterized in terms of 4 parameters, or $N^2 - (2N - 1) = (N - 1)^2$ in the case of N generations. Of these, $N(N - 1)/2$ can be taken as real mixing angles, and the remaining $(N - 1)(N - 2)/2$ as CP violating phases that make $V_{\rm CKM}$ complex.

For the standard three generation case, a parameterization that is usually adopted is the one depending on the three mixing angles θ_{12}, θ_{23} and θ_{13} and on one CP violating phase δ through

$$V_{\rm CKM} = R_{23}\Gamma_\delta R_{13}\Gamma_\delta^\dagger R_{12}. \tag{3.12}$$

Here the matrix R_{ij} represents a rotation by an angle θ_{ij} of the rows and columns i and j, while $\Gamma_\delta = {\rm diag}(1, 1, e^{i\delta})$. One hence obtains

$$V_{\rm CKM} = \begin{pmatrix} 1 & 0 & 0 \\ 0 & c_{23} & s_{23} \\ 0 & -s_{23} & c_{23} \end{pmatrix} \begin{pmatrix} c_{13} & 0 & s_{13}e^{-i\delta} \\ 0 & 1 & 0 \\ -s_{13}e^{i\delta} & 0 & c_{13} \end{pmatrix} \begin{pmatrix} c_{12} & s_{12} & 0 \\ -s_{12} & c_{12} & 0 \\ 0 & 0 & 1 \end{pmatrix} \tag{3.13}$$

$$= \begin{pmatrix} c_{12}c_{13} & s_{12}c_{13} & s_{13}e^{-i\delta} \\ -s_{12}c_{23} - c_{12}s_{23}s_{13}e^{i\delta} & c_{12}c_{23} - s_{12}s_{23}s_{13}e^{i\delta} & s_{23}c_{13} \\ s_{12}s_{23} - c_{12}c_{23}s_{13}e^{i\delta} & -c_{12}s_{23} - s_{12}c_{23}s_{13}e^{i\delta} & c_{23}c_{13} \end{pmatrix},$$

where $c_{ij} \equiv \cos\theta_{ij}$ and $s_{ij} \equiv \sin\theta_{ij}$. The CKM matrix has been determined combining a large number of experiments, leading to $\theta_{12} \simeq 13°$, $\theta_{13} \simeq 0.2°$, $\theta_{23} \simeq 2.4°$ and $\delta \simeq 69°$. Note that in the limit $\theta_{13} \to 0$ and $\theta_{23} \to 0$ one would recover the two generation Cabibbo mixing, with $\theta_C \simeq \theta_{12}$. Given the small values of θ_{13} and θ_{23}, the mixing of the third generation with the first two is rather small for the quarks. On the other hand, the CP violating angle δ is found to be sizable.

3.2 The Dirac equation

Before proceeding to discuss the possible neutrino mass terms, it is useful to recall some of the properties of the different spinor representations, which will be used to introduce the Majorana mass terms.

The Dirac equation for a free particle is

$$(i\partial\!\!\!/ - m)\Psi = 0. \tag{3.14}$$

The Dirac matrices satisfy

$$\{\gamma^\mu, \gamma^\nu\} = 2\,g^{\mu\nu} \ , \quad \gamma^0\gamma^{\mu\dagger}\gamma^0 = \gamma^\mu. \tag{3.15}$$

The first condition, where the Minkowski metric is $g = \mathrm{diag}(1,-1,-1,-1)$, guarantees that the components of the spinor field satisfy the Klein-Gordon equation, since applying $(i\partial\!\!\!/ + m)$ to the Dirac equation one gets

$$0 = (-\partial_\mu\partial_\nu\gamma^\mu\gamma^\nu - m^2)\Psi = (-\frac{1}{2}\partial_\mu\partial_\nu\{\gamma^\mu,\gamma^\nu\} - m^2)\Psi = -(\Box + m^2)\Psi. \tag{3.16}$$

This ensures the validity of the relativistic dispersion relation $E^2 = p^2 + m^2$. Note that the Dirac equation can also be written as a Schrödinger-like equation, $i(\partial/\partial t)\Psi = \mathcal{H}\Psi$, where identifying $\vec{p} = -i\nabla$ the Hamiltonian is $\mathcal{H} = \vec{\alpha}\cdot\vec{p} + \beta m$, with $\vec{\alpha} = \gamma^0\vec{\gamma}$ and $\beta = \gamma^0$.

The second relation in Eq. (3.15), which is a compact way of stating that γ^0 is hermitian while γ^i are anti-hermitian, ensures that both $\vec{\alpha}$ and β, and hence also the Hamiltonian, are hermitian.

Another useful matrix, called chirality, is $\gamma_5 \equiv i\gamma^0\gamma^1\gamma^2\gamma^3$, which satisfies

$$\{\gamma_5, \gamma^\mu\} = 0 \ , \quad \gamma_5^\dagger = \gamma_5 \ \text{and} \ \gamma_5^2 = 1. \tag{3.17}$$

This matrix allows to define the chirality projectors $P_{\mathsf{L,R}} \equiv (1 \mp \gamma_5)/2$ satisfying $P_\mathsf{L}^2 = P_\mathsf{L}$, $P_\mathsf{R}^2 = P_\mathsf{R}$ and $P_\mathsf{L}P_\mathsf{R} = 0$.

Note that given one representation γ for the gamma matrices, the set of matrices $\gamma' \equiv U\gamma U^\dagger$, with U unitary, is also a valid representation in which $\Psi \to U\Psi$.

One commonly used representation for the gamma matrices is the chiral (or Weyl) representation

$$\gamma^0 = \begin{pmatrix} 0 & 1 \\ 1 & 0 \end{pmatrix} \quad , \quad \gamma^i = \begin{pmatrix} 0 & \sigma_i \\ -\sigma_i & 0 \end{pmatrix} \quad , \quad \gamma_5 = \begin{pmatrix} -1 & 0 \\ 0 & 1 \end{pmatrix}, \tag{3.18}$$

in which each element is a 2×2 matrix, with σ_i being the Pauli matrices. In this representation the chiral projectors take a particularly simple form, with $P_L = \mathrm{diag}(1,0)$ just selecting the two upper components of Ψ while $P_R = \mathrm{diag}(0,1)$ selecting the two lower ones.

Another set of matrices is the Dirac representation, which is particularly useful when studying the low-energy limit of the Dirac equation. In this representation

$$\gamma^0 = \begin{pmatrix} 1 & 0 \\ 0 & -1 \end{pmatrix} \quad , \quad \gamma^i = \begin{pmatrix} 0 & \sigma_i \\ -\sigma_i & 0 \end{pmatrix} \quad , \quad \gamma_5 = \begin{pmatrix} 0 & 1 \\ 1 & 0 \end{pmatrix}. \tag{3.19}$$

The Majorana representation, in which the matrices are imaginary while the fields are real, is instead

$$\gamma^0 = \begin{pmatrix} 0 & \sigma_2 \\ \sigma_2 & 0 \end{pmatrix} \quad , \quad \gamma^1 = \begin{pmatrix} i\sigma_3 & 0 \\ 0 & i\sigma_3 \end{pmatrix} \quad , \quad \gamma^2 = \begin{pmatrix} 0 & -\sigma_2 \\ \sigma_2 & 0 \end{pmatrix} \quad , \quad \gamma^3 = \begin{pmatrix} -i\sigma_1 & 0 \\ 0 & -i\sigma_1 \end{pmatrix}$$

$$\gamma_5 = \begin{pmatrix} \sigma_2 & 0 \\ 0 & \sigma_2 \end{pmatrix}. \tag{3.20}$$

3.3   The antiparticle field

In order to write Lorentz invariant terms in the Lagrangian, it is useful to introduce the adjoint field $\overline{\Psi} \equiv \Psi^\dagger \gamma^0$, so that for instance the bilinear term $\overline{\Psi}\Psi$ is Lorentz invariant while $\overline{\Psi}\gamma^\mu\Psi$ transforms as a four-vector and leads to a Lorentz invariant term when contracted with another four-vector.

A particularly relevant spinor turns out to be the antiparticle field, described by the conjugate spinor Ψ^c, which transforms as Ψ under Lorentz transformations but has the opposite charges. Consider for instance the Dirac equation for a fermion with electric charge eq in the presence of an electromagnetic field A_μ, which is obtained from the free Dirac equation making the substitution $\partial_\mu \to \partial_\mu - ieqA_\mu$, so that

$$[i(\partial\!\!\!/ - ieq A\!\!\!/) - m]\, \Psi = 0. \tag{3.21}$$

If we consider the complex conjugate of this equation, multiply on the left by $\gamma^{0\mathsf{T}}$ and use that $\gamma^{0\mathsf{T}}\gamma^{\mu*}\gamma^{0\mathsf{T}} = \gamma^{\mu\mathsf{T}}$, one gets

$$\left[-i(\partial_\mu + ieqA_\mu)\gamma^{\mu\mathsf{T}} - m\right]\overline{\Psi}^\mathsf{T} = 0. \tag{3.22}$$

The conjugate field is introduced through $\Psi^c \equiv C\overline{\Psi}^{\mathsf{T}}$, where in order that Ψ^c be properly normalized C has to be a unitary matrix. Since $\Psi^c \equiv C\gamma^{0\mathsf{T}}\Psi^*$, this field has the opposite charges as Ψ. If we then require that

$$C\gamma^{\mu\mathsf{T}}C^{-1} = -\gamma^\mu, \tag{3.23}$$

this leads to

$$\left[i(\slashed{\partial} + ieq\slashed{A}) - m\right]\Psi^c = 0, \tag{3.24}$$

so that the field Ψ^c will indeed satisfy the Dirac equation with a charge opposite to that of Ψ, and hence C is called the charge conjugation matrix. Note that Eq. (3.23) leaves the freedom of an overall phase in C, and that if C satisfies the equation also C^{T} satisfies it. It can indeed be shown that C is antisymmetric,[2] in which case one has that $(\Psi^c)^c = -CC^*\Psi = \Psi$. The matrix C then satisfies

$$C^{-1} = C^\dagger = -C^*. \tag{3.25}$$

Another useful relation is that $\overline{\Psi^c} = -\Psi^{\mathsf{T}}C^\dagger$. In the most common representations of the Dirac matrices, the matrix C can be taken to be real, in which case $C^\dagger = C^{\mathsf{T}} = -C$ and one gets $\overline{\Psi^c} = \Psi^{\mathsf{T}}C$. In particular, in the Dirac and Weyl representations one can take $C = i\gamma^2\gamma^0$ which, as can be directly checked, is real and satisfies all the necessary conditions.

3.4 Dirac, Weyl and Majorana spinors

A Dirac spinor Ψ, such as the one used to describe a charged particle, contains four degrees of freedom, annihilating the two polarizations of the particle and creating the two polarizations of the corresponding antiparticle. One can write the free particle field as an expansion over plane waves

$$\Psi = \sum_{s=1,2} \int \frac{\mathrm{d}^3 p}{(2\pi)^{3/2}\sqrt{2E}} \left[b_s(p)u_s(p)e^{-ip\cdot x} + d_s^\dagger(p)v_s(p)e^{ip\cdot x}\right]. \tag{3.26}$$

The polarizations may correspond for instance to $s_z = \pm 1$ (alternatively, the decomposition may be done in terms of the L and R chirality states). The wave functions $u_s(p)$ and $v_s(p)$ are the positive and negative frequency solutions, such that

$$(\slashed{p} - m)u_s(p) = 0 \quad , \quad (\slashed{p} + m)v_s(p) = 0, \tag{3.27}$$

---

[2]This can be seen considering the Lorentz invariant bilinear $\overline{\Psi}_i\Psi_j^c$. Transposing it should leave it unchanged, and using that the fermionic fields anticommute one gets $\overline{\Psi}_i\Psi_j^c = \Psi_i^\dagger\gamma^0 C\gamma^{0\mathsf{T}}\Psi_j^* = -\Psi_j^\dagger\gamma^0 C^{\mathsf{T}}\gamma^{0\mathsf{T}}\Psi_i^*$. Considering the case $i = j$ it is clear that C needs to be antisymmetric.

and are normalized such that $u_s(p)^\dagger u_{s'}(p) = v_s(p)^\dagger v_{s'}(p) = 2E\delta_{ss'}$. The operators b_s will annihilate the particle with polarization s, while $d_s^\dagger$ will create the antiparticle with polarization s. These operators satisfy anti-conmutation relations, for instance $\{b_s(p), b_{s'}^\dagger(p')\} = \delta^3(\vec{p} - \vec{p'})\delta_{ss'}$, and similarly for d_s. On the other hand, the conjugate field Ψ^c will create the particle states and annihilate the corresponding antiparticle states.

The chiral fields Ψ_L and Ψ_R, usually referred to as Weyl spinors, describe each of them just two degrees of freedom. Using that $C^{-1}\gamma_5 C = \gamma_5^T$, and hence that $C^{-1}P_{L,R}C = P_{L,R}^T$, one has that the conjugates of the chiral fields are

$$(\Psi_{L,R})^c = (\Psi^c)_{R,L}. \tag{3.28}$$

The fields Ψ_L and its conjugate $(\Psi_L)^c$ contain the same two degrees of freedom, corresponding to the left-handed particle and the right-handed antiparticle, but one field creates the states that the conjugate field annihilates and viceversa. Note that the conjugation operation changes both the charges and the chirality of the Weyl field, and hence is related to the CP conjugation rather than just charge conjugation.

It is also useful to introduce the concept of a Majorana field, which treats in a more symmetric way particles and antiparticles. This can be achieved by means of the state

$$\chi = \Psi_L + e^{i\theta}(\Psi_L)^c, \tag{3.29}$$

where we allowed for a relative phase factor $e^{i\theta}$. This phase is called the Majorana creation phase because

$$\chi^c = (\Psi_L)^c + e^{-i\theta}\Psi_L = e^{-i\theta}\chi. \tag{3.30}$$

This implies that the Majorana field coincides, up to an overall phase factor, with its conjugate field.

A fermion with four degrees of freedom, such as the electron, can be described in general by a Dirac spinor Ψ or, alternatively, by its two chiral projections $\Psi_{L,R}$, or even by two Majorana spinors, such as $\chi_1 = \Psi_L + (\Psi_L)^c$ and $\chi_2 = \Psi_R + (\Psi_R)^c$. This description would also apply to the neutrinos if their masses were of the Dirac type.

As we already mentioned, for a massless Dirac fermion there would be no coupling between the two chiralities and one may hence consider independently the left and right-handed chiralities, each with two degrees of freedom. A logical possibility for a massless fermion would then be that the right-handed chiralities actually be absent from the theory, as was considered to be the case at some point when the neutrinos were believed to be massless. On the other hand, if neutrinos were massive but their masses were due to lepton number violating Majorana mass terms, as will be discussed below each neutrino mass eigenstate would have just two degrees of freedom, and it would have to be described by one single Majorana spinor rather than by a Dirac one.

3.5 Neutrino masses

The origin of neutrino masses is much more speculative and uncertain than that of the charged fermion masses, since there is a larger variety of possible ways to generate them. In general, a fermionic mass term always involves a flip of chirality, coupling a left-handed field to a right-handed one. Since $SU(2)_L$ singlet right-handed neutrinos would have no weak, electromagnetic nor strong interactions, this means that it would not be possible to produce or detect them through any known gauge interaction. This is why there is no real need to introduce them to account for the usual particle physics accelerator phenomenology. If one considers the *minimal* version of the Standard Model in which no right-handed neutrinos are introduced, and in which the only Higgs boson present is the standard $SU(2)_L$ doublet one, there is no way to generate a mass term for the neutrinos via Yukawa couplings analogous to those that give masses to the charged fermions. This is why it is often said that in the Standard Model the neutrinos are strictly massless. In this sense, the non-vanishing neutrino masses that have been inferred from different observations provide the first clear experimental evidence requiring the presence of physics beyond the minimal Standard Model.

3.5.1 *Dirac neutrino masses*

The simplest way to give neutrinos a mass would be to introduce the right-handed neutrinos (one for each generation) and couple them through a Yukawa interaction of the form

$$\mathcal{L}_Y = -\left(h^\nu_{\alpha\beta} \epsilon_{ij} \overline{L^i_\alpha} H^{j*} \nu_{R\beta} + \text{h.c.} \right). \tag{3.31}$$

After the electroweak symmetry breaking, the resulting neutrino mass term will be

$$-\mathcal{L}_m = (m_D)_{\alpha\beta} \overline{\nu_{\alpha L}} \nu_{\beta R} + \text{h.c.}, \tag{3.32}$$

where $m_D \equiv h^\nu \langle H^0 \rangle$. This mass is in principle non-diagonal in flavor space, but it is possible to diagonalize it, as we did with the quarks, through a bi-unitary transformation such that $U_L^\nu m_D U_R^{\nu\dagger} = \text{diag}(m_1, m_2, m_3)$, and one can define the mass-eigenstates as $\nu_{i\text{L,R}} = \left(U_{\text{L,R}}^\nu\right)_{i\alpha} \nu_{\alpha\text{L,R}}$. The Dirac neutrino fields are introduced as

$$\nu_i \equiv \nu_{i\text{L}} + \nu_{i\text{R}}, \qquad (3.33)$$

so that

$$-\mathcal{L}_m = \sum_i m_i \overline{\nu_i} \nu_i. \qquad (3.34)$$

For each neutrino mass eigenstate, the fields ν_i contain four degrees of freedom (left and right neutrino and antineutrino chiralities), similarly to what happens in the case of the charged fermions. It is clear also that this so-called Dirac mass term preserves the global lepton number symmetry corresponding to $\nu_j \to e^{i\theta}\nu_j$, in the same way as the charged lepton mass term preserves lepton number or the quark mass term preserves baryon number.

Although this mechanism to generate neutrino masses is very simple, its main drawback is that since the Higgs VEV is at the electroweak scale ($\langle H^0 \rangle \sim 10^2\,\text{GeV} = 10^{11}\,\text{eV}$), in order to generate masses below one eV the Yukawa couplings have to be extremely small, $h^\nu < 10^{-11}$. This is in particular much smaller than the known Yukawa couplings of the charged fermions, for which the smallest one is that of the electron, which is of order 3×10^{-6}, while the largest one is that of the top quark, which is of order unity. In the absence of any appealing explanation for such a hierarchy between neutral and charged fermion Yukawa couplings, the plain Dirac neutrino masses look then unnaturally small.

3.5.2 *Majorana neutrino masses*

The two experimentally known neutrino states with electron flavor are the left-handed electron neutrino, produced e.g. in a β^+ decay in association with a positron ($A \to A' + e^+ + \nu_e$), and the right-handed electron antineutrino, produced e.g. in a β^- decay in association with an electron ($A \to A' + e + \overline{\nu}_e$). Something similar also happens with the muon and tau neutrino flavors produced through weak interactions. These states are conveniently described by Weyl spinors, which have definite chiralities and hence contain just two degrees of freedom, i.e.

$$\Psi_\text{L} = \int \frac{\text{d}^3 p}{(2\pi)^3 \sqrt{2E_\nu}} \left[b_\text{L}(p) u_L(p) e^{-ip\cdot x} + d_\text{R}^\dagger(p) v_R(p) e^{ip\cdot x} \right], \qquad (3.35)$$

with $E_\nu = \sqrt{p^2 + m^2}$. Here the operator b_L annihilates a left-handed particle while $d_R^\dagger$ creates a right-handed antiparticle.

One may envisage the possibility of using just these two degrees of freedom to write down a mass term involving the required L $\leftrightarrow$ R transition. This possibility was first suggested by Majorana in 1937, in a paper named *Symmetric theory of the electron and positron*, which was devoted mainly to the problem of getting rid of the negative energy sea filled with fermions that had been associated to the Dirac equation [Ma37]. As a side product, he found that for neutral particles there was *no more any reason to presume the existence of antiparticles*, and that *it was possible to modify the theory of beta emission, both positive and negative, so that it came always associated with the emission of a neutrino.* In other words, according to this hypothesis the mass eigenstate neutrino field and its antiparticle field coincide, just as happens with the photon or with the neutral pion π^0, which coincide with their antiparticles.

To see how this works, let us consider the antiparticle field, $(\nu_L)^c$, which is a right-handed field, and write the advertised Majorana mass term as

$$- \mathcal{L}_M = \frac{1}{2} m [\overline{\nu_L}(\nu_L)^c + \overline{(\nu_L)^c}\nu_L]. \qquad (3.36)$$

This mass term has the required Lorentz structure with the L $\leftrightarrow$ R transition, but it just involves two degrees of freedom. One can see that this mass term does not preserve any $U(1)$ phase symmetry, violating the so-called lepton number by two units. If we introduce the associated Majorana field $\nu \equiv \nu_L + (\nu_L)^c$, which under conjugation transforms into itself ($\nu^c = \nu$), the mass term becomes

$$\mathcal{L}_M = -\frac{m}{2} \overline{\nu}\nu. \qquad (3.37)$$

Up to now we have introduced the Majorana mass m by hand, contrary to what was done in the case of the charged fermions where it arose from a Yukawa coupling in a spontaneously broken theory. To follow a similar procedure with the neutrinos presents however a difficulty, because the Standard Model neutrinos belong to $SU(2)_L$ doublets, and hence to write an electroweak singlet Yukawa coupling it is necessary to introduce an $SU(2)_L$ triplet Higgs field $\vec{\Delta}$. The coupling $\mathcal{L} \propto \overline{L^c}\vec{\sigma}L \cdot \vec{\Delta}$, with $\vec{\sigma}$ the Pauli matrices, would then lead to the Majorana mass term after the neutral component of the scalar triplet gets a VEV.[3] Alternatively, the Majorana mass term could arise from a loop effect in models where the neutrinos have lepton number

---

[3]Note that the isosinglet lepton bilinear combination $\epsilon^{\alpha\beta} L_\alpha^c L_\beta$ does not contain the term $\nu^c \nu$ that could give rise to a neutrino mass term.

violating couplings to new scalars, as in the so-called Zee models [Ze80] or in the supersymmetric models with R-parity violation. These models have the interesting feature that the masses are naturally suppressed by a loop factor, and they could also be attractive if one looks for scenarios where the neutrinos have relatively large electromagnetic dipole moments, since a photon can be directly attached to the charged particles in the loop.

Probably the nicest mechanism to give neutrinos a mass is the so-called Type-I see-saw model [Mi77; Ge79; Ya79; Mo80]. In this scenario, which naturally occurs in grand unified theories (GUTs) such as $SO(10)$, one introduces the $SU(2)_\mathsf{L}$ singlet right handed neutrinos N_R and let them acquire a Majorana mass M through the VEV of an $SU(2)_\mathsf{L}$ singlet Higgs. The natural scale for the singlet VEV is the scale of the breaking of the grand unified group, i.e. typically in the range 10^{12}–10^{16} GeV. Allowing also for a Dirac mass term resulting from an ordinary Yukawa coupling after the electroweak symmetry gets broken, the mass terms in the Lagrangian will be

$$-\mathcal{L}_M = \frac{1}{2}(\overline{\nu_\mathsf{L}}, \overline{(N_\mathsf{R})^c}) \begin{pmatrix} 0 & m_D \\ m_D & M \end{pmatrix} \begin{pmatrix} (\nu_\mathsf{L})^c \\ N_\mathsf{R} \end{pmatrix} + \text{h.c.} \qquad (3.38)$$

The mass eigenstates which result from the diagonalisation of this mass matrix are two Majorana fields with masses $m_\text{light} \simeq m_D^2/M$ and $m_\text{heavy} \simeq M$. Since $m_D/M \ll 1$, we see that $m_\text{light} \ll m_D$, and hence the lightness of the known neutrinos is here related to the heaviness of the sterile states N_R.

If we introduce one singlet neutrino per family, the different entries in the mass matrix in Eq. (3.38) are 3×3 matrices and one ends up with a 6×6 neutrino mass matrix, which has to be symmetric.[4] In the see-saw limit, corresponding to $m_D \ll M$, this matrix can be block diagonalized and the resulting mass matrix in the sector of the three light neutrinos is $M_\text{light} = -m_D^\mathsf{T} M^{-1} m_D$.

Note that if m_D is similar to the up-type quark masses, as happens for instance in $SO(10)$ grand unified theories, one would expect $m_{\nu_3} \sim m_t^2/M \simeq 0.04\,\text{eV}(10^{15}\,\text{GeV}/M)$. It is clear then that in these scenarios the observation of neutrino masses near $0.1\,\text{eV}$ would point out to new physics at about the GUT scale. On the other hand, for $m_D \sim$ GeV the

---

[4]This can be seen writing $-\mathcal{L}_m = \nu_{\mathsf{L}\alpha}^\mathsf{T} C M_{\alpha\beta} \nu_{\mathsf{L}\beta} = -\nu_{\mathsf{L}\beta}^\mathsf{T} C^\mathsf{T} M_{\alpha\beta} \nu_{\mathsf{L}\alpha}$, where we transposed the Lorentz structure and got the minus sign because the fermion fields anticommute. Using that C is antisymmetric and exchanging the indices α and β one then gets $M_{\alpha\beta} = M_{\beta\alpha}$.

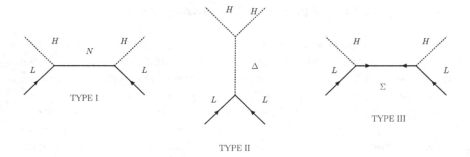

Fig. 3.2 Diagrams corresponding to the different types of see-saw mechanisms.

singlet neutrino masses would be required to lie at an intermediate scale, $M \sim 10^{10}$–10^{12} GeV, which is also of great theoretical interest.

The most general form of the mass matrix involving ν_L and N_R is

$$- \mathcal{L}_M = \frac{1}{2} (\overline{\nu_\mathsf{L}}, \overline{(N_\mathsf{R})^c}) \begin{pmatrix} m_\mathsf{T} & m_D \\ m_D^\mathsf{T} & M \end{pmatrix} \begin{pmatrix} (\nu_\mathsf{L})^c \\ N_\mathsf{R} \end{pmatrix} + \text{h.c.}, \qquad (3.39)$$

where m_T could be generated by the VEV of a triplet Higgs, m_D by the standard Higgs doublet VEV while M by that of a singlet Higgs. The case of Dirac neutrinos corresponds to $m_\mathsf{T} = M = 0$, while otherwise the neutrinos will be Majorana particles.

Other possibilities still exist, such as the type-II seesaw, in which instead of the heavy singlet neutrino one introduces a heavy scalar triplet Δ which is then coupled to the triplet combination of two Higgs doublets. The light neutrino masses in this model are then proportional to v^2/m_Δ. Yet another alternative is the type-III seesaw model, in which the lepton doublet couples to a fermion triplet Σ and to the Higgs doublet. The exchange of the fermion triplet can then lead to a mass term proportional to v^2/m_Σ. The different diagrams leading to the neutrino mass terms in these three scenarios are illustrated in Fig. 3.2. All these possibilities lead, at low energies, to an effective operator

$$\mathcal{L} = -\frac{c_{\alpha\beta}}{\Lambda} \left(\overline{L_\alpha^c} \tilde{H}^* \right) \left(\tilde{H}^\dagger L_\beta \right) + \text{h.c.}, \qquad (3.40)$$

where $\tilde{H}_i = \varepsilon_{ij} H_j^*$. This so-called Weinberg operator [We79] has mass dimension five (3/2 for each fermionic field and 1 for each bosonic field), and is hence suppressed by the high-energy scale Λ that is related to the mass of the exchanged particle in each model. After the electroweak symmetry breaking this operator leads to a Majorana mass term for the neutrinos of the form $c_{\alpha\beta} v^2/\Lambda$.

3.6   Experimental signatures of Majorana neutrinos

If neutrinos are Majorana particles, there are some processes involving lepton number violation that become possible and that could be used, if the masses are not too small, to distinguish between the Dirac or Majorana nature of the neutrinos. One is the oscillation between neutrinos and antineutrinos [Po57], that could be observed for instance if a muon neutrino produced together with a positive muon interacts as if it were an antineutrino, i.e producing a positive muon. These kind of processes are proportional to $(m_\nu/E_\nu)^2$, and they are hence expected to be quite small for the standard light neutrinos. A possible exception could be the search for lepton number violating processes at high-energy colliders, such as through the production of pairs of leptons with the same charge associated to the exchange of heavy Majorana neutrinos. For this to have chances of being observable the heavy neutrino masses should be at the TeV scale. Note however that TeV scale neutrinos no longer explain in a natural way the lightness of the ordinary neutrinos via the see-saw mechanism.

The most promising process to test the Majorana nature of the neutrinos is the so-called neutrinoless double-beta decay, first discussed by Furry in 1939 [Fu39]. In this case, a nucleus suffers simultaneously two beta decays, via $(A, Z) \to (A, Z + 2) + 2e$, so that two electrons get emitted. While in the normal double-beta decay [Go35] also two antineutrinos get emitted, in the neutrinoless channel the antineutrino emitted in the vertex where one of the electrons is produced gets absorbed, as if it were a neutrino, in the other vertex, and as a result no neutrino gets emitted. This implies that the lepton number L (and actually also $B - L$, where B is the baryon number) gets violated in the decay. The main signature of this process would be that the sum of the energies of the two electrons amounts to the total available energy, while in the standard double-beta decay the spectrum of the sum of the two electron energies is continuously distributed because the two emitted antineutrinos carry a fraction of the available energy (see Fig. 3.3).

Being a second order weak process, which depends upon the values of the neutrino Majorana masses, the lifetimes associated to the double-beta decays are huge, and to observe this decay one needs to consider nuclei in which the single beta decay is not allowed. This is actually the case for some nuclei having even numbers of protons and of neutrons, for which the possible final states of a single beta decay, having an odd number of protons and neutrons, would have a higher mass, making the single beta decay channel to be forbidden. There are 41 isotopes for which this happens

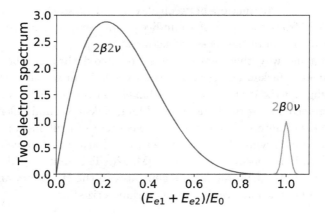

Fig. 3.3 Double-beta decay spectrum as a function of the sum of the two electron energies normalized to the end-point energy E_0. The small peak at the endpoint would be the smoking gun signature of the neutrinoless mode, and its width is related to the energy resolution of the experiment (considered here as 5%).

(35 $\beta^-\beta^-$ and 6 $\beta^+\beta^+$) and the two neutrino double-beta decay mode has indeed been directly observed in about a dozen of them (such as in ^{48}Ca, ^{76}Ge, ^{100}Mo, ^{136}Xe, ^{130}Te, etc., which have lifetimes of the order of 10^{19}–10^{21} yr). By precisely measuring the spectrum of the two electrons near the endpoint, searching for the expected peak from the neutrinoless double-beta decay, one can then set bounds, or eventually one day measure, the associated Majorana neutrino mass. Present lower bounds on the lifetimes of the neutrinoless double-beta decay mode are typically larger than 10^{25} yr.

3.7 Neutrino mixing

When considering the weak interactions of the leptons, one chooses the flavor basis such that for the charged leptons the flavor eigenstates coincide with the mass eigenstates. In this way, the e, μ and τ leptons are identified by measuring their masses. The neutrino flavor eigenstates ν_α, with $\alpha = e$, μ, τ, are just the states coupling in the W boson mediated CC interactions with the corresponding charged lepton mass eigenstates. If neutrinos are massive, there is no reason to expect that the mass eigenstates ν_k (with $k = 1, 2, 3$) should coincide with the flavor (gauge) eigenstates ν_α, and hence the CC weak interaction will in general couple each of the charged leptons with all the different neutrino mass eigenstates. Note that for the leptonic case the distinction between flavor and mass eigenstates will be already clear from the type of subindices employed, and hence no prime will be used to denote the mass eigenstates.

In the same way that quark states are mixed through the Cabibbo, Kobayashi and Maskawa matrix, neutrinos would be mixed through the leptonic mixing matrix V such that $\nu_\alpha = V_{\alpha k}\nu_k$. This leptonic mixing matrix is usually referred to as the Pontecorvo, Maki, Nakagawa and Sakata matrix (PMNS), since Pontecorvo introduced the concept of neutrino–antineutrino oscillations [Po57] while Maki, Nakagawa and Sakata introduced the neutrino flavor mixing between ν_e and ν_μ [Ma62]. This matrix will appear in the couplings of the leptonic mass eigenstates to the W boson, and for the three lepton generation case it can be parameterized as

$$V = \begin{pmatrix} c_{12}c_{13} & s_{12}c_{13} & s_{13}e^{-i\delta} \\ -s_{12}c_{23} - c_{12}s_{23}s_{13}e^{i\delta} & c_{12}c_{23} - s_{12}s_{23}s_{13}e^{i\delta} & s_{23}c_{13} \\ s_{12}s_{23} - c_{12}c_{23}s_{13}e^{i\delta} & -c_{12}s_{23} - s_{12}c_{23}s_{13}e^{i\delta} & c_{23}c_{13} \end{pmatrix} P_M,$$

where now the mixing angles involved are those of the neutrino sector. The diagonal matrix $P_M \equiv (e^{i\alpha_1}, e^{i\alpha_2}, 1)$ contains two additional phases. If neutrinos are Dirac particles, these phases can be reabsorbed in the definition of the fields, as is actually done for the quarks. If the neutrinos are Majorana particles, the phases $\alpha_{1,2}$ cannot be removed because left and right-handed neutrino fields are no longer independent from each other, and hence such rotations would necessarily introduce a complex phase in the neutrino masses. Note that due to the freedom of performing an overall phase rotation of the charged fermion fields appearing in the CC, one of the diagonal entries of P_M can be made equal to unity, and hence only the relative phases between different generations enter into it. The parameterization adopted imposes $(P_M)_{33} = 1$. The mixing angles can be chosen to be in the first quadrant, $0 \le \theta_{ij} \le \pi/2$, while the CP violating phase δ and the Majorana phases $\alpha_{1,2}$ can be in the range from 0 to 2π. Moreover, one generally defines ν_1 as the neutrino state with the largest ν_e component and ν_3 to be the one with the smallest ν_e component, so that $|V_{e1}|^2 \ge |V_{e2}|^2 \ge |V_{e3}|^2$. This corresponds to choosing θ_{13} to be in the first octant, i.e. in the range $[0, \pi/4]$, and satisfying $s_{13} \le s_{12}c_{13} \le 1/\sqrt{2}$. The precise values of these mixing angles, and in particular the octant of θ_{23}, as well as the different neutrino masses m_i, and in particular their ordering and the overall mass scale, have to be determined from observations.

Suggested exercises:

- Show that a Dirac neutrino mass term can be written in terms of two Majorana spinors, $\nu_i = \nu_{iL} + (\nu_{iL})^c$, where $\nu_{1L} = \nu_L + (N_R)^c$ and $\nu_{2L} = \nu_L - (N_R)^c$. Does this means that lepton number should be violated?
- Show that with a suitable rephasing of the field, the Majorana condition $\chi = e^{i\theta}\chi^c$ can be written in the simpler form $\psi = \psi^c$.
- Considering a Majorana field, check that the vector and tensor currents $\bar{\chi}\gamma_\mu\chi$ and $\bar{\chi}\sigma_{\mu\nu}\chi$ are both zero, and therefore χ cannot couple directly to the electromagnetic field.
- Convince yourself that the above result does not contradict the statement that a Dirac field can be decomposed into two Majorana fields.

Chapter 4

Neutrino Oscillations

The possibility that the neutrino flavor eigenstates be a superposition of mass eigenstates allows for the phenomenon of neutrino oscillations. Being this a quantum mechanical interference effect, it is sensitive to quite small mass splittings. It arises because the different mass eigenstates evolve differently as the neutrinos propagate and, as a consequence, the flavor composition of a neutrino state can change with time. The observation of flavor oscillations as the neutrinos propagate from the sources to the detectors has allowed to determine the mass squared differences between mass eigenstates as well as the mixing angles involved. Upper bounds on their masses have also been obtained in more direct searches and through their impact on cosmology.

4.1 Neutrino oscillations in vacuum

To study the neutrino oscillation phenomena, consider a flavor eigenstate neutrino ν_α with momentum p that is produced at time $t = 0$ (this could be for instance a ν_μ produced in the decay $\pi^+ \to \mu^+ + \nu_\mu$). The initial state is then

$$|\nu_\alpha\rangle = \sum_k V_{\alpha k}^* |\nu_k\rangle. \tag{4.1}$$

Note that since the neutrino state $|\nu_\alpha\rangle$ is created by the operator $b_\alpha^\dagger$ acting on the vacuum, the conjugate matrix V^* appears in the mixing between neutrino states, while it was instead V that appeared in the mixing between the fields ν_α. On the other hand, for antineutrinos it is V that appears in the mixing between states.

We know that the mass eigenstates evolve with time according to

$$|\nu_k(t, x)\rangle = \exp[i(\vec{p} \cdot \vec{x} - E_k t)]|\nu_k\rangle. \tag{4.2}$$

In the relativistic limit relevant for neutrinos, one has that the energy of a neutrino with mass m_k is $E_k = \sqrt{|\vec{p}|^2 + m_k^2} \simeq |\vec{p}| + m_k^2/(2|\vec{p}|)$, and thus the different mass eigenstates will acquire different phases as they propagate. Hence, the probability of observing a flavor ν_β at time t, i.e. after traversing a distance $L \simeq ct$, is (setting $E \equiv |\vec{p}|$)

$$P(\nu_\alpha \to \nu_\beta) = |\langle \nu_\beta | \nu(t) \rangle|^2 = \left| \sum_k V_{\alpha k}^* V_{\beta k} \exp\left(-i\frac{m_k^2}{2E}L\right) \right|^2$$

$$= \delta_{\alpha\beta} - 4 \sum_{k>j} \mathrm{Re}(V_{\alpha k}^* V_{\beta k} V_{\alpha j} V_{\beta j}^*) \sin^2\left(\frac{\Delta m_{kj}^2 L}{4E}\right)$$

$$+ 2\sum_{k>j} \mathrm{Im}(V_{\alpha k}^* V_{\beta k} V_{\alpha j} V_{\beta j}^*) \sin\left(\frac{\Delta m_{kj}^2 L}{2E}\right). \qquad (4.3)$$

This probability depends on the mass squared difference $\Delta m_{kj}^2 \equiv m_k^2 - m_j^2$, since this is what determines the phase difference affecting the propagation of the different mass eigenstates. Taking into account the explicit expression for the mixing matrix V, it is easy to convince oneself that the Majorana phases α_1 and α_2 do not enter in the oscillation probability. Hence, flavor oscillation phenomena cannot tell whether neutrinos are Dirac or Majorana particles.

We note that to derive Eq. (4.3) we made the simplifying assumption that all mass eigenstates had the same momentum $\vec{p}$ while the energies $E_k = \sqrt{|\vec{p}|^2 + m_k^2}$ differed. The same result could have been obtained assuming the energies to be the same and the momenta to differ. Actually, none of these assumptions is strictly correct, but performing a more accurate analysis using wave-packets instead of plane waves, so as to allow for a spread in the values of momenta and energies describing the neutrino state (with the associated spatial and temporal spreads) would lead to the same final result, as long as the coherence of the superposition between different mass eigenstates is not lost [Nu76].

If the phase δ were 0 or π, the last term in Eq. (4.3) would vanish and no CP violation would be present in neutrino oscillations. However, for generic values of δ this term does contribute to the transition probabilities. Its presence allows for a non-vanishing asymmetry between the oscillation probabilities of neutrinos and antineutrinos, given by

$$A_{\alpha\beta}^{\mathrm{CP}} \equiv P(\nu_\alpha \to \nu_\beta) - P(\bar{\nu}_\alpha \to \bar{\nu}_\beta) \equiv P_{\alpha\beta} - \overline{P}_{\alpha\beta}, \qquad (4.4)$$

where we introduced the shorthand notation

$$P_{\alpha\beta} \equiv P(\nu_\alpha \to \nu_\beta) \quad , \quad \overline{P}_{\alpha\beta} \equiv P(\bar{\nu}_\alpha \to \bar{\nu}_\beta). \qquad (4.5)$$

Taking into account that the probabilities for the transitions between antineutrinos are obtained by replacing V with V^* in Eq. (4.3), one gets

$$A_{\alpha\beta}^{\mathsf{CP}} = 4\sum_{k>j} \mathrm{Im}(V_{\alpha k}^* V_{\beta k} V_{\alpha j} V_{\beta k}^*) \sin\left(\frac{\Delta m_{kj}^2 L}{2E}\right)$$
$$= 4 s_{\alpha\beta} J_{\mathsf{CP}} \left(\sin\frac{\Delta m_{32}^2 L}{2E} + \sin\frac{\Delta m_{21}^2 L}{2E} + \sin\frac{\Delta m_{31}^2 L}{2E}\right). \qquad (4.6)$$

Here $s_{\alpha\beta}$ just stands for a sign, with $s_{\mu e} = 1 = s_{\tau\mu} = -s_{\tau e}$, and the Jarlskog invariant is

$$J_{\mathsf{CP}} \equiv \mathrm{Im}\left(V_{\mu 3} V_{e3}^* V_{e2} V_{\mu 2}^*\right) = \frac{1}{8} c\theta_{13} s2\theta_{12} s2\theta_{23} s2\theta_{13} s\delta. \qquad (4.7)$$

It is clear that to have a non-vanishing value of J_{CP} one needs that the three mixing angles and the phase δ be all non-zero. A non-vanishing asymmetry $A_{\alpha\beta}^{\mathsf{CP}}$ also requires that $\alpha \neq \beta$ and that the neutrino masses be all different.

In the simplified case in which one considers that the oscillations take place just between two generations, which is often a good working approximation, V can be taken as the 2×2 rotation matrix with mixing angle θ given by

$$R_\theta = \begin{pmatrix} \cos\theta & \sin\theta \\ -\sin\theta & \cos\theta \end{pmatrix}. \qquad (4.8)$$

One finds after a simple computation that in this case the transition probability is

$$P_{\alpha\beta} = \sin^2 2\theta \ \sin^2\left(\frac{\Delta m^2 L}{4E}\right), \qquad (4.9)$$

with the amplitude of the flavor oscillations being given by $\sin^2 2\theta$ and $\Delta m^2 \equiv m_2^2 - m_1^2$ is the mass squared difference of the two mass eigenstates involved in the mixing between the states ν_α and ν_β. The flavor oscillation performs a complete cycle after the neutrinos travel a distance equal to the oscillation length L_{osc}, which is given by

$$L_{\mathrm{osc}} \equiv \frac{4\pi E}{\Delta m^2} \simeq 2.5 \ \mathrm{m} \frac{E\,[\mathrm{MeV}]}{\Delta m^2\,[\mathrm{eV}^2]}. \qquad (4.10)$$

We see then that neutrinos, having sub-eV masses, will oscillate with a macroscopic wavelength.

In the case of neutrino mixing among three flavors, one gets from Eq. (4.3) a survival probability

$$P_{\alpha\alpha} = \overline{P}_{\alpha\alpha} = 1 - 4\sum_{k>j} |V_{\alpha k}|^2 |V_{\alpha j}|^2 \sin^2 \Delta_{kj}, \qquad (4.11)$$

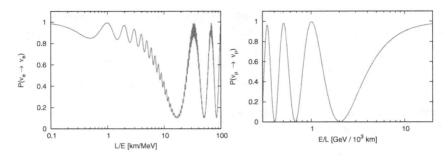

Fig. 4.1 Left panel: Electron neutrino survival probability as a function of L/E, in the range relevant for reactor experiments (note that $P_{ee} = \overline{P}_{ee}$). We adopted the central values of the measured neutrino mixings and mass differences. Right panel: Muon neutrino survival probability as a function of E/L, in the range relevant for long-baseline accelerator experiments.

where $\Delta_{kj} = \Delta m_{kj}^2 L/(4E)$. In particular, considering the case of reactor $\overline{\nu}_e$, their survival probability is

$$\overline{P}_{ee} = 1 - c^4\theta_{13}s^2(2\theta_{12})s^2\Delta_{21} - s^2(2\theta_{13})[c^2\theta_{12}s^2\Delta_{31} + s^2\theta_{12}s^2\Delta_{32}]. \quad (4.12)$$

This survival probability is plotted in the left panel of Fig. 4.1, adopting the actual present central values for the mixing angles and neutrino mass differences, as a function of L/E. Two clear patterns of oscillations can be identified in the plot. The first one with a large amplitude, given by $s^2(2\theta_{12}) \simeq 0.86$, and with an oscillation length determined by $\Delta m_{21}^2 \simeq 7.4 \times 10^{-5}\,\text{eV}^2$ (resulting in a first deep minimum at $L/E \simeq 20\,\text{km/MeV}$). The other one has a smaller amplitude, given by $s^2(2\theta_{13}) \simeq 0.1$, and has an oscillation length determined by $\Delta m_{31}^2 \simeq 2.5 \times 10^{-3}\text{eV}^2$ (resulting in a first local minimum at $L/E \simeq 0.5\,\text{km/MeV}$).

These features have been observed using reactor antineutrinos with energies of few MeV. In particular, the KamLAND experiment [Ar05b], located near the center of Japan, detected neutrinos from all the Japanese reactors which, being near the shores, lie at typical distances of 150 to 220 km. The determination of the electron antineutrino survival probability was then sensitive to the first two deep minima, which are associated to θ_{12}, as is shown in the left panel of Fig. 4.2. Later on, detectors with good energy resolution lying at a distance of about 1 km from powerful reactors, such as those of Daya Bay in China [An12] or RENO in Korea [Ah12], were able to see the smaller modulations of the survival probability that are due to θ_{13}.

These kind of experiments look for the disappearance of the reactor $\overline{\nu}_e$, i.e. for a reduction in their expected flux. Given the low neutrino

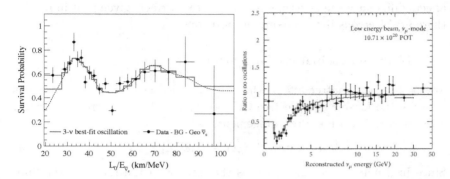

Fig. 4.2 Electron antineutrino survival probability as a function of L/E measured by KamLAND (left panel, from [PDG]) and muon neutrino survival measured by MINOS (right panel, from [Ev13]). Also shown as histograms are the expectations for the best fit oscillation parameters.

energies, it is however not possible to detect the appearance of a different neutrino flavor via its CC interactions. When one uses neutrino beams from accelerators, which have energies of few GeV, it is instead possible to study not only the disappearance of muon neutrinos that get converted into another flavor, but one can also search for the appearance of a flavor different from the original one. This has the advantage that one becomes sensitive to very small oscillation amplitudes, because the observation of just a few events of a different flavor is enough to establish a positive signal of oscillations. The survival probability for the case of muon neutrinos is shown in the right panel of Fig. 4.1, and the corresponding observations with the MINOS long-baseline experiment are shown in the right panel of Fig. 4.2. The appearance of electron type neutrinos has been observed in long-baseline experiments with muon neutrino beams, such as K2K, T2K, MINOS and NOνA. Also the appearance of a few ν_τ using a beam of ν_μ produced at CERN was observed with the OPERA detector at the Gran Sasso Laboratory.

Note that the neutrino survival probabilities $P_{\alpha\alpha}$ are independent of the CP violating phase δ. A search for CP violating effects can be performed looking for a difference between the neutrino and the antineutrino oscillation probabilities between different flavors. This difference can arise from the phase δ in the leptonic mixing matrix, as discussed in relation with Eq. (4.4), but it is also influenced by the effects of the neutrino propagation through the matter of the Earth, that as we demonstrate in the next section affects differently the neutrinos and the antineutrinos, given that in matter there are electrons but there are no positrons.

4.2   Neutrino oscillations in matter

To see how the matter affects the neutrino propagation, it is convenient to write the low-energy effective CC interaction of the electron neutrinos, after performing a Fierz rearrangement, as

$$\mathcal{H}_{CC} = \sqrt{2}G_F[\bar{e}\gamma_\mu(1-\gamma_5)e][\bar{\nu}_{eL}\gamma^\mu\nu_{eL}]. \tag{4.13}$$

Since in a normal medium, such as the interior of the Earth or the Sun, the electrons are non-relativistic, in this limit the electron vector current averaged over the background becomes $\langle\bar{e}\gamma_\mu e\rangle \to (N_e, \vec{0})$, where N_e is the electron density. On the other hand, for the axial vector part one gets $\langle\bar{e}\gamma_\mu\gamma_5 e\rangle \to (0, \vec{S}_e)$. Hence, for an unpolarized medium in which the average electron spin density $\vec{S}_e$ vanishes, this axial vector term will not contribute to the effective interaction. As realized by Wolfenstein [Wo78], this means that the electron neutrinos will feel a potential

$$V_{CC} \simeq \sqrt{2}G_F N_e, \tag{4.14}$$

while for the antineutrinos the potential will have a minus sign in front.

To understand the main consequences arising from this effective potential, it is convenient to consider the simplified case of just two-flavors, in which the electron neutrino mixes with a state ν_α. The flavor α could be μ or τ, or actually could consist of some admixture of both. The evolution of the neutrino states will hence be determined by the Schrödinger-like equation

$$i\frac{d}{dt}\begin{pmatrix}\nu_e\\\nu_\alpha\end{pmatrix} = \left\{ R_\theta \begin{bmatrix} p+\frac{m_1^2}{2E} & 0 \\ 0 & p+\frac{m_2^2}{2E} \end{bmatrix} R_\theta^T + \begin{bmatrix} \sqrt{2}G_F N_e & 0 \\ 0 & 0 \end{bmatrix} + NC \right\}\begin{pmatrix}\nu_e\\\nu_\alpha\end{pmatrix}, \tag{4.15}$$

where θ is the vacuum mixing angle appearing in the rotation R_θ given in Eq. (4.8) and $p = |\vec{p}| = E$. The term indicated as NC corresponds to the effective potential induced by the neutral current interactions of the neutrinos with the medium. Given that the neutral currents are flavor blind, this term is proportional to the identity matrix and hence it does not affect the flavor oscillations.[1] In order to study the flavor oscillations of the

---

[1]Note that these NC terms could however be relevant when studying oscillations between the usual neutrinos and sterile neutrinos which, unlike the active ones, do not feel the NC interactions.

standard neutrinos, one can drop the NC term as well as that proportional to p, and it is also convenient to subtract a diagonal term $\lambda \mathbf{I}$, with $\lambda = (m_1^2 + m_2^2)/(4E) + G_F N_e/\sqrt{2}$, to get the more symmetric equation

$$i\frac{d}{dt}\begin{pmatrix} \nu_e \\ \nu_\alpha \end{pmatrix} = \frac{\Delta m^2}{4E}\begin{bmatrix} -c2\theta + a & s2\theta \\ -s2\theta & c2\theta - a \end{bmatrix}\begin{pmatrix} \nu_e \\ \nu_\alpha \end{pmatrix}, \tag{4.16}$$

where

$$a \equiv \frac{\sqrt{2}G_F N_e}{\Delta m^2/(2E)} \tag{4.17}$$

is just the ratio between the effective CC matter potential and the energy splitting between the two vacuum mass eigenstates. This can also be rewritten as $a = L_{\rm osc}/L_m$, where the matter induced refraction length is

$$L_m \equiv \frac{2\pi}{\sqrt{2}G_F N_e} \simeq 7{,}600\,\text{km}\left(\frac{0.5}{Y_e}\right)\left(\frac{5\,\text{g cm}^{-3}}{\rho}\right), \tag{4.18}$$

where we used that $N_e \equiv Y_e \rho/m_p$, where the number of electrons per nucleon is $Y_e \equiv N_e/(N_n + N_p)$. Note that for oscillations between antineutrinos, the sign of the parameter a would be reversed.

To solve this equation, it is convenient to introduce the so-called mixing angle in matter, θ_m, and define the neutrino matter eigenstates

$$\begin{pmatrix} \nu_1^m \\ \nu_2^m \end{pmatrix} \equiv R_{\theta_m}^{\mathsf{T}}\begin{pmatrix} \nu_e \\ \nu_\alpha \end{pmatrix}, \tag{4.19}$$

such that the evolution equation becomes

$$i\frac{d}{dt}\begin{pmatrix} \nu_e \\ \nu_\alpha \end{pmatrix} = \frac{1}{4E}R_{\theta_m}\begin{bmatrix} -\Delta\mu^2 & 0 \\ 0 & \Delta\mu^2 \end{bmatrix}R_{\theta_m}^{\mathsf{T}}\begin{pmatrix} \nu_e \\ \nu_\alpha \end{pmatrix}. \tag{4.20}$$

It is simple to show that to have such diagonalization of the effective Hamiltonian, the mixing angle in matter needs to satisfy

$$s^2 2\theta_m = \frac{s^2 2\theta}{(c2\theta - a)^2 + s^2 2\theta}, \tag{4.21}$$

and the mass squared difference appearing in Eq. (4.20) will be

$$\Delta\mu^2 = \Delta m^2\sqrt{(c2\theta - a)^2 + s^2 2\theta}. \tag{4.22}$$

Looking at these expressions one can see that, as pointed out by Mikheyev and Smirnov [Mi85], there will be a resonant behavior for densities near the value for which $a = c2\theta$, i.e. for

$$\Delta m^2 c2\theta = 2\sqrt{2}G_F N_e E. \tag{4.23}$$

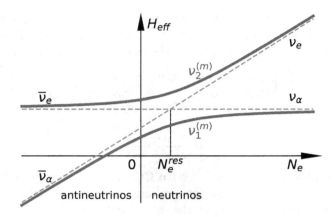

Fig. 4.3   Effective Hamiltonian for the neutrino matter mass eigenstates as a function of the electron density. Positive densities are for the neutrinos while the negative densities are for the case of anti-neutrinos with densities $|N_e|$. A positive value of Δm^2 is considered.

At the resonance the matter mixing angle becomes maximal, i.e. $\theta_m = \pi/4$, while the effective mass splitting in matter becomes minimum, taking the value $\Delta \mu^2|_R \simeq \Delta m^2 s 2\theta$. On the other hand, for densities much larger than the resonant one the matter mixing angle approaches $\pi/2$, so that one would get in this case that $\nu_e \simeq \nu_2^m$. This is illustrated in Fig. 4.3, where the effective masses of the matter eigenstates are plotted as a function of the density, considering just the mixing between two neutrinos. Here negative densities actually represent antineutrinos in positive densities.

The resonance condition for the neutrinos can also be rewritten as

$$\Delta m^2 c 2\theta \simeq \left(\frac{Y_e}{0.7}\right) \left(\frac{E}{10 \text{ MeV}}\right) \frac{\rho}{100 \text{ g cm}^{-3}} 10^{-4} \text{ eV}^2. \qquad (4.24)$$

Note that for the Sun $Y_e \sim 0.7$–0.8, due to the large H fraction present, while instead for the Earth $Y_e \simeq 0.5$.

When neutrinos propagate in a medium with constant density, as is sometimes a good approximation for the propagation through the Earth, the matter effects just change the mixing angle and the frequency of the oscillations among neutrinos. In this case the transition amplitude would be

$$P_{\alpha\beta} = \sin^2 2\theta_m \sin^2 \left(\frac{\Delta \mu^2 L}{4E}\right) \simeq s^2 2\theta \sin^2 \left(\frac{\Delta \mu^2 L}{4E}\right) \frac{\Delta m^2}{\Delta \mu^2}. \qquad (4.25)$$

If neutrinos propagate instead in a medium with varying density, as is the case inside the Sun or in a Supernova, the mixing angle in matter would change continuously.

For instance, in the case of the Sun one has that the density decreases approximately exponentially with the distance r from the center of the Sun, with

$$\rho \simeq 150 \, \frac{\text{g}}{\text{cm}^3} \exp(-r/h), \tag{4.26}$$

where the scale height is $h \simeq 0.1 R_\odot$ in terms of the solar radius $R_\odot \simeq 7 \times 10^5$ km. The solar neutrinos, which are produced near the center of the star, will then cross a resonance in their way out only if $E > (\Delta m^2 \, c2\theta / 10^{-5} \, \text{eV}^2)$ MeV. For lower energies, the resonance density would however turn out to be larger than the central density of the Sun. Moreover, only if $\Delta m^2 > 0$ the resonance is present for neutrinos, while for negative values of Δm^2 only antineutrinos, which are however not produced in fusion processes, could meet a resonance in matter.

The resonance condition will be satisfied at the layer for which $a = c2\theta$. One can also associate a width δ_R to the resonance, defined as the distance from the layer for which $|c2\theta - a| \simeq s2\theta$. The resonance width should then satisfy

$$\delta_\text{R} \simeq \frac{s2\theta}{|da/dr|_\text{R}}, \tag{4.27}$$

what leads to $\delta_\text{R} \simeq h \tan 2\theta$. This width is useful to characterize the two basic regimes of resonant flavor conversions. The first one is the adiabatic regime, taking place when the oscillation length in matter at the resonance is smaller than the resonance width, i.e. for

$$\frac{4\pi E}{\Delta \mu^2|_\text{R}} = \frac{4\pi E}{\Delta m^2 s2\theta} < h \tan 2\theta. \tag{4.28}$$

In this case the neutrino states can adjust to the changing density and they essentially remain as matter mass eigenstates as the resonance is crossed. The second regime, which is called non-adiabatic, corresponds to the opposite case in which the resonance is so narrow that the oscillating neutrinos effectively do not see it, and hence no significant flavor transition occurs during the resonance crossing. Since the matter mass eigenstates do change across the resonance, this implies that a significant transition between matter mass eigenstates has to take place as the resonance is crossed in the non-adiabatic regime.

The adiabatic condition can be rewritten as

$$\frac{s^2 2\theta}{c2\theta} > \left(\frac{E}{10 \, \text{MeV}} \right) \left(\frac{6 \times 10^{-8} \text{eV}^2}{\Delta m^2} \right) \left(\frac{h}{0.1 R_\odot} \right). \tag{4.29}$$

To better understand the flavor transition during the resonance crossing, it proves convenient to write down the evolution equation for the matter mass eigenstates, which is

$$i\frac{\mathrm{d}}{\mathrm{d}x}\begin{pmatrix} \nu_1^m \\ \nu_2^m \end{pmatrix} = \begin{pmatrix} -\frac{\Delta\mu^2}{4E} & -i\frac{\mathrm{d}\theta_m}{\mathrm{d}x} \\ i\frac{\mathrm{d}\theta_m}{\mathrm{d}x} & \frac{\Delta\mu^2}{4E} \end{pmatrix}\begin{pmatrix} \nu_1^m \\ \nu_2^m \end{pmatrix}. \tag{4.30}$$

The adiabatic case corresponds to the situation in which the off-diagonal terms in this equation are negligible. This means that during the adiabatic resonance crossing the matter mass eigenstates remain themselves, so that the flavor of the neutrinos change just following the change of the matter mixing angle with the varying electron density. For instance, when electron neutrinos are produced in the high-density core of a star, where the matter mixing angle is θ_m^0, the initial neutrino states will be $\nu_e = c\theta_m^0 \nu_1^m + s\theta_m^0 \nu_2^m$ and, as the neutrinos propagate adiabatically through the star, they will evolve as

$$|\nu(t)\rangle = c\theta_m^0 \exp(i\,\delta t)|\nu_1^m\rangle + s\theta_m^0 \exp(-i\,\delta t)|\nu_2^m\rangle, \tag{4.31}$$

where $\delta t = \int_0^t \mathrm{d}t' \Delta\mu^2/(4E)$. The survival probability when the neutrino exits the star, where the mixing becomes the vacuum one, is then

$$P_{ee} = \left| c\theta_m^0 \exp(i\,\delta t)c\theta + s\theta_m^0 \exp(-i\,\delta t)s\theta \right|^2$$
$$= c^2\theta_m^0 c^2\theta + s^2\theta_m^0 s^2\theta + \frac{1}{2}s(2\theta_m^0)s(2\theta)c(2\,\delta t). \tag{4.32}$$

When the resonance crossing is instead non-adiabatic, the off-diagonal terms in Eq. (4.30) are non-negligible and induce transitions between the different matter mass eigenstates as the resonance is crossed [Pa86; Ha86]. Indeed, the probability of jumping from one matter eigenstate to the other during resonance crossing can be written, for an exponential density profile, as [Pe88]

$$P_c(\nu_1^m \to \nu_2^m) = \frac{\exp\left(-\gamma \sin^2\theta\right) - \exp\left(-\gamma\right)}{1 - \exp\left(-\gamma\right)}, \tag{4.33}$$

where the adiabaticity parameter is $\gamma \equiv \pi h \Delta m^2/E$. For an electron density varying in a more general way, not just exponentially, it is usually a good approximation to replace the scale height h in the above expressions by $|(\mathrm{d}N_e/\mathrm{d}r)/N_e|_\mathrm{R}^{-1}$.

4.3 Averaged neutrino oscillations

There are many situations in which only averaged neutrino oscillations can be observed. This happens for instance when the region of production of the neutrinos (such as the core of the Sun), or eventually the detector size, is much larger than the neutrino oscillation length. Since the neutrino oscillation length $L_{\text{osc}} = 4\pi E/\Delta m^2$ is energy dependent, also the finite detector energy resolution can lead to an averaging of the oscillation probability. In those cases, the oscillating terms in the conversion probability in vacuum in Eq. (4.3) get averaged, so that $\langle \sin^2(\pi L/L_{\text{osc}}) \rangle \to 1/2$ and $\langle \sin(2\pi L/L_{\text{osc}}) \rangle \to 0$. This leads to a transition probability in vacuum

$$\langle P_{\alpha\beta} \rangle = \sum_k |V_{\alpha k}|^2 |V_{\beta k}|^2. \tag{4.34}$$

This is to be interpreted as the incoherent sum of the production of the mass eigenstates ν_k with probability $|V_{\alpha k}|^2$ and their posterior observation as a flavor ν_β with probability $|V_{\beta k}|^2$. The interference between the amplitudes corresponding to different mass eigenstates get then effectively washed out in the averaging process.

In the case of two flavors, the averaged conversion probability in vacuum is then

$$\langle P_{\alpha\beta} \rangle_{2f} = \frac{1}{2} s^2 2\theta. \tag{4.35}$$

For the solar neutrinos, the neutrino producing region turns out to be much larger than the neutrino oscillation length, and hence the oscillations do get averaged. Taking into account the matter effects, the ν_e get produced in the high-density core where the matter mixing angle is θ_m^0. In the two flavor approximation, that would correspond to the limit $\theta_{13} \simeq 0$, one has then that the initial neutrino state is $\nu_e = c\theta_m^0 \nu_1^m + s\theta_m^0 \nu_2^m$. If the propagation is adiabatic, the averaged ν_e survival probability is given by Eq. (4.32) but with the last term averaged to zero. In this case, $\langle P_{ee} \rangle_{2f} = c^2\theta_m^0 c^2\theta + s^2\theta_m^0 s^2\theta$ is just the incoherent sum of the probabilities of producing ν_1^m or ν_2^m and then detecting them as ν_e. If the resonance crossing were instead non-adiabatic (something which will turn out not to be the case for solar neutrinos, given their inferred mass-squared differences and the condition in Eq. (4.29)), one has to allow for an eventual jump, with probability P_c, between the matter mass eigenstates as they cross the resonance. In this case, the averaged two-flavor survival probability would be

$$\langle P_{ee} \rangle_{2f} = \left[c^2\theta_m^0 c^2\theta + s^2\theta_m^0 s^2\theta\right](1 - P_c) + \left[c^2\theta_m^0 s^2\theta + s^2\theta_m^0 c^2\theta\right] P_c$$
$$= \frac{1}{2}\left[1 + (1 - 2P_c)c2\theta c2\theta_m^0\right]. \tag{4.36}$$

Note that if the neutrinos were produced at densities much larger than the resonance one, as actually happens for solar neutrinos with $E \gg 2\,\text{MeV}$,

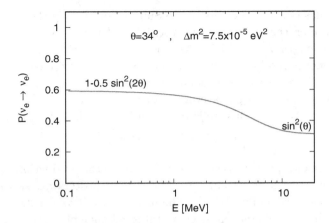

Fig. 4.4 Survival probability of electron neutrinos exiting from the Sun as a function of their energy, for the masses and mixing angles that have been experimentally determined.

one would have in this case that $\theta_m^0 \simeq \pi/2$ and hence $\langle P_{ee}\rangle_{2f} \simeq s^2\theta$ if the resonance crossing is adiabatic. On the other hand, when there is no resonance crossing because the resonance density turns out to be higher than the density at which the neutrinos are produced, as actually happens for solar neutrinos with $E < 2\,\text{MeV}$, one would get that the averaged survival probability should approach the vacuum value. This overall behavior is illustrated in Fig. 4.4.

In order to account for the effects of three-flavor mixing for solar neutrinos, it is a good approximation to include the mixing with the third mass eigenstate as $\nu_e = c\theta_{13}\nu_\ell + s\theta_{13}\nu_3$, where the ν_ℓ is the mixture of ν_1^m and ν_2^m discussed before and one can neglect the matter effects on ν_3, given that the associated mass splitting turns out to be much larger. Averaging out the ν_3 oscillations one has then

$$\langle P_{ee}\rangle_{3f} \simeq c^4\theta_{13}\langle P(\nu_e \to \nu_e)\rangle_{2f} + s^4\theta_{13}. \qquad (4.37)$$

For supernova neutrinos, in which case all three flavors of neutrinos and antineutrinos get produced, actually two different resonances can appear (associated to the two different mass squared differences). This makes the oscillation phenomenology richer but also more complex, as will be discussed in Chapter 7. Other cases in which the neutrino oscillations get averaged is for the very-high energy astrophysical neutrinos produced at cosmological distances.

On the other hand, non-averaged neutrino oscillations have been observed at reactors, both at short baselines of less than 1 km or with the

KamLAND experiment over baselines of about $200\,\mathrm{km}$, at long-baseline accelerator experiments over distances of about $1,000\,\mathrm{km}$ and with atmospheric neutrinos over baselines up to $10^4\,\mathrm{km}$.

Note that in the regime of averaged oscillations, the CP violating asymmetries $A_{\alpha\beta}^{\mathrm{CP}}$ will vanish, but however one may still have some sensitivity to the phase δ by accurately measuring the probabilities of transition between different neutrino flavors. In particular, one can convince oneself that for instance $\langle P_{e\mu}\rangle = \langle \overline{P}_{e\mu}\rangle$ and $\langle P_{e\tau}\rangle = \langle \overline{P}_{e\tau}\rangle$ depend both on δ (if $\theta_{13} \neq 0$), with $P_{e\mu} + P_{e\tau} = 1 - P_{ee}$ being in turn independent of δ (since P_{ee} does not depend on it), so that the δ dependent term of the oscillation probabilities has to appear with opposite signs in $P_{e\mu}$ and $P_{e\tau}$. However, given the smallness of θ_{13} these effects are estimated to be small and difficult to determine (see e.g. [Pa15]).

4.4 Quantum mechanical decoherence

Besides the averaging effect that results when considering neutrinos that have travelled different distances (due to the finite size of the source and of the detector) or that have different energies within the resolution of the detectors (and hence contribute to a given energy bin with different relative phases), a more fundamental quantum mechanical decoherence can affect the neutrino flavor conversion. This decoherence appears after the neutrinos have travelled long distances, and leads to similar averaged expressions for the oscillation probabilities. While the first type of averaging is of a statistical nature, resulting from the incoherent average of the oscillations of many neutrinos with different energies or having travelled different distances, the second one appears already for a single individual neutrino, and it arises due to a totally different reason.

To understand the main cause of this effect, one has to account for the fact that the neutrino wave-function is not a delocalized plane wave, but rather a wave-packet having a certain spatial spread, σ_x, which is ultimately related to the localization of the neutrino production process [Nu76; Ka81; Ki96]. On the other hand, when a given neutrino flavor is produced, the different superimposed mass eigenstates ν_i will have different group velocities, $v_i = \partial E/\partial p_i = p_i/E$, so that in the relativistic limit the difference between the mass eigenstate neutrino wave-packet velocities is $|\Delta v_{ij}| \simeq c|\Delta m_{ij}^2|/(2E^2)$. This implies that the wave-packets of the different mass components will tend to separate from each other as they travel, and their wave functions will no longer have a significant overlap after they traverse a distance $L_{\rm coh}$ such that $|\Delta v_{ij}|L_{\rm coh}/c = \sigma_x$. When this happens, any measurement of the flavor content performed on a time scale shorter than the difference in travel time between the mass eigenstate neutrinos will only be sensitive to the incoherent sum of the individual probabilities, and no interference pattern between the different mass eigenstates is observble. The associated coherence length is

$$L_{\rm coh} = \frac{c\sigma_x}{|\Delta v|} \simeq 2 \times 10^9 \, {\rm km} \frac{\sigma_x}{10^{-10}\,{\rm m}} \left(\frac{E}{\rm GeV}\right)^2 \frac{10^{-4}\,{\rm eV}^2}{\Delta m^2}. \qquad (4.38)$$

Regarding the size of the wave-packet σ_x, it depends on the properties of the interactions affecting the neutrino production process. For instance, if the neutrino is produced in the weak decay of an isolated particle (such as a nucleus, a pion or a muon), σ_x is given by the particle decay length, eventually Lorentz contracted if the decaying particle is relativistic. In particular, for the case of muon neutrinos produced in the decay of a relativistic pion having a Lorentz factor Γ, and considering that the typical neutrino energy in the rest frame of the pion is $E'_\nu \simeq m_\pi/4$, the neutrinos emitted in the forward direction will have an associated size $\sigma_x \simeq c\tau_\pi/\Gamma \simeq c\tau_\pi m_\pi/(4E) \simeq 0.3\,{\rm m}\,{\rm GeV}/E$ [Fa08]. The wave-packet size can get significantly reduced when the decay takes place in a dense medium, since the coherence cannot build over times longer than the one associated to the interactions of the decaying particle, if these ones lead to a significant change in its momentum. This time is typically of the order of the interatomic separation divided by the thermal velocity $v_T = \sqrt{3T/m}$ of the particles. For instance, for the case of the Sun where the medium consists mostly of hydrogen nuclei with the density reaching values of $\sim 100\,{\rm g\,cm}^{-3}$ near the center, where the typical temperature is in the keV range, one would have $\sigma_x \simeq n^{1/3}/v_T \simeq 10^{-8}\,{\rm m}$. A comparable value also results near the neutrinospheres in supernovae, where the densities are much larger ($\sim 10^{12}\,{\rm g\,cm}^{-3}$) but also the temperatures are larger (of order few MeV) [Ke16]. When the relevant neutrino producing process is an EC, where an electron from the plasma gets captured by an essentially point-like hadron, the wave-packet length σ_x is mostly determined by the corresponding length of the electron wave-packet times its thermal velocity. The electron wave-packet length is in turn determined by its collision rate associated to the Coulomb interactions with the protons or electrons in the medium. The neutrino wave-packet length may also be shortened if the decaying particle is significantly deflected by magnetic fields, as could happen in some sources of ultrahigh-energy cosmic rays, since in this case the coherence in the neutrino wave function resulting from the decay cannot build up.

As an example, one can check that for MeV neutrinos from the Sun the typical length for decoherence is $L_{\text{coh}} \simeq 10^5$ km, which is much smaller than the distance to the Sun, and hence their oscillations indeed decohere by the time they reach the Earth (besides being averaged by the finite source size and the finite energy resolution). A similar conclusion also applies to supernova neutrinos. Regarding the very-high energy (TeV to PeV) astrophysical neutrinos originating from extragalactic sources at distances much larger than a Mpc ($\gg 3 \times 10^{19}$ km), their loss of coherence would depend on the generation mechanism producing them. In particular, if they result from the decays of free pions (or muons), they will in general preserve the coherence at $E \gg$ TeV, while if interactions with radiation or magnetic fields shorten considerably their spread σ_x, the coherence may be lost [Fa08]. Anyhow, when averaging the contribution from astrophysical sources at different distances the oscillations will be effectively averaged out. On the other hand, neutrinos from reactors, from accelerators or those from the atmosphere involve baselines which are much smaller than the typical associated coherence lengths, so that in principle their interfering effects can be (and indeed have been) observed.

Note that if oscillations into sterile neutrinos were to take place involving mass squared differences larger than $1\,\text{eV}^2$, the coherence conditions may not hold even for relatively short baselines. By the way, the loss of coherence is also the fundamental reason explaining why no oscillation effects are observable between charged leptons, whose much larger mass differences lead to an abrupt loss of coherence as soon as these particles get produced [Ak19].

4.5 Status of the determination of the neutrino masses and mixings

Neutrino oscillation phenomena, which were observed studying solar, atmospheric, reactor and accelerator neutrinos, have established that neutrino masses are non-vanishing. These observations have allowed to determine the squared mass differences $\Delta m_{21}^2 \simeq 7.4 \times 10^{-5}\,\text{eV}^2$ and $|\Delta m_{32}^2| \simeq 2.4 \times 10^{-3}\,\text{eV}^2$ (with 3% and 1% accuracies respectively).

The result on Δm_{21}^2 was first hinted, as will be discussed in Chapter 5, by the deficit of solar neutrinos. Here the matter effects in the Sun are relevant and allow to infer also the sign of Δm_{21}^2, because the resonant conversion is present for the neutrinos. This was then confirmed by the KamLAND experiment that measured oscillations of reactor electron antineutrinos over baselines of $\sim 180\,\mathrm{km}$, with the results shown in Fig. 4.2.

The result on $|\Delta m_{32}^2|$ was first obtained studying atmospheric neutrinos, in particular from the zenith angle dependent suppression of the flux of muon neutrinos, as will be discussed in Chapter 8. It was then confirmed by accelerator ν_μ experiments using long-baselines, e.g. from KEK and Tokai to Kamioka (K2K [Ah06] and T2K [Ab18]) in Japan and from Fermilab to the MINOS [Ad14] or NOνA [Ac19] detectors in Minnesota.

The strong suppression of the survival probabilities observed in these experiments indicates that the mixing angles involved in the oscillations are large, with $\theta_{12} \simeq 33°$ and $\theta_{23} \simeq 45°$. The disappearance of reactor $\bar{\nu}_e$ on baselines of $\sim 1\,\mathrm{km}$, which are due to oscillations at the frequency associated to the mass splitting Δm_{31}^2 (note that $\Delta m_{31}^2 = \Delta m_{32}^2 + \Delta m_{21}^2 \simeq \Delta m_{32}^2$), was observed more recently by the Daya Bay [An12] and RENO [Ah12] experiments, indicating that $\theta_{13} \simeq 9°$. Since the matter effects on these terrestrial experiments are quite small, the sign of Δm_{32}^2 is still unknown, with the two possible scenarios being the normal ordering (NO), in which $m_1 < m_2 < m_3$, or the inverted ordering (IO), in which $m_3 < m_1 < m_2$ (and hence $\Delta m_{32}^2 < 0$). Recent results exploiting the long-baseline experiments NOνA and T2K, as well as atmospheric neutrino measurements by Super-Kamiokande, favor at about the 3σ level the NO scenario. There are good expectations to measure in the near future the sign of Δm_{32}^2 with higher significance in these long-baseline experiments, as well as exploiting the matter effects in atmospheric neutrinos (IceCube, ORCA and INO experiments), or with accelerator experiments with larger baselines (such as with the DUNE experiment at $1{,}300\,\mathrm{km}$ from Fermilab), or alternatively in experiments using reactor antineutrinos and large detectors with very good energy resolution at baselines $> 50\,\mathrm{km}$, such as with JUNO. Long-baseline accelerator neutrino experiments using both ν and $\bar{\nu}$ could be able to determine the CP violating phase δ. Also the octant of θ_{23} is still unknown, i.e. whether the state ν_2 has a ν_μ component larger than the ν_τ component (first octant) or vice-versa (second octant), and long-baseline accelerator experiments could help to determine it.

Several groups regularly perform global fits to the available oscillation data to infer the mass squared differences and mixing angles. Table 4.1 summarizes the results obtained by the NuFIT Collaboration [Es20] for the normal and inverted mass ordering cases.

Given that the neutrino mass splittings are so small, this suggests that the neutrino masses themselves are below $0.1\,\mathrm{eV}$. A possible exception could be in scenarios in which the three neutrinos were almost degenerate and

Table 4.1 Best fit parameters (by 2021) for the neutrino mixing angles and mass-squared differences, where $\Delta m_{3\ell}^2 = \Delta m_{31}^2$ for NO while it is Δm_{32}^2 for IO (from http://www.nu-fit.org/, v.5.1).

Ordering	θ_{12} [deg]	θ_{23} [deg]	θ_{13} [deg]	δ [deg]	Δm_{21}^2 [10^{-5}eV^2]	$\Delta m_{3\ell}^2$ [10^{-3}eV^2]
NO	$33.45^{+0.77}_{-0.75}$	$42.1^{+1.1}_{-0.9}$	$8.62^{+0.12}_{-0.12}$	230^{+36}_{-25}	$7.42^{+0.21}_{-0.20}$	$2.510^{+0.027}_{-0.027}$
IO	$33.45^{+0.78}_{-0.75}$	$49.0^{+0.9}_{-1.3}$	$8.61^{+0.14}_{-0.12}$	278^{+22}_{-30}	$7.42^{+0.21}_{-0.20}$	$-2.490^{+0.026}_{-0.028}$

heavier, so that $m_1 \simeq m_2 \simeq m_3 \gg \sqrt{|\Delta m_{31}^2|}$. All the attempts to determine the absolute neutrino masses have up to now only established upper limits on their values. The most restrictive bounds are those from cosmology, further discussed in Chapter 10, which set a constraint on the sum of the neutrino masses of about $\sum m_i < 0.12\,\text{eV}$ [Ag20], with the exact bound depending somewhat on the cosmological priors adopted and the data included in the analysis. Note that combining this bound with the known values of the mass-squared differences, one can conclude that the heaviest neutrino (which must be heavier than about $\sqrt{\Delta m_{32}^2} \simeq 0.05\,\text{eV}$) should also be lighter than about $0.059\,\text{eV}$ for the NO case, and lighter than about $0.052\,\text{eV}$ in the IO case, while the lightest neutrino must be lighter than about $0.03\,\text{eV}$ for the NO case, and lighter than about $0.016\,\text{eV}$ in the IO case.

Direct bounds on the neutrino masses are obtained from the study of the shape of the electron spectrum from tritium beta decay near the endpoint energy E_0. This rate should get suppressed if neutrino masses are non-vanishing. The differential rate for beta decay in terms of the energy of the emitted electron is

$$\frac{d\Gamma}{dE_e} = C\,F(E,Z)p_e(E_e + m_e)(E_0 - E_e)\sum_{i=1}^{3}|V_{ei}|^2\sqrt{(E_0 - E_e)^2 - m_{\nu_i}^2},$$

(4.39)

where $C \equiv G_F^2 \cos^2\theta_C |M|^2/(2\pi^3)$, with M being the associated nuclear matrix element and the Fermi function $F(E,Z)$ is related to the Coulomb corrections to the beta decay. Expanding the previous equation in the limit of $m_{\nu_i} \ll E_0 - E_e$, one can show that

$$\frac{d\Gamma}{dE_e} \simeq C\,F(E,Z)p_e(E_e + m_e)(E_0 - E_e)\sqrt{(E_0 - E_e)^2 - m_\beta^2},$$

(4.40)

where the effective neutrino mass m_β satisfies

$$m_\beta^2 \equiv |V_{e1}|^2 m_1^2 + |V_{e2}|^2 m_2^2 + |V_{e3}|^2 m_3^2.$$

(4.41)

The expression in Eq. (4.40) provides an accurate fit also near the endpoint of the spectrum when the mass splitting between neutrinos is much smaller than the energy resolution, as is the case for the present generation of tritium decay experiments. The quantity m_β is then constrained by the measurement of the shape of the electron spectrum near the endpoint. The present result from the KATRIN experiment is $m_\beta < 0.8\,\text{eV}$ [Ak22].

Scenarios in which neutrinos have Majorana masses are also constrained from the non-observation of neutrinoless double-beta decay, which is sensitive to the quantity

$$m_{\beta\beta} \equiv |V_{e1}^2 m_1 + V_{e2}^2 m_2 + V_{e3}^2 m_3|. \tag{4.42}$$

Note that unlike m_β, which depends on $|V_{ei}|^2$, the effective mass $m_{\beta\beta}$ depends on V_{ei}^2, and hence is sensitive to the Majorana phases α_1 and α_2. The present bound is $m_{\beta\beta} \leq 0.1\text{–}0.2\,\text{eV}$ [Ga16; An19; Ag20c], depending on the experiment considered and on the theoretical estimate adopted for the nuclear matrix elements involved in the corresponding transitions, which are not known with high precision.

There are good prospects to improve the sensitivity to the neutrino masses, in particular with new CMB and large-scale structure observations which may increase the sensitivity to the sum of neutrino masses, with the KATRIN tritium beta decay experiment that could become sensitive down to $m_\beta \simeq 0.2\,\text{eV}$, and with new double beta decay experiments that may reach a sensitivity down to the level of $m_{\beta\beta} \simeq 0.02\,\text{eV}$ in the next decade.

Figure 4.5 summarizes the range of theoretical expectations for $m_{\beta\beta}$ as a function of the lightest neutrino mass, both for the NO (top panel) and IO (bottom panel) cases, as well as the present upper-bounds from the searches with ^{136}Xe decays by the KamLAND-Zen experiment [Ga16] ($m_{\beta\beta} < 61$ to $165\,\text{meV}$, depending on the nuclear matrix element adopted) and those derived from cosmology ($\sum m_i < 0.12\,\text{eV}$).

Suggested exercises:

- Prove the expressions for the 3-flavor neutrino conversion probability, for the average survival probability and for the CP asymmetry
- Prove the approximate equality in Eq. (4.40)
- Reproduce Fig. 4.5

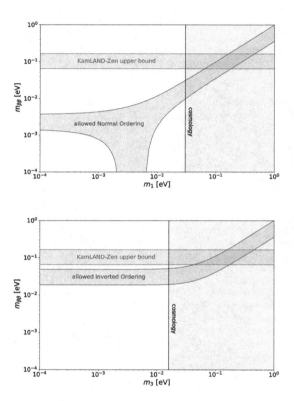

Fig. 4.5 Theoretically allowed region for $m_{\beta\beta}$ as a function of the lightest neutrino mass, obtained by letting the Majorana phases to vary. Also shown is the range of upper-bounds from the KamLAND-Zen experiment and the region excluded by the cosmological bound. Top panel is for NO, bottom panel for IO.

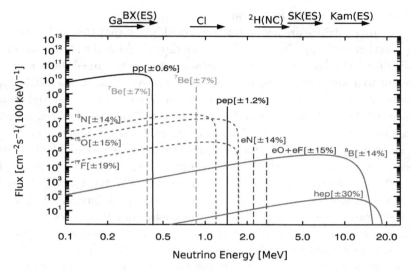

Fig. 5.2 Spectrum of the different solar neutrino contributions. The fluxes are in units of $cm^{-2}s^{-1}$, with the continuous spectra being shown per energy bins of 100 keV. The thresholds of the different experiments are also indicated. The detectors based on electron scattering (ES) can obtain spectral information above their thresholds (adapted from [PDG]).

pp-I processes roughly scaling as T^4 while the CNO ones as T^{20}. Indeed, the larger is the charge of the nucleus involved in a process, the stronger will be the Coulomb barrier that needs to be overcome for it to capture a proton, and hence the threshold temperatures will be higher and also the resulting temperature dependencies will be more pronounced. The larger Coulomb barriers affecting heavier nuclei also account for the fact that ^8B neutrinos tend to be produced closer to the core of the star (mostly at radii $r < 0.1R_\odot$) than the ^7Be neutrinos (at $r < 0.15R_\odot$), and these in turn are more centrally produced than the pp neutrinos (at $r < 0.25R_\odot$).

To predict the fluxes of solar neutrinos from all these processes, it is necessary to make a model of the Sun starting from the time when the fusion became the main energy source of the star and evolve it up to the present time. The initial gas mass of $1\,M_\odot$ is assumed to contain an homogeneous mixture of hydrogen, helium and metals, and the initial abundances are chosen so as to reproduce the present solar luminosity $L_\odot$, radius $R_\odot$ and surface metallicities. Since the metals determine eventually the radiative opacities, and hence the temperature gradients in the radiative zone, the uncertainties in their abundances can directly reflect into uncertainties in the temperature profile of the Sun.

The pp neutrinos are accurately predicted, given that they are the starting reaction in the pp-chain and hence are directly related to the solar luminosity $L_\odot$. Also the pep neutrinos are accurately determined, because they amount to a well determined fraction of the pp ones, $\Phi_{pep} \simeq 2.5 \times 10^{-3} \Phi_{pp}$. The fluxes of CNO neutrinos have uncertainties related to the actual abundances of the C, N and O elements in the central part of the Sun, besides those related to the uncertainties in the inferred central temperatures.

A detailed knowledge of the nuclear cross sections of the different processes involved in the pp-chain and CNO-cycle is required in order to obtain the different neutrino fluxes [Ad11]. To compute the total fluxes the neutrino production rates from these reactions have to be integrated over the different radial regions of the central Sun where they take place.

As a side remark, let us mention that in more massive stars, as the hydrogen is consumed in the main sequence (mostly through the CNO-cycle) and a He core forms, H fusion continues in a shell around the growing He core. He fusion becomes operative when the central temperature of the star reaches 10^8 K, leading to the reaction $^4\text{He} + {}^4\text{He} \rightarrow {}^8\text{Be}$, followed by $^4\text{He} + {}^8\text{Be} \rightarrow {}^{12}\text{C}$ (i.e., the so-called triple alpha process), together with $^4\text{He} + {}^{12}\text{C} \rightarrow {}^{16}\text{O}$ and $^4\text{He} + {}^{16}\text{O} \rightarrow {}^{20}\text{Ne}$. When He gets depleted from the core, and eventually burns in shells, further reactions proceed in the core, such as $^{12}\text{C} + {}^{12}\text{C} \rightarrow {}^{16}\text{O} + 2\,{}^4\text{He}$ or $^{16}\text{O} + {}^{16}\text{O} \rightarrow {}^{28}\text{Si} + {}^4\text{He}$, until Fe gets eventually produced. Since Fe is the nucleus having the maximum binding energy per nucleon, and hence the minimum mass per nucleon, no further energy can be gained by fusing Fe to produce heavier elements. This is why its production essentially represents the end point of nuclear fusion reactions in stars. The production of elements heavier than Fe takes place in endothermic processes, mostly by slow neutron capture processes occurring in evolved intermediate mass stars and massive stars ending their life in a supernova explosion. They may also be produced in the event of a neutron star binary merger, where the extremely neutron-rich matter naturally favors the production of heavy elements through rapid neutron capture processes.

Note that the nuclear reactions beyond the pp and CNO cycles do not produce significant amounts of neutrinos, since in most of them the number of neutrons and protons is conserved. However, during the later stages of the evolution of the massive stars, large amounts of neutrinos get produced in thermal processes and beta reactions. As the central temperatures of these stars grow, the neutrino emission becomes increasingly important, carrying away most of the energy produced in the fusion processes and eventually determining the lifetime of the different stages of nuclear fusion.

5.3 Observations of solar neutrinos and inferred neutrino properties

Many experiments have looked for the solar neutrinos: the radiochemical experiments with ^{37}Cl at Homestake [Cl98] or those with ^{71}Ga at SAGE [Ab09] in Baksan, and GALLEX [Ha99] and GNO [Al05] at the Gran Sasso Laboratory, the water Cherenkov detectors (Super-)Kamiokande [Fu96; Ab16] in Japan and the heavy water Subdury Neutrino Observatory (SNO) [Ah13] in Canada, as well as the liquid scintillator detectors Borexino [Ag18] at the Gran Sasso and KamLAND [Ab11] in Japan.

Note that radiochemical experiments are only sensitive to ν_e, while the electron scattering (ES) process, which is measured in water and scintillator detectors, is also sensitive to the other flavors although with a reduced strength, so that the ES rate is approximately proportional to $\Phi_{\nu_e} + 0.16(\Phi_{\nu_\mu} + \Phi_{\nu_\tau})$. On the other hand, the heavy water experiment allowed to separately detect the CC (ν_e) and NC ($\nu_e + \nu_\mu + \nu_\tau$) channels, besides the ES events. Also a major difference between radiochemical experiments and ES ones is that the first ones only obtain an integrated rate above the corresponding threshold energy and integrated over an exposure of several weeks, while the Cherenkov and scintillator detectors can measure the differential rate as a function of the energy transferred to the electrons, for all energies above the threshold of each detector, and do this in real time. The SNO NC detection in the process $\nu_x + d \rightarrow \nu_x + p + n$ (with $x = e$, μ or τ), via the observation of the produced neutrons, has no information on the neutrino energy, just that it is above the threshold of 2.23 MeV. The Cherenkov detectors also have information on the neutrino arrival direction, while no information about it can be retrieved from the isotropically emitted scintillation light. On the other hand, scintillator detectors produce a much larger number of photoelectrons and can achieve excellent radio-purity standards. These circumstances allow for observational energy thresholds which are low enough so as to be sensitive to all the contributions to the spectrum of solar neutrinos.

The characteristics of the different experiments that have observed the solar neutrino fluxes are summarized in Table 5.1, and having different energy thresholds they were sensitive to the oscillation probabilities in different energy ranges.

Table 5.1   Experiments that studied solar neutrinos.

Experiment	Reaction	Threshold [MeV]	Mass [tonne]	years
Homestake	$\nu_e\,^{37}\mathrm{Cl} \to e\,^{37}\mathrm{Ar}$	0.814	615	1967-1994
SAGE	$\nu_e\,^{71}\mathrm{Ga} \to e\,^{71}\mathrm{Ge}$	0.233	50	1989-
Gallex&GNO	$\nu_e\,^{71}\mathrm{Ga} \to e\,^{71}\mathrm{Ge}$	0.233	30	1991-2003
Kamiokande	$\nu_x e \to \nu_x e$	7.5	3,000	1986-1996
Super-Kamiokande	$\nu_x e \to \nu_x e$	5	32,000	1996-
SNO [ES]	$\nu_x e \to \nu_x e$	3.7	3,000	1999-2006
SNO [NC]	$\nu_x d \to \nu_x p\,n$	2.23		
SNO [CC]	$\nu_e d \to e\,p\,p$	4.9		
KamLAND	$\nu_x e \to \nu_x e$	0.5	1,000	2009-2011
Borexino	$\nu_x e \to \nu_x e$	0.2	300	2007-2022

The results of these experiments, which have puzzled physicists for almost thirty years, is that only between 1/2 to 1/3 of the expected ν_e fluxes were actually observed. Moreover, water Cherenkov detectors allowed to look for a possible diurnal modulation resulting from the matter effects suffered by the solar neutrinos that cross the Earth before being detected during night-time observations. In this way, it was found by Super-Kamiokande that, when observed in the high-energy ^{8}B neutrinos, the Sun looks actually brighter during the night by about 3.3% [Ab16].

A crucial measurement was the independent determinations of the CC and NC interactions of the solar neutrinos using the heavy water experiment at the Subdury Neutrino Observatory [Ah13]. The result is that the NC rate, which is sensitive to the three flavors of active neutrinos, is indeed consistent with the solar model expectations for the flux of ν_e in the absence of oscillations, while the CC rate measured with the process $\nu_e + d \to e + p + p$, which is sensitive to the electron neutrinos alone, shows a deficit by a factor of about 1/3. This indicates that the oscillations have indeed occurred, and that they converted a large fraction of the electron neutrinos into the other active neutrino flavors (ν_μ and ν_τ). This is illustrated in Fig. 5.3, which shows the determination of the fluxes of ν_e (Φ_e) and $\nu_\mu + \nu_\tau$ ($\Phi_{\mu\tau}$). While the Φ_e flux is about 1/3 of the expectation from the standard solar model for the ^{8}B neutrino flux of $\Phi = (5.46 \pm 0.66) \times 10^6\,\mathrm{cm}^{-2}\mathrm{s}^{-1}$, the total flux $\Phi_e + \Phi_{\mu\tau}$ is consistent with it.

Remarkably, even before the first observation of a solar neutrino deficit by Davis at Homestake, it was pointed out by Pontecorvo [Po68; Gr69] that neutrino oscillations could reduce the expected rates. Since the bulk of solar neutrinos have typical energies $E \simeq 0.1$–$10\,\mathrm{MeV}$, their oscillation

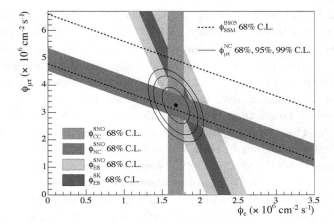

Fig. 5.3 Bounds from the SNO experiment on the Φ_e–$\Phi_{\mu\tau}$ plane. Blue band is the NC result sensitive to $\Phi_e + \Phi_{\mu\tau}$, the red band is the CC result just sensitive to Φ_e while the green band is the ES result, sensitive approximately to $\Phi_e + \Phi_{\mu\tau}/6$, with the grey band being the ES result from the much larger Super-Kamiokande detector. The region between the dotted lines is the flux expected from the standard solar models allowing for oscillations between active neutrinos (figure from [PDG]).

length in vacuum would be of the order of the distance from the Sun to the Earth ($1\,\mathrm{AU} \simeq 1.5 \times 10^{11}\,\mathrm{m}$) for $\Delta m^2 \sim 10^{-12}\text{–}10^{-10}\,\mathrm{eV}^2$, and hence even those tiny neutrino mass differences could have had observable effects if the neutrino mixing angles were large. This possibility was referred to in the past as the *just so* solution to the solar neutrino problem, but turned out however not to be realized in nature.

Much more interesting became the possibility of explaining the puzzle by the resonantly enhanced oscillations of the neutrinos as they propagate outwards through the matter in the Sun. This exploits the fact that the solar medium affects the ν_e differently than the $\nu_{\mu,\tau}$, since only the first interact through charged currents with the electrons present in it. This interaction modifies the neutrino oscillations in a beautiful way, as was discussed in detail in the previous chapter, through the interplay between neutrino mixings and matter effects, in the so called Mikheyev-Smirnov-Wolfenstein (MSW) effect [Mi85; Wo78].

The solar neutrino measurements have converged over the years towards the so-called *large mixing angle* (LMA) solution, which allows to account for all the different observations. Considering the simplified, but still accurate, case of mixing between two flavors, this solution corresponds to the mixing of ν_e with a combination of comparable amounts of ν_μ and ν_τ flavors, with a mixing angle given by $\theta_{\mathrm{sol}} \simeq 33°$. The mass splitting between the mass eigenstates involved is $\Delta m^2_{\mathrm{sol}} \simeq +7.5 \times 10^{-5} \, \mathrm{eV}^2$. These values imply that for energies $E_\nu > 2 \, \mathrm{MeV}$ the resonance layer lies near the center of the Sun, and that the resonance is quite wide, with a width $\delta_{\mathrm{R}} \simeq 0.2 R_\odot$. This makes the matter oscillations to be well in the adiabatic regime. For energies smaller than $2 \, \mathrm{MeV}$, the density required for a resonance to take place would be larger than the central density of the Sun, which is $\rho_0 \simeq 150 \, \mathrm{g \, cm}^{-3}$. This implies that for these low energies the solar neutrinos do not cross a resonance in their way out of the Sun, and they are hence affected mostly by the vacuum oscillations. In particular, this implies that the suppression expected in the radiochemical experiments based on Ga, which are mostly sensitive to the low-energy pp neutrinos, should be milder than that expected in the experiments with higher thresholds, as is indeed observed.

The mixing parameters involved in the LMA scenario have also been confirmed by the observation of oscillations of electron antineutrinos produced by a large number of Japanese reactors, using the 1 kt scintillator detector KamLAND. This experiment was able to measure oscillations over distances of about 180 km. The reduction in the flux, with respect to the expectations based on the power produced at each reactor, was found to agree with the predictions from the LMA parameters. These results actually restricted the mass splitting that is involved to a very narrow range around $\Delta m^2 \simeq 8 \times 10^{-5} \, \mathrm{eV}^2$ [Ar05b], thanks to the observed energy dependence of the oscillation length (see Fig. 4.2). To precisely determine the mixing parameters one actually has to perform a three flavor fit, since besides the dominant mixing angle θ_{12} we now know that θ_{13} is also nonzero. A global fit to all the relevant oscillation measurements leads to the preferred values that were shown in Table 4.1.

In recent years, the Borexino Collaboration has managed to detect ES events down to neutrino energies of about 300 keV (corresponding to visible energies of 150 keV, below which the background from $^{14}\mathrm{C}$ decays from the organic scintillator is overwhelming). After a series of scintillator purifications and implementing background reduction techniques, they were able to detect in real time the $^7\mathrm{Be}$ line of 0.86 MeV, which produces a Compton-like shoulder below an energy of 0.66 MeV in the electron spectrum from ES interactions. They were also able to determine the pp neutrino flux and the shoulder from pep neutrinos too, in addition to the higher energy $^8\mathrm{B}$ neutrinos. These results are shown in Fig. 5.4. The measurement of the CNO fluxes was more challenging, because they have a shape similar to that of

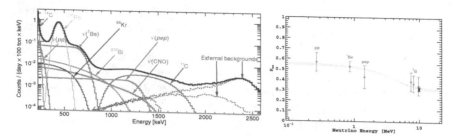

Fig. 5.4 Left panel: Spectrum of the different solar neutrino components expected at Borexino using ES events, together with the different backgrounds (from [Ag20f]). Right panel: P_{ee} survival probability of the different solar neutrino components measured by Borexino and at the highest energies by Super-Kamiokande (from [PDG]).

the larger background from radioactive Bi decays (coming from the U and Th chain), but its detection has been achieved recently [Ag20d]. The right panel of Fig. 5.4 displays the survival probability P_{ee} of the different solar neutrino components measured by Borexino and, at the highest energies, by Super-Kamiokande, with the results being in good agreement with the MSW expectations, shown in light-blue.

5.4 Impact of solar neutrinos on our understanding of the Sun

The solar neutrino problem established by the Homestake, (Super)-Kamiokande, SAGE, Gallex and GNO experiments represented an inconsistency between the electron neutrino fluxes reaching the Earth and those predicted by the solar models. The measurement of neutral currents in SNO corroborated the correctness of the SSM in 2002, and made it possible to conclude beyond any doubt that solar neutrinos indeed oscillate. The KamLAND measurements reported on the same year consolidated the conclusion, and also contributed to the knowledge of the value of the squared mass difference involved. Borexino allowed to observe the shape of P_{ee} (see Fig. 5.4), adding confidence to this interpretation. Global analyses of the data give support to the hypothesis that there are three light standard neutrinos oscillating among each other (with all the cautions about possible small additional exotic particle physics effects for which we have no evidence at the moment). Under this situation we can consider that the oscillation parameters are known with sufficient precision, and use the observations of solar neutrinos to actually study the Sun.

Taking oscillations into account, the SSM and neutrino measurements are in good agreement, and their comparison leads to the following remarks:

- boron and beryllium neutrino measurements are more accurate than the theoretical predictions, by factors of 2 and 4 respectively
- the measurements of pp and pep neutrinos are still more uncertain than the predictions, by about an order of magnitude
- the measurements of CNO neutrinos are about twice less precise than the expectations.

These considerations illustrate the importance of still continuing with the measurements of the pp, pep and CNO neutrinos in order to reduce their uncertainties, and also the need to improve the theoretical modelling of the Sun as well as to achieve a solid determination of the surface metal abundances. It would also be very desirable to independently repeat, and possibly improve, the pioneering results obtained by Borexino, which made it possible to isolate the various components of the solar neutrinos. In addition, one should measure more accurately the boron neutrino spectrum that was seen by Super-Kamiokande, SNO and Borexino, as well as attempt to measure the hep neutrino fluxes.

Regarding the implications of the measurements for the SSM, the boron and beryllium neutrinos are strongly dependent on the central temperature of the Sun, and therefore they allow to determine it precisely, with the results being in agreement with the SSM. The flux of pp (and pep) neutrinos can be easily estimated already from the solar luminosity, as roughly sketched in Eq. (5.1). This can be expressed more quantitatively with the so-called luminosity constraint [Ba02], which states that the energy released in the fusion of four protons into a ^{4}He nucleus gets transformed into the solar radiation and into the emitted neutrinos.[1] This constraint is

$$\frac{L_\odot}{4\pi(\mathrm{AU})^2} = \sum_i \alpha_i \Phi_i, \qquad (5.2)$$

where Φ_i are the fluxes of the different neutrino contributions ($i =$ pp, pep, ...) and α_i are the available energies ending up into radiation in association with each process, essentially $\alpha_i = \sum_{\mathrm{init}} M_i - \sum_{\mathrm{final}} M_i - \langle E_\nu \rangle_i$, which is the difference between the masses of the initial particles and that of the final particles and the average energy of the emitted neutrinos. Using the detailed branching ratios between the different fusion processes and the

---

[1] Eventually one can also account for small additional effects, such as the change in the gravitational energy of the Sun or non-equilibrium features, such as those leading to a secular increase in the total number of ^{3}He or ^{13}N nuclei [Ve21].

known average neutrino energies in each case, one can obtain for instance that [Ve21]

$$\Phi_{pp} + 0.946\,\Phi_{CNO} = 6.00 \times 10^{10}\text{cm}^{-2}\text{s}^{-1}, \tag{5.3}$$

with the CNO fluxes being actually two orders of magnitude smaller than the pp ones.

Finally, CNO neutrinos can provide a determination of the content of some of the most abundant *metals* in the center of the Sun, which are the C, N and O nuclei acting as catalysts for these reactions. In the last decades, the change in the results of the solar surface metal abundances toward lower values has affected the predicted CNO neutrino fluxes. Given that the presently favored *low Z* scenarios are in tension with the helioseismological determination of the speed of sound in the solar interior, an interesting interplay between these two aspects of the problem appears, and the more accurate measurement of the CNO neutrinos could help to clarify the situation and eventually indicate whether changes in the SSM would be required to achieve a better agreement with observations.

Regarding the near future, one expects improvements in the measurements of the different solar neutrino components to be obtained with SNO+ (which is a scintillator as big as KamLAND and as pure as Borexino) and with JUNO (a 20 kt scintillator). Also the ^{8}B neutrino spectrum will be measured more precisely down to few MeV with the Super-Kamiokande and Hyper-Kamiokande detectors. This should allow to better study the change in the ν_e survival probability that is expected from the transition between the regimes of low-energy vacuum oscillations and the high-energy MSW conversions in the Sun. Also a more precise determination of the day-night asymmetries due to the matter effects in the Earth will be achieved. All these improvements should help to better constrain the neutrino mixing parameters and should also provide useful information about the solar models.

Suggested exercises:

- Knowing the atomic masses of the deuterium, proton and neutron, calculate the energy thresholds in the neutral and charged current neutrino reactions in the SNO detector. What advantage do these detection reactions have over the one used in Super-Kamiokande (which, on the other hand, is much larger than SNO)?

- Compare the oscillation length of solar neutrinos and the size of the region where they get produced. Are oscillations averaged?
- This is an exercise to better understand the solar neutrino detection through the reaction $\nu + e \to \nu + e$ in Borexino.

  (1) Supposing that it is possible to observe electrons with kinetic energies larger than 150 keV, calculate the corresponding minimum neutrino energy E_ν^{min} required to produce such electrons.
  (2) Calculate the total cross section as a function of E_ν for this detector.
  (3) Supposing that the fiducial mass of the detector in the search for Be neutrinos is 100 t and that it is composed by a hydrocarbon with formula C_3H_4, calculate the number of target electrons N_e.
  (4) Using that the ^{7}Be decays 90% of the time producing a neutrino of 862 keV, estimate the flux of these neutrinos at the Earth and their daily rate at Borexino.
  (5) Discuss the effects of neutrino oscillations for this Be neutrino signal.

Recommended reading:

Neutrino Astrophysics, J.N. Bahcall, Cambridge University Press (1989)

Chapter 6

Geoneutrinos

6.1 The internal heat of the Earth

Four and a half billion years ago, the Earth formed by the coalescence of planetesimals, themselves in turn being aggregates of interstellar dust that had gathered in the primeval solar nebula. For the inner rocky planets, the planetesimals were rich in silicates and iron, which would condense at high temperatures, while poor in volatile elements, such as water, carbon dioxide or ammonia, that would be unable to solidify. For the outer planets instead, the lower ambient temperatures would allow the volatiles to freeze, leading to a different planetesimal composition that would allow them to condense into larger bodies, able to also gravitationally accrete the abundant H and He elements.

Driven by their density contrast, the iron and the silicates present in the proto-Earth differentiated, with the denser iron (and nickel) falling into the core region while the silicates accumulated in the Earth mantle. Today the Earth has a solid inner core region, at radii smaller than 1,200 km, a fluid outer core extending up to about 3,500 km radius, a viscous mantle, whose convection is also responsible for the plate tectonics, and a non-uniform rigid crust with a typical thickness of about 30 km, but being the continental component thicker than the oceanic one.

The gravitational contraction and differentiation heated the primordial Earth, and the planet has been cooling since its formation. At present it is loosing heat at a rate of about 47 TW, which has been determined through the measurement of the temperature gradient in more than 30,000 boreholes in different locations, combined with the inferred thermal conductivities. Note that this energy loss is about three times larger than the human energy consumption, but three orders of magnitude less than the energy received from the Sun. The temperature gradient is maximum near the surface (lithosphere), where it is about $25°\mathrm{C\,km^{-1}}$, being less steep in the Earth interior. At the center the temperature reaches about $7{,}500°\mathrm{C}$.

In 1862 Kelvin estimated that in order for the Earth to cool from its original hot state to one with the present surface temperature gradient, its age had to be of the order of few tens of million years. This estimate, which fell short by about two orders of magnitude, did not take however into account the mantle convection, which transports efficiently the heat to its upper levels and increases the gradient in the crust with respect to a conductive only model.[1] Moreover, the estimate did not include the radiogenic heat production inside the Earth, with Gyr time scale, which will be the main subject of the present chapter. Comprehensive reviews of the topics to be discussed here can be found in [Fi07; Dy12; Sm19; Be22].

6.2   Main radioactive decays in the Earth

In most of the plausible models of the Earth, it turns out that indeed about half of the present surface heat flux is due to the energy generated by radioactivity within the Earth, with just the rest being due to the secular cooling of the interior of the Earth. The main processes responsible for the radiogenic heat production are the α and β decays involved in the $^{238}\mathrm{U}$ and $^{232}\mathrm{Th}$ decay chains, as well as the β decay of $^{40}\mathrm{K}$.

The end products of the uranium chain are

$$^{238}\mathrm{U} \to {}^{206}\mathrm{Pb} + 8\alpha + 6e + 6\bar{\nu}_e + 51.7\,\mathrm{MeV}. \qquad (6.1)$$

This decay chain starts with the α decay $^{238}\mathrm{U} \to {}^{234}\mathrm{Th} + \alpha$, having a half-life of $4.47\,\mathrm{Gyr}$. This is comparable to the age of the Earth, implying that about half of the initial $^{238}\mathrm{U}$ nuclei have already decayed by now. The subsequent radioactive decays in the chain, involving protactinium, radium, radon, astatine, polonium, bismuth, thallium, mercury and lead, all take place at a much faster rate. The energy released is carried by the kinetic energy of the decay products (including some γ rays), which heat up the Earth with the exception of the antineutrinos emitted in the beta decays of the neutron rich intermediate isotopes, which escape almost unimpeded.

---

[1] Kelvin believed in a rigid and homogeneous Earth, and used the theoretical expression of the thermal gradient, $\mathrm{d}T/\mathrm{d}z = T_0/\sqrt{\pi\kappa t}$ as a function of the initial temperature T_0, of the thermal diffusivity κ and of the age of the Earth t. It was Kelvin's assistant Perry who demonstrated that if the hypothesis of heat conduction is valid only for a layer 50 to 100 km underneath the surface, there is no contradiction with the Earth being few Gyr old.

Regarding the end products of the thorium chain, they are

$$^{232}\text{Th} \rightarrow {}^{208}\text{Pb} + 6\alpha + 4e + 4\bar{\nu}_e + 42.7\,\text{MeV}. \qquad (6.2)$$

This chain starts with the α decay $^{232}\text{Th} \rightarrow {}^{228}\text{Ra}+\alpha$, which has the longer half-life of 14 Gyr, to then quickly decay to ^{208}Pb through actinium, radium, radon, polonium, lead, bismuth and thallium. Note that even if thorium is at present about four times as abundant as uranium, being its half-life about three times longer makes the contribution to the radiogenic heat production from the two elements to be comparable, of about 40% each. The remaining 20% of the heat is contributed by the potassium beta decay

$$^{40}\text{K} \rightarrow {}^{40}\text{Ca} + e + \bar{\nu}_e + 1.31\,\text{MeV}. \qquad (6.3)$$

In about 11% of the cases the ^{40}K would decay to ^{40}Ar by electron capture, being this channel the main source of the argon present in the atmosphere, but in this case a neutrino is emitted rather than an antineutrino. Although the energy released per decay is much smaller than in the U and Th chains, the ^{40}K decay has a shorter half-life of 1.25 Gyr, what explains the sizeable heat production associated to it (although the element potassium is much more abundant than uranium, the ^{40}K isotope fraction is small, resulting in its abundance being similar to that of ^{238}U). Note also that given the shorter potassium half-life, its contribution to the heat production relative to uranium changed with time, and it was actually bigger than this last when the Earth was born. Also the isotope ^{235}U is radioactive, decaying by α emission to ^{231}Th with a half-life of 0.76 Gyr. Although its present abundance is just 0.7% of that of ^{238}U, so that its contribution to the radiogenic heat is now negligible, it was almost 30% as abundant as ^{238}U when the Earth was born. Given its faster decay, it contributed initially to the radiogenic heat even more than ^{238}U, through the chain

$$^{235}\text{U} \rightarrow {}^{207}\text{Pb} + 7\alpha + 4e + 4\bar{\nu}_e + 46.4\,\text{MeV}. \qquad (6.4)$$

Anyhow, in the initial stages of the Earth the radiogenic heat production was actually dominated by the much faster decays of ^{26}Al, with a half-life of 0.7 Myr, but this source of heat was quickly exhausted.

The total amount of the radiogenic U, Th and K elements, and their distribution in the Earth, is hard to estimate. Being lithophilic (easily bound chemically to oxygen and silicate compounds), they are expected to be mostly in the crust and the mantle, but not in the metallic core. Moreover, since the mantle crystallized from the core-mantle boundary outwards, they preferred to be in the melted phase towards the crust. For instance, the typical abundance of U in the continental crust is of order 1 μg/g, that

in the oceanic crust is about an order of magnitude smaller while that in
the mantle is expected to be on average about another order of magnitude
smaller. The overall abundance in the Earth, relative to silicon, of the
elements U and Th can be estimated from the abundances measured in
chondritic meteorites. These are the most abundant meteorites found and
they are believed to have originated together with the planetesimals that
made the Earth, so that their composition should be similar to that of the
primordial Earth. A clear advantage they have is that, contrary to what
happened in the present Earth, the various constituents of the meteorites
have not been differentiated.[2] One hence expects that the relative mass
abundances of thorium and uranium be close to the chondritic value of
$Th/U \simeq 3.9$, while the relative abundance of the more volatile K element
should be about $K/U \simeq 1.4 \times 10^4$. On the other hand, the present isotopic
abundance of ^{232}Th is almost 100%, that of ^{238}U is 99.3% while that of
^{40}K is just 0.012%. Different estimates of the overall abundance of U in
the primeval bulk silicate Earth (BSE), which ended up forming the mantle and the crust, allowed to predict that the radiogenic heat produced at
present should be somewhere between 10 and 30 TW. In the crust, where
the absolute abundance of U is better known through more direct measurements, one estimates that about 7 TW of this heat should be produced,
and the detailed production in each location depends on the local crustal
properties. The more uncertain remainder (3 TW to 23 TW) should be instead produced in the mantle, with the actual value depending on the total
amount of radioactive elements present initially. Antineutrinos offer us a
unique opportunity to explore this contribution.

6.3   Expected antineutrino fluxes

Besides producing heat, the decays of U, Th and K also produce a large
number of electron antineutrinos with MeV energies, which carry away
about 20% of the energy from the radioactive decays and typically lead
to an antineutrino flux at the surface of the Earth of a few $10^6 \, \mathrm{cm^{-2} s^{-1}}$.
Although this flux is much smaller than the flux of solar neutrinos, which
is about $10^{11} \, \mathrm{cm^{-2} s^{-1}}$, this last is largely dominated by the pp neutrinos
with energies below 0.4 MeV. The other solar neutrinos from ^7Be, pep and

---

[2]For the refractory elements (i.e. those with high condensation temperatures), such as
uranium and thorium, the relative abundances determined in the chondritic meteorites
is also quite similar to the abundances inferred from the photosphere of the Sun, but the
volatile elements abundances are instead different.

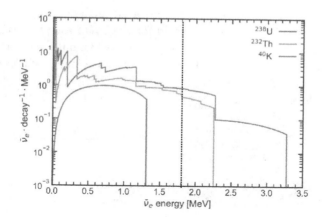

Fig. 6.1   Geoneutrino spectra per decaying nuclei for ^{238}U, ^{232}Th and ^{40}K. The vertical line indicates the threshold for the inverse beta decay process (adapted from [Be22]).

CNO have energies below 1.7 MeV, while above this energy there is the high-energy tail from ^{8}B neutrinos, which represents just about 0.1% of the total solar neutrino flux, and the much smaller flux of hep neutrinos. Moreover, being the geoneutrinos actually antineutrinos, they can be detected using liquid scintillator detectors via the inverse beta decay process, which above the threshold of 1.8 MeV has a cross section much larger than the electron scattering process used to detect the solar neutrinos. The IBD has also the clear signature of the prompt positron annihilation followed by the delayed neutron capture in protons emitting a 2.2 MeV gamma ray.

The detection of the geoneutrinos could provide an interesting handle to study the energy production inside the Earth [Kr84], to determine the fraction of the heat escaping from the surface of the Earth which is of radiogenic origin and to determine its distribution across the mantle and the crust. One may also learn about the contribution from the continental crust, which is about 2 Gyr old, and that from the oceanic crust, which is less than 200 Myr old, which are expected to be quite different given their different depths and compositions. One may also eventually measure the fraction of the heat which is due to the different radioactive elements, exploiting the different spectral shapes of the antineutrino fluxes from the different elements.

The shape of the antineutrino spectra from the different decays involved are shown in Fig. 6.1 (normalized to the number of $\bar{\nu}_e$ emitted in each decay chain). The ones from the U and Th are actually the superposition of the several spectra from the beta decays involved in the corresponding chains, and they extend beyond the threshold for the IBD process (vertical line at 1.8 MeV). Instead, those from the K beta decay can only reach a maximum energy of 1.31 MeV, and hence they unfortunately cannot be probed by this reaction.

The $\bar{\nu}_e$ flux of terrestrial origin at a given location is given by

$$\frac{\mathrm{d}\Phi}{\mathrm{d}E_\nu}(E_\nu, \mathbf{r}) = \sum_{i=\text{isotopes}} \frac{\mathrm{d}n}{\mathrm{d}E_\nu}(E_\nu) \int_{V_\oplus} \mathrm{d}^3 r' \frac{A_i(\mathbf{r}')\rho(\mathbf{r}')P_{ee}(E_\nu, |\mathbf{r}-\mathbf{r}'|)}{4\pi|\mathbf{r}-\mathbf{r}'|^2},$$

(6.5)

where $\mathrm{d}n/\mathrm{d}E_\nu$ is the spectral distribution of the $\bar{\nu}_e$ emitted per decaying nucleus plotted before, and the specific activity of isotope i is

$$A_i(\mathbf{r}') \equiv \frac{a_i(\mathbf{r}')C_i}{\tau_i m_i},$$

(6.6)

with $a_i(\mathbf{r}')$ the mass of element i per unit rock mass, C_i the fraction of the relevant isotope, τ_i is the lifetime and m_i the atomic mass of the isotope. The rock density is ρ, so that $A_i\rho$ is the rate of decays per unit time and volume. Finally, $P_{ee}(E, L)$ is the $\bar{\nu}_e$ survival probability after traversing a distance L, which takes into account that flavor oscillations reduce the amount of the electron antineutrino flavor, which is the one that is detectable. Given that the oscillation length of the neutrinos is

$$L_{\text{osc}} = \frac{4\pi E_\nu}{\Delta m^2} \simeq 100\,\text{km}\frac{E_\nu}{3\,\text{MeV}}\frac{7.5 \times 10^{-5}\,\text{eV}^2}{\Delta m^2},$$

(6.7)

we see that the geoneutrino flavor oscillations will be largely averaged when adding up neutrinos from different distances, so that to a good approximation one may replace P_{ee} by the averaged expression (see Eq. (4.12))

$$\langle P_{ee} \rangle \simeq 1 - 0.5(\cos^4\theta_{13}\sin^2 2\theta_{12} + \sin^2 2\theta_{13}) \simeq 0.55.$$

(6.8)

This shows that due to the oscillations, almost half of the $\bar{\nu}_e$ emitted in the Earth become undetectable to the IBD reaction, and hence it is very important to account for this effect when inferring the radiogenic energy production from the measured neutrino fluxes.[3] These fluxes can then be convoluted with the IBD cross section and the experimental efficiencies to obtain the rates in liquid scintillator detectors.

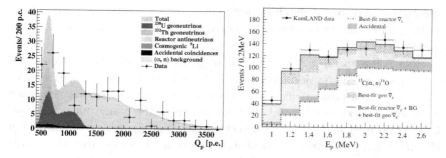

Fig. 6.2 Left panel: geoneutrino spectra measured with the detectors Borexino, from [Ag20b] (https://doi.org/10.1103/PhysRevD.101.012009). Right panel: the same for KamLAND (reprinted figure with permission from [Ga13], copyright 2022 by the American Physical Society). The energy of the prompt signal, denoted by Q_p in the left panel and by E_p in the right one, is just the sum of the kinetic energy of the positron plus $2m_e$. It corresponds to $E_\nu - 0.72\,\text{MeV}$, and hence allows to measure the energy of the antineutrino.

6.4 Observational results and issues at stake

The KamLAND and Borexino detectors, consisting respectively of 1 kt and 300 tons of liquid scintillator, have actually been able to detect the geoneutrino fluxes in recent years [Ar05; Be10; Ga13; Ag20b]. The resulting spectra are displayed in Fig. 6.2. The main backgrounds in these searches are the nuclear reactor $\bar{\nu}_e$ resulting from the neutron induced fission of U and Pu nuclei, whose spectrum extends up to about 8 MeV. They affect particularly the KamLAND experiment, given that many reactors exist in Japan, and indeed the detection of the reactor antineutrinos to measure their oscillations over distances of $\sim 200\,\text{km}$ was the main motivation for this experiment. This background has to be estimated from the knowledge of the power output of the nuclear reactors, and it was actually strongly reduced after the reactors shutdown in 2011 following the Fukushima accident, something which turned out to be beneficial for the geoneutrino detection. Another background in this experiment was from contamination of radioactive elements present in the detector, with α particles initiating the $^{13}\text{C}(\alpha,n)^{16}\text{O}$ reaction with the natural ^{13}C isotopes present in the scintillator's hydrocarbons. The decay of the excited O nucleus could provide the prompt signal and then there will be the delayed n capture, mimicking

---

[3]Some small corrections to the averaged oscillation expression exist, particularly given that about a quarter of the signal measured in a detector comes from the nearby crust within 50 km of it. The additional corrections due to matter effects are also at the percent level.

the IBD signature. A significant reduction of radioactive elements, such as the ^{210}Po from radon decays, was required in order to achieve a cleaner measurement.

Regarding the Borexino detector in Italy, the background from european nuclear reactors is in this case not so large, giving a signal smaller than that from geoneutrinos in the relevant energy range, and the other radioactive backgrounds are under control given the many purification efforts performed to be able to detect the low energy solar neutrinos. On the other hand, the overall geoneutrino rates in Borexino are smaller due to the smaller fiducial volume of this detector.

Note that even if the contribution to the radiogenic heat of the U and Th chains are comparable, the expected signal in a scintillator from the uranium is a factor of about 3.5 times larger than that from thorium, due to the higher associated neutrino energies, with the endpoint of the ^{238}U chain being 3.3 MeV while that of the ^{232}Th chain being just 2.25 MeV. One for instance expects a radiogenic signal in KamLAND from the local crust near the detector of about 11.2 TNU from U and 3.2 TNU from Th [Fi07], where a terrestrial neutrino unit (TNU) corresponds to one event per year in a fully efficient detector containing 10^{32} protons (which corresponds to about 1 kt of scintillator). At the Gran Sasso location instead, the different geology of the Apennine range (richer in carbonate sediments) leads to a predicted rate from the local crust, in TNU, which is about 30% smaller. There is also a comparable contribution from the reminder of the crust all over the surface of the Earth, which can be estimated using different crust models.

The contribution from the mantle is instead more uncertain due to the poor knowledge of the absolute abundances of radiogenic elements in it, which have to be inferred indirectly. If one adopts for the bulk silicate Earth a *geochemical model* which assumes that the composition of refractories is similar to that of carbonaceous chondritic meteorites and that the radiogenic nuclei are excluded from the core, the mantle could add to the geoneutrino rates an extra 11 TNU if most of the U and Th are near the mantle-core boundary, or 16 TNU if they are more homogeneously distributed across it. Other different predictions rely for instance in the *cosmochemical model*, which adopts for the BSE the composition of the refractory elements observed in a different type of meteorites, the enstatite chondrites, which actually show an Fe abundance more in line with that of the Earth. In this case, one expects a smaller total radiogenic heat production of about 11 TW, with about 7 TW from the crust and just about 4 TW from the mantle, with a correspondingly reduced signal in liquid scintillator detectors. On the other extreme, there are the so-called *geodynamical models*, which take into account the dynamics of the mantle convection and try to reproduce the present heat loss without requiring a too high core temperature in the proto-Earth. These models suggest that the radiogenic heat could be as high as 33 TW, arising mostly from the mantle. The actual measurements can hence in principle be used to distinguish among these different possibilities.

From the most recent results by KamLAND and by Borexino, based on the detection in total of about 200 antineutrino events of radiogenic origin, it has been inferred [Be22] that the signal from U and Th geoneutrinos at KamLAND is 32.1 ± 5.0 TNU, while that at Borexino is $47.0^{+8.6}_{-8.1}$ TNU. If one subtracts the more accurately known contribution from the lithosphere (both the local crust from within ~ 100 km and the far field lithosphere from all the rest of the Earth crust), one can conclude that the mantle contribution to the KamLAND measurement is just $4.8^{+5.6}_{-5.9}$ TNU, while that to Borexino is $20.8^{+9.4}_{-9.2}$ TNU. Some tension is apparent between these two values, the first one being closer to the cosmochemical estimate while the last one is more in the middle range derived in geochemical models (or even marginally consistent with geodynamical models), but the uncertainties are still large so that a wide range of possibilities remain open. If the data are combined and one adds the estimated contribution from K decays as well as that from the lithosphere, one can infer a total radiogenic heat of $20.8^{+7.3}_{-7.9}$ TW, right in the middle between the cosmochemical and geochemical estimates. This implies that approximately half of the total measured heat flux of about 47 TW is of radiogenic origin, the rest being due to the secular cooling. More data and new experiments, such as SNO+, JUNO and Jinping, will certainly help to clarify these issues and to further develop this fascinating new field of geoneutrino science.

Suggested exercises:

- In ref. [Be22], the following result is quoted: with a flux of $10^6 \, \bar{\nu}_e \, \text{cm}^{-2}\text{s}^{-1}$ and neglecting oscillations, an ideal detector with 10^{32} protons would see 12.8 events per year from the U chain and 3.2 from the Th chain. Check the plausibility of this result using the known IBD cross section and the spectra of Fig. 6.1.
- The number of detected events collected to date is about 200. Show that this is consistent with the expected antineutrino fluxes, time of data taking and detector properties.

Chapter 7

Supernova Neutrinos

Supernova (SN) explosions signal the end of the nuclear burning phase in the life of a massive star. They represent a spectacular astrophysical process in which the neutrinos play a preponderant role. A detailed knowledge of the physics of the neutrinos is required in order to understand the SN explosions. In turn, the observation of those neutrinos can provide crucial insights into the different stages of the SN evolution, and may also allow us to learn about the properties of the neutrinos themselves.

7.1 Generalities about core collapse supernovae

Astronomy It is quite rare to see with the naked eye the appearance of a new very bright star in the sky. According to historical records from the last 2,000 years, this happened on average about once per century. Eight of these events were surely supernovae that exploded in the Milky Way (including the Crab, Tycho's and Kepler's SNe), the rest probably being the more frequent but fainter novae associated to cataclysmic events in which a white dwarf star suddenly brightens as a result of a burst of accretion from a binary companion. Since due to the Galactic dust attenuation the visible light that is emitted in the Milky Way can reach us only from distances of 2 to 3 kpc, just the closest events that happened in the sky of the northern hemisphere regions, such as in China or Europe, were registered and contributed to the historical records.[1] In the directions towards these explosions we see today a supernova remnant, namely a cloud of gas expanding radially at a velocity of several thousand $km\,s^{-1}$. Few other young remnants with ages of less than 1,000 years have been identified in

---

[1]Looking at wavelength such as IR or X-rays, a future Galactic SN happening anywhere inside the Milky Way should now be observable.

the Milky Way, signaling that a SN exploded there but was not observed at that time (as for instance Cas A, at 3.4 kpc distance, whose observation was missed around 350 yrs ago). Sometimes there is also a compact stellar remnant that can be seen as a young pulsar.

Several thousands of supernovae have been observed in the whole Universe up to now. The electromagnetic emission of a SN remains very bright for a few months, with a typical luminosity of about $2 \times 10^8 L_\odot$, what amounts to a total energy budget in radiation of about 10^{49} erg. The analysis of the absorption lines in their spectra has led astronomers to classify supernovae either as type I (without hydrogen lines) or as type II (with hydrogen lines). Type I SN are further divided between the supernovae without helium and with strong silicon lines (type Ia), those with helium lines (Ib) and those without any helium nor silicon lines (Ic). Supernovae of type Ia appear in any type of galaxy, while the other ones appear mostly in spiral and irregular galaxies because they are associated with young stellar populations. Supernovae Ia are produced when a C/O white dwarf star accretes gas from a binary companion until it exceeds the Chandrasekhar mass of about $1.4 M_\odot$, so that electron degeneracy pressure can no longer prevent the star from collapsing. In this situation, the collapsing star heats, C fusion is ignited and the star explodes, without leaving any compact remnant nor producing significant neutrino emission through fusion processes. Some neutrinos can still be produced thermally and through beta processes, with energies of few MeV given that the density is not high enough to trap the neutrinos and further heat the star. The neutrino luminosity of type-Ia SNe turns out to be about four orders of magnitude smaller than in the other types of SNe [Od11]. Anyway, if a SN Ia were to take place very nearby, so that its neutrinos become observable, some useful information about the explosion mechanism may be obtained [Wr17]. The other SN types, namely type II, Ib and Ic, are believed instead to be linked to the gravitational collapse of the core of a very massive star. They are called core collapse supernovae (CCSN). In this process, a compact remnant is produced and a huge amount of energy, of the order of a few 10^{53} erg, ends up being emitted mostly as neutrinos, and this is why we will be interested in them here. We note that direct observations of the supernova remnants show that the kinetic energy of the expanding debris is of the order of 10^{51} erg, which amounts to the kinetic energy of $10 M_\odot$ flying at a speed of few thousand km s^{-1}. This corresponds to about 1% of the energy released in the collapse. On the other hand, even if during a few months a SN can be as bright as a whole galaxy, the total energy emitted as light is only a fraction of about 10^{-4} of the total energy released.

The compact-star connection The principles of catastrophic gravitational collapse of massive stars were uncovered by Chandrasekhar in 1930, and speculations about the possible existence of compact stars were then discussed by Landau. Few years later, just after the discovery of the neutron, Baade and Zwicky remarked that supernovae could herald the formation of a neutron star, implying a prodigious release of gravitational energy. At the end of the thirties, Oppenheimer and Snyder studied the formation of what is now known as a black hole, and the possible existence of quark stars has also been speculated more recently. We now describe the general astrophysical picture that is believed to lead to the supernova phenomenon.

The evolution of the stars results from the permanent competition between the gravitational attraction, that tends to produce a collapse, and the repulsive force due to the gas pressure which is maintained by the nuclear fusion reactions taking place in the interior of the hot stars. Remarkably, the larger is the star mass, and hence the larger the gravitational pull, the faster need the fusion reactions to occur and hence the shorter is the resulting star's lifetime. For instance, while after 5 Gyr the Sun is still in the middle of its hydrogen burning phase, stars with masses in excess of $8\,M_\odot$ can complete the burning of H into He in about 10^7 yr, and then in increasingly rapid stages the nuclear fusion produce C, O, Mg, Si and finally Ni and Fe, resulting in an onion like structure with the heavier elements located closer to the center of the stars.

Since Fe is the element having the minimum energy per nucleon, its fusion into heavier elements does not produce more energy. The Fe core then contracts until it is prevented from further collapse by the pressure exerted by the degenerate electrons. This purely quantum mechanical effect can be roughly understood by considering that in the stellar core, neglecting temperature effects, all the momenta of the electrons will be filled up to the Fermi level p_F. The number of electrons in the core, N_e, should then satisfy

$$N_e \simeq 2V \int_0^{p_F} dp \, \frac{4\pi p^2}{(2\pi)^3} = V \frac{p_F^3}{3\pi^2}, \qquad (7.1)$$

where we took into account the two spin degrees of freedom of the electrons and V is the volume of the core. This implies that $p_F \simeq N_e^{1/3}/R_c$, with $R_c \simeq 10^3$ km being the core radius. Actually, the core reaches temperatures in excess of 10^9 K ($\sim$ MeV), so that one may consider that the electrons are mildly relativistic, having energies $\varepsilon_F \simeq p_F$. In this case, the total energy associated to this Fermi motion is $E_F \simeq N_e \varepsilon_F \simeq N_e^{4/3}/R_c$. On the other hand, omitting factors of order one, the gravitational energy of the core is $E_g \sim -G_N M_c^2/R_c \sim -N_b^2 (m_p/M_{Pl})^2/R_c$, with N_b the number of nucleons in the core, m_p the proton mass and $M_{Pl} \sim G_N^{-1/2} \simeq 10^{19} m_p$ being the Planck mass. Setting $N_b \simeq N_e$, one finds that $E_g \simeq -E_F$, an indication that the degeneracy pressure can no longer prevent the collapse, for $N_b > (M_{Pl}/m_p)^3$, i.e. for $M_c > 10^{57} m_p \simeq M_\odot$. The detailed computation performed by Chandrasekhar [Ch35], solving the hydrostatic equations with the appropriate equation of state for the relativistic electrons, led indeed to a value for the limiting mass beyond which the core collapse should occur of $M_{Ch} \simeq 1.4 M_\odot$.

Note that the average density of the Fe core, which is a solar mass object contained in a Moon size volume,[2] is about $10^9 \, \mathrm{g\,cm^{-3}}$. When the Fe core reaches the Chandrasekhar mass, it collapses almost in free fall and in a few ms reaches a density exceeding the nuclear density $\rho_n \simeq 3 \times 10^{14} \, \mathrm{g\,cm^{-3}}$. At this point, the compressed nuclear core bounces back, sending a shock wave through the remaining accreting matter, that heats and eventually expels the external layers of the star. A compact remnant, such as a neutron star or a black hole, is expected to remain in the core.

Stars with initial masses below $8 M_\odot$ do not succeed in burning C, but rather cool into a degenerate C/O white dwarf after having expelled their envelopes (these are the candidates for type Ia SN if they form part of a binary system). Stars with masses $8 < M/M_\odot < 10$ may not be able to burn Ne, and hence have O-Ne-Mg degenerate cores which can collapse into neutron stars once they reach the Chandrasekhar mass, leading to core collapse supernovae (typically of type II). Stars with initial masses in excess of $10 \, M_\odot$ do produce an Fe core, which will hence collapse as described before. In stars with masses larger than $\sim 20 \, M_\odot$, intense stellar winds can wipe out the outermost layers of the mantle before the explosion, depleting the hydrogen or even the helium in the envelope and leading to supernovae of type Ib or of type Ic. The amount of blown-out material from the envelope depends sensitively on the star's metallicity, which determines the radiative opacities. The envelope may also be depleted as a result of interactions with a binary stellar companion. It is plausible that the cores of the stars with initial mass in excess of 20–$30 \, M_\odot$ will end up as black holes.

---

[2] The Fe core has about 900 km radius, while the Si core has a radius of about 4,000 km.

Numerical simulations of the sequence of events following gravitational collapse are reaching an impressive level of sophistication. They are much more demanding than the simulations needed to understand our Sun, and they show that in the very early moments after the infall a hot proto-neutron star forms in the center of the collapsing star. There is however a persisting difficulty in explaining in detail how the explosion works. It is important to note that the energy that must be released in the formation of a neutron star is very large, of the order of several times 10^{53} erg. This follows from the expression for the gravitational energy of the compact remnant

$$E_{\rm g} \simeq -\frac{3}{5} G_{\rm N} \frac{M^2}{R_{\rm c}} \simeq -3 \times 10^{53} \left(\frac{M}{1.4 M_\odot}\right)^2 \left(\frac{10\,{\rm km}}{R_{\rm c}}\right) \ {\rm erg}, \qquad (7.2)$$

where M is the mass of the compact remnant and $R_{\rm c}$ is its radius.[3] The energy released in the supernova explosion is actually much more than the total nuclear energy released by the fusion processes that took place in the course of the entire star's lifetime, what seems a curious revenge of the ideas of Kelvin concerning the role of gravity as a source of stellar energy!

Neutrinos are responsible for carrying away about 99% of the energy released in the supernova, in an emission having a complex temporal structure and lasting about ten seconds. Their observation offers a unique chance to look into the processes taking place during the formation of a compact star. Moreover, neutron stars are observed to have large peculiar velocities, from 100 up to 1,000 km s^{-1}, which are plausibly produced at the moment of their formation as a result of an asymmetric neutrino emission. It should also be recalled that neutron stars can rotate quite fast and are usually endowed with high magnetic fields, due to the conservation of the angular momentum and of the magnetic flux during the collapse. This could be potentially relevant to understand the star's evolution during the first instants after the explosion. Also the presence of companion stars may further complicate the picture of the pre-supernova.

Astrophysical expectations for the SN explosion The process of a SN explosion consists mainly of four stages: the infall, the neutronization

---

[3] A more precise value for the neutron star's binding energy BE, which accounts for the difference between baryonic and gravitational neutron star masses, should also account for the effects of the nuclear interactions, and hence depends on the equation of state (EOS) adopted for the nuclear matter. A numerical expression which approximately reproduces the results obtained with different EOS is $BE \simeq 0.6 \beta M / (1 - 0.5\beta)$, where $\beta = G_{\rm N} M / R_{\rm c}$ is the so-called compactness parameter [La01]. In particular, for $M = 1.4 M_\odot$ and $R_{\rm c} = 10$ km one gets $\beta \simeq 0.21$, so that $BE \simeq 0.14 M$.

Table 7.1   Schematic description of the collapse and neutrino emission in the supernova delayed explosion scenario, for a progenitor mass of about 10 to 16 $M_\odot$. The available energy is $\mathcal{E} \equiv |E_g|$. In the first four rows the main phases of the collapse are identified, while the last row refers to the newborn neutron star (adapted from [Ca04]).

Collapse Phase	Dynamics	ν Process	Duration	Energetics
Infall neutronization of inner $\sim 0.6 M_\odot$ of core	iron core collapse $\gamma + \mathrm{Fe} \to 13\alpha + 4n$ $\alpha \to 2n + 2p$	ν_e-emission $e^- p \to n \nu_e$ ν_e-trapping $\nu_e A \to \nu_e A$ $\nu_e n \to p e^-$	~ 100 ms	$\lesssim 1\% \, \mathcal{E}$
Flash neutronization of outer $\sim 0.4 M_\odot$ of core	bounce/shock wave $\gamma + \mathrm{Fe} \to 13\alpha + 4n$	ν_e-burst $e^- p \to n \nu_e$ at ν_e-sphere	$[t \equiv t_b]$ $\lesssim 10$ ms	$\sim 1\% \, \mathcal{E}$
Accretion neutronization of inner $\sim 0.5 M_\odot$ of mantle delayed shock revival	shock-wave stalling $\gamma \to e^+ e^-$ proto n-star formation SN explosion	$\bar\nu_e$-emission $e^+ n \to p \bar\nu_e$ ν_i-emission $e^+ e^- \to \nu_i \bar\nu_i$ ν-heating $\nu_e n \rightleftharpoons p e^-$ $\bar\nu_e p \rightleftharpoons n e^+$	$\lesssim 500$ ms	10–20 % $\mathcal{E}$
Cooling residual neutronization	mantle contraction $\gamma \to e^+ e^-$	ν_i-emission $e^+ e^- \to \nu_i \bar\nu_i$ at ν_i-sphere	~ 10 s	80–90 % $\mathcal{E}$
neutron star $M_{ns} \sim 1.4 M_\odot$ $R_{ns} \simeq 18$ km $\rho \simeq 3\,10^{14}$ g cm^{-3}	steady state $T < 10^9$ K	ν-fading $n\,n \to n\,p\,e^- \bar\nu_e$ $n\,p\,e^- \to n\,n\,\nu_e$	$\sim 10^5$ yr	few % $\mathcal{E}$

burst, the accretion phase and the cooling phase, with their main features being summarized in Table 7.1. The infall phase starts just when the core reaches the Chandrasekhar mass and lasts for less than 100 ms, during which the collapsing inner core is compressed and heated. Fe nuclei falling towards the center are disintegrated, first into alpha particles and then partly into nucleons (it takes about 2 MeV per nucleon to dissociate Fe into $13\alpha + 4n$, but then it takes about 7 MeV per nucleon to completely dissociate an α particle). Some electrons start then to be captured by protons to produce neutrons, with the associated emission of ν_e. These processes are endothermic and about 10% of the energy gained in the collapse is spent on them. When nuclear densities are reached, a bounce takes place, and this moment is usually adopted in the simulations as the reference time

t_b, with subsequent times being named *post-bounce*. The resulting shock wave expands then through the remaining infalling matter. For densities larger than about $10^{12}\,\mathrm{g\,cm^{-3}}$, the neutrinos actually get trapped, having to diffuse out up to the so-called neutrino sphere, some kind of surface of last scattering at a radius of few tens of km from where they can leave the proto-neutron star. One of the relevant neutrino interactions at this stage is the coherent NC with nuclei, which is enhanced by a factor N^2 (see Eq. (2.8)). Although below the shock most nuclei get disintegrated, the infalling matter above the shock is rich in Fe nuclei for which the large number of neutrons, $N = 30$, leads to a strong enhancement of the NC cross section. Also the CC processes contribute to the neutrino trapping.

The neutronization burst is characterized by a strong peak in the emitted ν_e flux, lasting for about 10 ms, which is caused by the deleptonisation of the outer part of the Fe core. This ν_e emission amounts to about 1% of the total SN luminosity. A large fraction of the shock energy is spent however in dissociating the infalling Fe nuclei, so that the shock loses power, generally stalling at a radius of few hundred km. At this point, the stalled shock-wave revives as a result of several factors, including the residual degeneracy pressure from electrons and trapped neutrinos that prevents a rapid recollapse or the weakening ram pressure from the remaining infalling matter that eventually subsides. The most important contribution, however, is that from the neutrinos leaving the star's core which deposit a fraction of their energy in the matter behind the shock and, helped by the convective instabilities resulting from this heating from below, eventually relaunch the shock wave. These convective effects are essentially three dimensional, and their study requires quite demanding simulations [Ja16]. This delayed explosion scenario represents nowadays the most accepted scenario for core collapse supernova. The success or failure to achieve such delayed explosions depends on many uncertain inputs, such as the equation of state at nuclear densities or the treatment of convection (see [Ja01] for a review).

During the accretion phase, which lasts for about 0.5 s, a very high neutrino luminosity is achieved and about 10 to 20% of the total energy gets emitted [Na78; Be85; Ja01]. In the delayed explosion scenario, after the shock revival and the successful explosion comes the cooling phase, that lasts for about 10 s, and in it the remaining 80 to 90% of the SN energy is released, mostly in neutrinos and antineutrinos of all three flavors.

During the initial core collapse, the outer mantle of the star remains essentially unaware of this, but during the cooling phase the shock wave sweeps the mantle of the star and later continues heating and accelerating the star's envelope. After a few hours, the shock eventually breaks out, giving rise to the explosion that is visible in light. Note that after the moment when the explosion is launched, the heating by the shock of the outer core triggers some nuclear fusion, in particular through alpha captures that lead to Fe peak elements such as ^{56}Ni, liberating some extra energy that contributes to the explosion. Also the neutron rich ambient is favorable to the formation of elements heavier than Fe by r-processes, in which rapid neutron captures take place on timescales shorter than the typical beta decay lifetimes. Electron neutrinos in turn contribute to increase the nuclear charges through charged current interactions with the neutron rich elements. In this way, an important fraction of the elements heavier than iron get produced (the rest being likely produced in binary neutron-star mergers). These heavy elements can subsequently be dispersed into the galactic environment, and they eventually contribute to the material from which new generations of stars, and also planets, can be formed. The radioactive decays of ^{56}Ni into ^{56}Co (lifetime of 6.1 d), and then to ^{56}Fe (lifetime of 77 d), are important to light up the SN in the few months following the explosion.

Frequency and distribution of Galactic SNe The knowledge of the frequency of core collapse supernovae in the Milky Way is very important in order to know what are the chances of observing one with the operating neutrino telescopes. Its value can be estimated using the average frequency of SNe in galaxies similar to ours, as determined in supernova surveys, or based on the number of supernova remnants observed in the Galaxy, or the already discussed frequency of historical SNe once selection effects are accounted for, or the observation of radioactive decays of ^{26}Al produced in SN explosions, etc. The combination of these results leads to a frequency of 1.63 ± 0.46 CCSN/century in the Milky Way [Ro21]. This gives hopes to the searches of neutrinos from a Galactic supernova, since the probability that such an explosion could take place within a person's lifetime is almost a certainty. Neutrino detectors sensitive to a Galactic supernova have been operating for the last three decades and, although no Galactic explosion occurred, the SN1987A that took place in the nearby Large Magellanic Cloud was actually observed, as will be discussed later.

Regarding the most likely location where a SN could take place in the Milky Way, it is sensible to assume that the distribution of the massive stars that explode as core collapse supernovae is proportional to the overall distribution of the stars. The simplest way to model this distribution is assuming that they lie in a flat disk with just an exponential radial profile

$$\frac{d^2 N_*}{dx\,dy} = \frac{N_*}{2\pi\,r_*^2} \exp(-r/r_*), \text{ with } r = \sqrt{x^2 + y^2}. \qquad (7.3)$$

We used as origin the Galactic center, lying at a distance $d_{\rm GC} \simeq 8.5\,{\rm kpc}$, and the x and y Cartesian coordinates are contained in the Galactic plane, with the x-axis pointing away from the Earth location. N_* is the total number of stars in the Galaxy and a reasonable value for the radial scale factor is $r_* \simeq 3\,{\rm kpc}$. This simple model could be improved in many ways, such as accounting for the spiral arms or specifying the distribution along the direction z perpendicular to the disk. However, for the purpose of estimating the distribution of the supernovae in the Milky Way the adopted exponential profile within the Galactic plane is sufficient. It is easy to obtain the distribution of the distances from us to the stars, $d = \sqrt{(x + d_{\rm GC})^2 + y^2}$, and of the angles with respect to the Galactic center, given by the galactic longitude ℓ, which is determined from the relation $\tan\ell = y/(x + d_{\rm GC})$. The resulting values for the average and dispersion of the distance and angle are

$$d_{\rm SN} = (10 \pm 5) \text{ kpc and } \ell_{\rm SN} = 0° \pm 33°. \qquad (7.4)$$

Note that the probability distribution for the observation of a Galactic supernova neutrino signal is quite different from the distribution of the stars that are visible in the night sky, due to the fact that neutrinos pass through Galactic matter unimpeded and thus they are much more likely to arrive from the central regions of the Galaxy. Considering the above discussion, the reference distance to a Galactic supernova will be assumed to be 10 kpc, but given the significant dispersion on the possible distance one should keep in mind that the neutrino fluxes expected from a Galactic supernova could typically vary by an order of magnitude.

7.2 Expectations for the neutrino emission

Flavor In the very beginning of the core collapse, mostly electron neutrinos are produced through the neutronization reaction $p + e \to n + \nu_e$. This emission is expected to amount to only a fraction of the order of 1% of the total emitted energy, while most of the energy is released in the subsequent accretion (10–20%) and cooling (80–90%) phases. Let us note that in an iron core of $1.4\,M_\odot$ there are about $N_e = 7 \times 10^{56}$ electrons. Had we assumed that when the neutron star forms the energy of 3×10^{53} erg is just carried away by a number of electron neutrinos comparable to N_e, each of them would have had about 300 MeV. This remark alone shows that the true number of emitted neutrinos, whose typical energies are about 20 times smaller, has to be more than an order of magnitude higher. This also implies that the asymmetry between the total number of electron neutrinos and antineutrinos finally emitted, fixed by the lepton number so that $N_{\nu_e} - N_{\bar{\nu}_e} \simeq N_e$, should be much smaller than N_{ν_e}.

After the core bounce, the central regions of the proto-neutron star reach temperatures up to 30 MeV, and neutrinos and antineutrinos are copiously produced in this hot and very dense region. Several processes contribute to this, including charged current interactions producing electron type (anti)neutrinos and NC interactions producing all three types of (anti)neutrinos, such as through pair production $e^+e^- \to \nu\bar{\nu}$ and $\nu_e\bar{\nu}_e \to \nu\bar{\nu}$, or through nucleon bremsstrahlung $NN \to NN\nu\bar{\nu}$. Note that it is not expected that a large amount of muons or taus be produced, due to their large masses. Thus, muon and tau (anti)neutrinos get produced mostly through neutral currents, and hence they should all be present in similar amounts. It is thus customary to label the muon and tau neutrinos and antineutrinos collectively as ν_x, and the four corresponding fluxes are assumed to be the same. In this picture we have then three different types of fluxes, those associated to ν_e, to $\bar{\nu}_e$ and to ν_x.

The neutrinos produced in the proto-neutron star are initially trapped and they have to diffuse outward. Eventually, neutrinos reach a layer, at densities 10^{11}–10^{12} g cm^{-3}, from which they can efficiently escape from the star without having further interactions with stellar matter. These imaginary boundary surfaces are called *neutrinospheres*, in analogy with the name photospheres used for stellar surfaces. These neutrino spheres are at a typical radius of 30 to 100 km, where the proto-neutron star temperature is of order 3 to 6 MeV. Since the neutrino interactions depend on energy, the neutrino spheres do depend on the energy and hence the outgoing spectra will not be exactly thermal (higher energy neutrinos escape from regions at larger radius where the density and temperature of the medium are lower). Also, since the neutrino interactions depend on the flavor considered, one expects that ν_e will have a larger neutrino sphere than $\bar{\nu}_e$ (due to the CC interactions with the more abundant neutrons), and that ν_x will have the smallest neutrino sphere.[4] This implies that one should also expect that $\langle E_{\nu_e} \rangle < \langle E_{\bar{\nu}_e} \rangle < \langle E_{\nu_x} \rangle$. In spite of this, after the initial neutronization burst the total luminosities in each neutrino species, $\mathcal{E}_i \equiv \int dt\, \mathcal{L}_i$, end up

---

[4]Actually, due to the difference between the ν and $\bar{\nu}$ NC interactions with nucleons, there is a slight difference between the $\nu_{\mu,\tau}$ and $\bar{\nu}_{\mu,\tau}$ distributions, but these differences can be safely neglected.

being similar, with $\mathcal{E}_{\nu_e} \simeq \mathcal{E}_{\bar{\nu}_e} \simeq \mathcal{E}_{\nu_x} \simeq 5 \times 10^{52}$ erg, since there is some compensation because the neutrinos with lower energies are emitted from larger surfaces.

Neutrino energy distributions and fluxes As just discussed, each neutrino species should have an approximate, but not exact, thermal distribution. Due to the energy dependence of the neutrinospheres, the actual distributions turn out to be narrower than a thermal one, what is usually referred to as a pinched distribution. The effective temperature (related to the average energy) and the degree of pinching depend on the flavor considered and also change with time. The distributions are often parameterized as a modified Maxwell-Boltzmann distribution

$$\phi(E, T, \alpha) = \frac{E^\alpha}{T^{\alpha+1}\Gamma(\alpha+1)} \exp(-E/T). \qquad (7.5)$$

One has in this case that $\langle E \rangle = (\alpha + 1)T$, and the spectral pinching α gets determined from $(\alpha+2)/(\alpha+1) = \langle E^2 \rangle / \langle E \rangle^2$. A Maxwell-Boltzmann distribution would have $\alpha = 2$, while for larger α the distribution becomes narrower since $\sigma_E/\langle E \rangle = 1/\sqrt{\alpha+1}$, with $\sigma_E = \sqrt{\langle E^2 \rangle - \langle E \rangle^2}$ measuring the spread of the distribution. Alternative parameterizations have also been considered, such as a modified Fermi-Dirac distribution with $\phi(E, T, \eta) \propto E^2/(1 + \exp(E/T - \eta))$, where the effective chemical potential η describes the pinching. The Fermi-Dirac distribution with $\eta = 0$ is actually quite similar to the modified Maxwell-Boltzmann distribution with $\alpha \simeq 2.3$, so that values of $\alpha > 2.3$ would correspond to pinched fermionic distributions.

An important issue for the eventual analysis of data is to have an accurate parametric description of the flux Φ_i reaching the Earth, for each of the neutrino species $i = \nu_e, \bar{\nu}_e, \nu_x$. This flux is approximately given by

$$\Phi_i(E, t) = \frac{\mathcal{L}_i}{4\pi D^2} \frac{\phi(E, T_i, \alpha_i)}{(\alpha_i + 1)T_i}, \qquad (7.6)$$

where $\mathcal{L}_i(t)$ is the SN luminosity (i.e. the emitted power), D the distance to the SN, $T_i(t)$ the effective temperature of each species and $\alpha_i(t)$ the corresponding pinching parameter.

The fluence F_i is the time integrated flux, and may be expressed as

$$F_i(E) = \int dt\, \Phi_i(E, t) \simeq \frac{\mathcal{E}_i}{4\pi D^2} \frac{\phi(E, \langle T_i \rangle, \langle \alpha_i \rangle)}{(\langle \alpha_i \rangle + 1)\langle T_i \rangle}, \qquad (7.7)$$

where $\langle T_i \rangle$ and $\langle \alpha_i \rangle$ are suitable average values. The neutrino emission will not be constant in time, and simulations suggest that a comparable amount

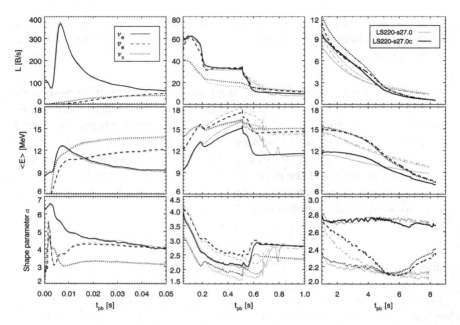

Fig. 7.1   Luminosities, average radiated energies and pinching parameter α obtained in simulations by the Garching group of a $27\,M_\odot$ precursor. Results are shown including convection (thick black lines) and without convection (thin red lines). Being this a 1D simulation, the explosion was induced at $\sim 0.5\,$s and $\sim 0.8\,$s post bounce times ($t_{\mathrm{pb}} \equiv t - t_{\mathrm{b}}$) in each case. Results are given for ν_e, $\bar{\nu}_e$ and ν_x. Units for the luminosity are in $\mathrm{B\,s^{-1}}$, where one Bethe stands for $B = 10^{51}$ erg. Panels from left to right correspond to the neutronization, accretion and cooling phases respectively (from [Mi16], with kind permission from the Società Italiana di Fisica).

of energy is emitted in each of the six neutrino and antineutrino species, a hypothesis called *equipartition* which is often adopted in phenomenological studies, but note that some simulations find deviations from this behavior by up to factors of two [Ke03].

As an example, we show in Fig. 7.2 the resulting values for the luminosities, average energies and pinching parameters as a function of time, obtained in a simulation of the collapse of a $27\,M_\odot$ star performed by the Garching group [Mi16]. Note the typical hierarchy between the different average neutrino energies that results during the accretion phase, while at late times one has that $\langle E_{\bar{\nu}_e}\rangle \simeq \langle E_{\nu_x}\rangle$, because in the cooling phase these neutrino types get mostly determined by NC processes. On the other hand, the ν_e average energies turn out to be smaller due to the effects of the CC interactions with the abundant neutrons, which imply that the neutrino-sphere radius of the ν_e is larger than those of the other neutrino types. Also note that the individual luminosities differ significantly during the first second, while they become more similar during the cooling phase. The pinching factors of the three neutrino species turn out to be different and they are also time dependent.

All these predictions depend on the progenitor mass and on the equation of state adopted, as well as on the details of the simulations performed. For instance, the figure shows the results obtained with and without the inclusion of convection, whose effects are important at the end of the accretion phase, during the shock revival and in the cooling phase.

The basic overall correctness of the core collapse scenario was validated with the observation of SN1987A in the Large Magellanic Cloud, but certainly much more insights would be gained if a Galactic supernova were to be observed in the future. In view of the significant uncertainties of the model predictions, the opportunity to obtain a detailed observation of the different stages of the explosion will be very important. There is a particular interest in monitoring the emission in the first fraction of a second, whose details are thought to be crucial to achieve a successful explosion. Also some effects of neutrino oscillations could become visible especially in the early stages, as the fluxes of the different flavours are expected to differ considerably in these phases; or perhaps also later due to the MSW effect from terrestrial matter affecting the high-energy tail of the different fluxes [Lu01].

Neutrino oscillations Neutrinos and antineutrinos are produced in certain amounts for each flavor, and they are affected by oscillations in matter as they travel through the supernova. They exit from it as an incoherent mixture of different mass eigenstates and, as such, they arrive to the Earth. If they are observed when the SN is below the horizon at the detector's site, they can also be affected by the oscillations taking place in terrestrial matter, but this is a small effect that we will ignore.

Oscillations among the three flavors can in principle produce differences between muon and tau neutrino fluxes, but given that the energies are below the threshold for the corresponding CC interactions, these differences would anyhow not be detectable. Thus, three flavor oscillations are fully described by the ν_e survival probability $P_{ee} \equiv P(\nu_e \rightarrow \nu_e)$ and by the fluxes Φ_e^0 and Φ_x^0 that would have been observed in the absence of oscillations. The flux

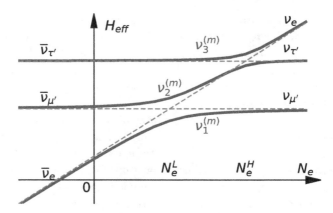

Fig. 7.2   Effective Hamiltonian for the neutrino matter mass eigenstates as a function of the electron density in a supernova, for the normal ordering case. Positive densities are for the neutrinos while the negative densities are for the case of anti-neutrinos with densities $|N_e|$.

of the electron neutrinos after oscillations is

$$\Phi_e = \sum_{\ell=e,\mu,\tau} P_{\ell e}\Phi_\ell^0 = P_{ee}\Phi_e^0 + (1 - P_{ee})\Phi_x^0. \qquad (7.8)$$

A similar expression holds for the electron antineutrinos in terms of the survival probability $\overline{P}_{ee} \equiv P(\overline{\nu}_e \to \overline{\nu}_e)$ and the $\overline{\nu}_e$ and $\overline{\nu}_x$ fluxes $\Phi_{\overline{e}}^0$ and $\Phi_{\overline{x}}^0$. The total flux obtained summing over the three flavors is, of course, not modified by oscillations.

It is clear that in order to have an observable effect due to the oscillations one needs to have $\Phi_e^0 \neq \Phi_x^0$. This condition does indeed hold, although to different levels during the different phases of the neutrino emission.

The usual MSW effect, arising from the CC coherent scattering of ν_e from electrons in the medium, is well understood [Di00]. In a supernova, the resonance condition can be fulfilled in two situations. The high (H) resonance involves the mixing θ_{13} and the mass splitting Δm_{31}^2. It corresponds to densities

$$\rho_{\rm H} = \frac{m_p Y_e}{2\sqrt{2}G_F E_\nu}\Delta m_{31}^2 \cos(2\theta_{13}) \simeq (10^3\text{--}10^4)\,\frac{\rm g}{\rm cm^3}. \qquad (7.9)$$

This resonance affects neutrinos if $\Delta m_{31}^2 > 0$ (NO), while it would affect antineutrinos if $\Delta m_{31}^2 < 0$ (IO). Similarly, there is the low (L) resonance, which involves the mixing θ_{12} and mass splitting Δm_{21}^2. It corresponds to densities $\rho_{\rm L} \simeq 10\text{--}100\,{\rm g\,cm}^{-3}$. This resonance affects neutrinos, since

$\Delta m_{21}^2 > 0$, and is similar to the resonance present in the Sun, while there is no H resonance in the Sun since $\rho_\odot < 150 \, \mathrm{g \, cm^{-3}}$. It is easy to verify that, given the observed values of the masses and mixing angles, the adiabaticity condition holds in both resonances. Hence, the flavor states that are produced in the very high-density regions near the neutrino-spheres, which are essentially coincident with neutrino matter mass eigenstates, will propagate remaining in these matter eigenstates until they exit the supernova. This is illustrated by the level-crossing diagram in Fig. 7.2. From it we see that in the by now favored case of normal ordering, which is the one plotted, the ν_e that is produced as a ν_3^m state in the very high-density core will exit the SN as a ν_3 mass eigenstate. The $\nu_{\mu'}$ state in the figure approximately stands for $(\nu_\mu - \nu_\tau)/\sqrt{2}$ (i.e. the state mixed with ν_e in the mass eigenstate ν_1, in the approximation that $\theta_{23} \simeq \pi/4$ and $\theta_{13} \simeq 0$), and the state $\nu_{\tau'}$ corresponds to the orthogonal combination $(\nu_\mu + \nu_\tau)/\sqrt{2}$ [Ku86]. Note that the negative densities considered in the plot actually just describe the case of antineutrinos in positive densities, and for the NO case the antineutrinos do not meet any resonance. In the case of an inverted mass ordering, one would have instead that the ν_e corresponds at high densities to the state ν_2^m, exiting from the SN as a ν_2, and the high resonance would affect the antineutrinos rather than the neutrinos.

One can then conclude that

$$P_{ee} = \begin{cases} |U_{e3}|^2 = \sin^2 \theta_{13} \simeq 0 & \text{for normal ordering} \\ |U_{e2}|^2 = \cos^2 \theta_{13} \sin^2 \theta_{12} \simeq 0.3 & \text{for inverted ordering,} \end{cases} \tag{7.10}$$

while for the antineutrinos

$$\overline{P}_{ee} = \begin{cases} |U_{e1}|^2 = \cos^2 \theta_{13} \cos^2 \theta_{12} \simeq 0.7 & \text{for normal ordering} \\ |U_{e3}|^2 = \sin^2 \theta_{13} \simeq 0 & \text{for inverted ordering.} \end{cases} \tag{7.11}$$

Note that there are some cases in which the survival probabilities are very close to zero or, in other terms, in which the flavor transformation is almost complete, what could make the effects of oscillations more likely to be observed. This is illustrated in Fig. 7.3, where the total rates from a Galactic supernova which are expected in different detectors are shown for SN models considering initial masses of $27 \, M_\odot$ or $11 \, M_\odot$. For the lower mass model, besides the results in the absence of oscillations also those including MSW oscillations for normal and inverted ordering scenarios are shown (indicated as NH and IH respectively). For instance, in water or scintillator detectors, which are mostly sensitive to $\overline{\nu}_e$ via the IBD process, only the rates during the infall and neutronization phases are significantly affected by oscillations. Instead, in the accretion and cooling phases the

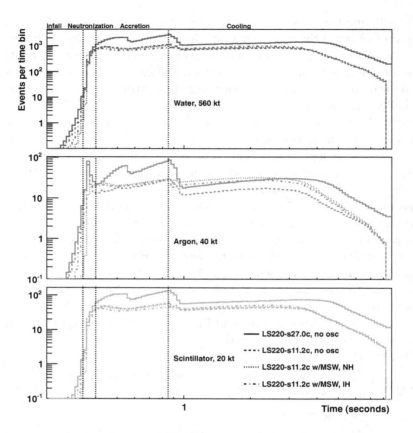

Fig. 7.3   Rates in different time bins from a Galactic SN at 10 kpc in different detectors obtained in simulations by the Garching group for precursors of 27 $M_\odot$ and 11 $M_\odot$ (from [Mi16], with kind permission from the Società Italiana di Fisica). Results are shown, from top to bottom, for water, argon and scintillator detectors. Rates are given without oscillations as well as with MSW oscillations in the NH and IH cases.

oscillations have almost no effect since the fluxes of $\bar{\nu}_e$ and $\bar{\nu}_x$ are quite similar. On the other hand, for the proposed DUNE argon detector, which is mostly sensitive to the ν_e fluxes via the CC interactions, the effects of oscillations are more pronounced in all the SN phases.

Besides the usual MSW transitions, a lot of work has been devoted to the study of the effects on the neutrino oscillations arising from the NC forward scattering of the outgoing neutrinos among themselves (see [Du10; Mi16] for reviews). These would take place mostly in the regions just outside the neutrino-spheres, i.e. for radii less than few hundred km, where the neutrino densities are huge. For instance, an electron neutrino propagating towards the observer through the background of muon neutrinos also emitted by the SN can transform into a muon neutrino without changing its direction, i.e. suffering a flavor changing forward scattering ν_e(to obs.) $+ \nu_\mu$(bkg) $\rightarrow \nu_\mu$(to obs.) $+ \nu_e$(bkg). Neutrino self-interactions can potentially give rise to peculiar effects, such as synchronized oscillations in which neutrinos of different energies oscillate with similar frequencies; bipolar oscillations in which the $\nu_e + \overline{\nu}_e$ transitions into $\nu_x + \overline{\nu}_x$ are very large; or flavor oscillations in which e.g. the ν_e and ν_x spectra get swapped in certain energy intervals (with energy splits delimiting the spectral swaps). However, the relevance of these phenomena to the supernova neutrino output is still a matter of debate since several effects, such as the averaging over different scattering angles or the suppression of the oscillations due to ordinary matter effects, probably make the neutrino self-interaction induced oscillations sub-dominant.

7.3 The observable neutrino signal

In the energy range of supernova neutrinos, $E_\nu \leq 50\,\text{MeV}$, neutrino telescopes can in principle tag three classes of events: charged current events due to $\overline{\nu}_e$, charged current events due to ν_e, and neutral current events probing also ν_x. To obtain as much information as possible, one would like ideally to study separately the various classes of events. However, their separation is not clear cut as some reactions, such as the elastic scattering on electrons, can be due to more than one class of events. At these energies, muon or tau (anti)neutrinos cannot be identified as such and, moreover, the difference between the interactions in the detector of neutrinos and antineutrinos of these flavors is not significant for isoscalar targets. There are also reactions, such as the charged current excitation of ^{12}C nuclei that is relevant in liquid scintillators, for which the electron neutrinos and the electron antineutrinos lead to similar signals, and hence their neat separation is not possible.

Some details on the most relevant processes that are used for supernova neutrino detection are provided in the following.

Inverse beta decay The usual type of supernova neutrino detectors, such as the ones that observed the ~ 20 events from SN1987A, have optimal response to electron antineutrino scattering on free protons (H nuclei).

These detectors are made of water or hydrocarbon compounds, that are rich in hydrogen. In the former case, the fraction of free protons per nucleon is $f_{H_2O} = 1/9$, while in the latter case the fraction depends on the actual composition of the detector. For instance, for linear alkyl benzene (LAB, which is the solvent providing the bulk of the target protons in many liquid scintillator detectors), having a chemical formula $C_6H_5C_nH_{2n+1}$, one has $f_{LAB}(n = 12) = 5/41$, which is just slightly larger than f_{H_2O}. For the water Cherenkov detector Super-Kamiokande, the fiducial mass that can be used for the detection of supernova neutrinos is $M_{SK} = 32$ kt, while at present the largest liquid scintillators, SNO+, KamLAND and LVD have a mass of just 1 kt each (while the projected JUNO scintillator detector will have a fiducial mass of 20 kt).

The reaction involved in the observation of the SN signal with these type of detectors is the inverse beta decay (IBD),

$$\bar{\nu}_e + p \to e^+ + n, \tag{7.12}$$

whose cross section is reliably known, being approximately $\sigma = 4G_F^2 p_e E_e/\pi$. More accurate expressions that take into account effects such as those due to nuclear recoils and form factors, which can be useful for precise numerical evaluations, can be found e.g. in [Vo99; St03].

The electron energy threshold in Super-Kamiokande is about 4 MeV, while in ultra-pure scintillators, such as Borexino, it can be as low as 150 keV. Note also that the positron energy correlates very closely with the electron antineutrino energy, but on the other hand the positron is emitted almost isotropically, giving essentially no information on the directionality of the antineutrino.

Although scintillators have a lower threshold for the electron energy that can be detected, this is not so relevant for the inverse beta decay event rate since the average SN neutrino energies are much larger than this threshold. Moreover, this reaction has a threshold in the neutrino energy of $m_n + m_e - m_p \simeq 1.8$ MeV. More crucial turns out to be the actual number of target protons, and thus only future multi-kilotonne scintillator detectors will be competitive with Super-Kamiokande for the detection of this kind of events. The much larger future Hyper-Kamiokande water detector, with a mass about 10 times greater than that of Super-Kamiokande, will also represent an important improvement for the SN detection.

To separate the IBD signal from other backgrounds involving electrons, the efficiency for tagging the neutron associated to the IBD process is crucial. At present, this efficiency is just about 20% in Super-Kamiokande, relying on the observation of the capture of the neutron by a proton to produce deuterium, releasing 2.2 MeV photons with a typical delay of about 200 μs. The neutron identification efficiency was proved to be larger than 60% in scintillators, for instance in the Large Volume Detector (LVD), and even more in ultra-pure scintillators such as Borexino, thanks to their lower threshold. This neutron tagging efficiency will be improved up to about 90% in the new Super-Kamiokande Gadolinium phase, in which 0.2% by mass of Gd were diluted in the water. The neutron captures by the Gd, in which about 8 MeV are released in gamma rays within about 30 μs, should then allow to efficiently tag the IBD processes.

Elastic scattering on electrons In this case the scattering is with the electrons, that are more numerous than the free protons, via the reaction $\nu+e \rightarrow \nu+e$. Although all neutrinos can interact, the cross section is much smaller than for the IBD. The typical total number of expected events from a SN due to the ES process is between 1/30 to 1/20 of those from the IBD reactions. Note also that a large fraction of the initial neutrino energy remains invisible in the neutrino elastic scattering off electrons. A peculiar aspect of water Cherenkov detectors is that one can use this process to measure the direction of the incoming neutrinos, since the Cherenkov radiation allows to reconstruct the direction of the electron, which is correlated with the incoming neutrino direction. This would allow to point back to a Galactic supernova with a precision of few degrees with current detectors, and hence one could approximately know the SN location before the light from the explosion actually reaches us. Indeed, before the light can be emitted from the envelope's photosphere the shock wave has to find its way through the stellar mantle, what typically takes several hours.

Given their low threshold, ultra-pure scintillators can be interesting for the study of the electron scattering process, and they may help us to learn about the electron neutrino flux since the associated cross section is largest for this neutrino flavor. The scintillation light has however no information on the directionality of the neutrino.[5]

Neutral current reactions The fluxes of non-electronic neutrinos and antineutrinos can be probed via neutral current events. Besides the electron

---

[5]Determining the positions of the positron and neutron could allow some determination of the arrival direction in future detectors. Also separating the small Cherenkov contribution to the signal from the larger scintillation one, using e.g. timing or spectral information, may allow some directionality reconstruction.

scattering events, some peculiar reactions that can be used to search for them are the observation in water Cherenkov detectors of excitation lines of the oxygen at 5–6 MeV and, for hydrocarbon detectors, the processes

$$\nu + {}^{12}\mathrm{C} \to \nu + {}^{12}\mathrm{C}^* \text{ followed by } \mathrm{C}^* \to \mathrm{C} + \gamma(15.1 \text{ MeV}). \qquad (7.13)$$

Also the elastic scattering on protons,

$$\nu + p \to \nu + p, \qquad (7.14)$$

can be observable in ultrapure scintillators. This process is somewhat similar to the electron scattering process, although the kinetic energy of the proton is small, $K_p < E_\nu^2/2m_p \sim 0.2\,\mathrm{MeV}(E_\nu/20\,\mathrm{MeV})^2$ and, moreover, only a fraction of the proton energy is visible, what is known as the *quenching* of the emitted light. Since the light emitted is only visible above a certain threshold, that in the best existing detector is presently about 0.2 MeV, only the high-energy tail of the SN neutrino spectrum can be observed through this channel.

7.4   SN1987A

The data   In the hours preceding the visible manifestations of the supernova SN1987A, that took place in the Large Magellanic Cloud (LMC) and was observed on February 23 1987, bursts of events were observed at the neutrino telescopes that were operative at the time. These were the water-Cherenkov detectors IMB [Bi87] and Kamiokande-II [Hi88] and the scintillator detector in Baksan [Al88].[6] The duration of the neutrino burst, as deduced from the data depicted in Fig. 7.4, was of about 10 seconds. Some significant features of the experiments are listed in Table 7.2.

The data are compatible with being due to the observation of electron antineutrinos from the SN explosion (see [Vi15b] for a summary).

Statistical inference of the SN fluence   From the couple dozens of events observed, one can roughly infer some characteristics of the SN1987A neutrino emission. The simplest reasonable form of the electron antineutrino fluence would be to adopt for it a Maxwell-Boltzmann type distribution

$$F(E_\nu) = \frac{\mathcal{E}}{4\pi D^2} \frac{E_\nu^2 \exp(-E_\nu/T)}{6T^4}, \qquad (7.15)$$

---

[6]A burst of 5 events was also observed by the LSD detector at the Mont Blanc, but it is usually considered to have been just a statistical fluctuation since it happened four hours before the other ones and nothing was observed at that time in the other detectors.

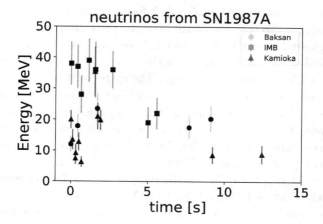

Fig. 7.4   Energy of the candidate neutrino events detected from SN1987A by IMB, Kamiokande II and Baksan detectors, as a function of time. The different event samples were synchronized considering that the first event from each detector arrived at $t = 0$.

Table 7.2   Relevant features of the neutrino telescopes in operation at the time of SN1987A, and of the pulses of events that they detected.

	protons [10^{32}]	threshold [MeV]	observed events	background [per 30 s]
Kamiokande-II	1.4	7.5	11	0.55
IMB	4.6	15	8	0.01
Baksan	0.2	10	5	1

with the distance to the LMC being $D \simeq 50\,\mathrm{kpc}$ and where the two free parameters $\mathcal{E}$ and T describe, respectively, the total energy radiated in electron antineutrinos and their average temperature (given the small number of events detected, a more detailed parameterization of the fluence is not justified). A maximum likelihood fit to the number of observed events and their energies, accounting for the detector thresholds and sensitivities, leads to best fit values of [Vi15b]

$$\mathcal{E} \simeq 5 \times 10^{52} \text{ erg and } T \simeq 4 \text{ MeV}, \tag{7.16}$$

which indeed agree well with the theoretical expectations.

Implications of SN1987A for particle physics   There are already several consequences that can be derived from the handful of neutrino events detected from SN1987A. The more direct ones are:

1) An upper limit of about 6 eV can be inferred on the mass of the neutrinos [Lo02; Pa10] (in this case one can assume the three neutrino masses to have a common value, given that the mass differences would be negligible). This limit is consistent, even if not competitive, with the ones obtained in the laboratory or derived from cosmology. The origin of this bound is from the non-observation of a dispersion of the neutrino arrival times as a function of the energy. It is simply understood as arising from the fact that the neutrino velocity is $\beta \simeq 1 - (m/E)^2/2$. If the data show a time structure of neutrino events with a duration Δt, without showing energy-dependent delays after a path of distance D, we can derive the limit $D/v - D/c < \Delta t$, and thus $m < E\sqrt{2c\,\Delta t/D}$. In the case of the 1987A supernova, using $D = 150$ klyr, $\Delta t \sim 1$ s and $E \sim 10$ MeV, this reads $m < 6$ eV. To improve this bound, one would need to know precisely the starting time of the emission by means of a gravitational-wave detection and/or to see for instance short-time structures in the data, such as those due to the dynamical oscillations occurring in the region around the protoneutron star, with duration of tens of ms, which can take place while the shock-wave waits to be relaunched (known as standing accretion shock instabilities, or SASI).

2) The observation of the neutrino burst just few hours before the observation of the emitted light, in accordance with the expected delay, allows to constrain the difference between the velocity of the neutrinos and that of light. Assuming that the precision of the agreement between both travel times amounts to less than $\Delta t \simeq 3$ h, one finds a bound on the neutrino velocity $|v_\nu/c - 1| < c\Delta t/D \simeq 2 \times 10^{-9}$.

3) The hypothesis that the heavier neutrinos could have decayed into the lighter one during their flight can be probed to some extent. In particular, if a large fraction of the heavier neutrinos had decayed in flight, in the case with inverse mass ordering we should have received a state very poor in electronic content, in contradiction with the actual observation of a significant amount of electron antineutrinos.

4) Exotic scenarios that could have led to a large disappearance of the flux of active neutrinos, such as those involving new hypothetical oscillations into sterile neutrinos, are disfavored due to the overall agreement of the observations with the expectations from a supernova model.

5) There is a general consensus that with the few events observed it was not possible to determine effects associated to three flavor oscillations, see e.g. [Vi15b].

7.5 Neutrinos from the next Galactic supernova

As we have discussed previously, there are very good reasons to expect that a Galactic supernova will happen sometime in the next decades, and the observation of the neutrinos from such an event should allow us to learn a lot. In this section we discuss briefly some of the major topics in which we expect to make progress and that should help to consolidate the scenarios that have been up to now only explored by means of computer simulations. It would however not be entirely surprising if neutrino observations also revealed previously unexpected situations and allowed us to learn important new things.

Number of events and distance The number of events that we expect to collect from a Galactic supernova is large, of several thousands IBD events already in Super-Kamiokande. Moreover, the Supernova Early Warning System (SNEWS) network [An04], which focuses on their detection, includes at present the detectors Super-Kamiokande (Japan), IceCube (South Pole), KM3NeT (Mediterranean), KamLAND (Japan), Daya Bay (China) and HALO (Canada), and should allow to warn astronomers about a SN explosion hours before the actual light can arrive. The neutrino emission from a supernova is expected to be almost isotropic.[7] The number of observed events depends strongly on the distance to the SN, and we could expect to observe a total of about $N_{\rm IBD} \simeq 6,000 \times (10~{\rm kpc}/D)^2$ with the SNEWS network of detectors. This means that from the neutrino signal one could determine the distance to the supernova with an uncertainty smaller than 10%, reasonably assuming that the total emitted energy is known with an accuracy of 20%. The distance should then become known with a much better precision after the astronomical identification of the star is achieved by means of the emitted electromagnetic radiation.

Locating the supernova in the sky by its neutrinos The elastic scattering events are directional and will allow the Super-Kamiokande to approximately reconstruct the supernova direction [To03]. The background for this determination is actually just due to the isotropic IBD events, but it may be somewhat reduced if the associated neutron is identified. Requiring that the energy of the electrons be below 30 MeV should reduce the IBD

---

[7]Note that even if the natal kicks of the pulsars were due to asymmetric neutrino emission, the associated kinetic energies would be less than 10^{49} erg, a tiny fraction of the total energy emitted in neutrinos.

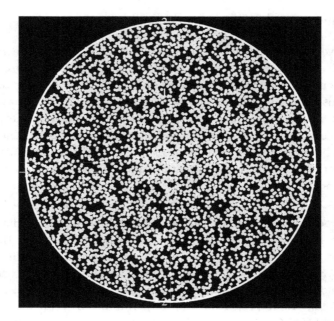

Fig. 7.5   Simulated event directions in the Super-Kamiokande detector from a future
Galactic supernova. The map is a Lambertian equal-area projection, with the SN located
at the center. The excess of events due to elastic scattering is clearly visible.

events by another 20%, without affecting the elastic scattering events that
have less visible energy due to the presence of the neutrino in the final
state. One then expects that, for a supernova located at 10 kpc, some
200 directional events will be observed on top of less than about 4,000 non-
directional (IBD) events [Pa09b]. The precision of the reconstruction of the
SN direction amounts then to 2 to 3 degrees. This precision should improve
for closer SNe due to the increased statistics, with the angular uncertainty
scaling approximately as the distance to the SN [To03; Pa09b]. Moreover,
the supernova will most likely be very close to the Galactic plane, what
corresponds to a small fraction of the sky.

Flavor   The certain fact is that we will identify (several) thousand of IBD
events and a useful sample of elastic scattering events. Although it is sure
that neutrino oscillations will occur, it is not clear whether they will be
identifiable, keeping also in mind the fact that we still lack a definitive
theoretical description of the oscillation effects induced by the neutrino

self-interactions that occur just outside the neutrino-spheres. An important consideration for the detection of oscillations is the possibility to observe neutral current events, that being independent from oscillations can provide a baseline for the interpretation. This is possible by the gamma lines of 5–6 MeV from interactions with O in Super-Kamiokande and in a potentially cleaner way with C in scintillators [Lu14], especially when new large ultra-pure detectors will be online. Note also that neutral current events will be needed to measure the total energy emitted by the supernova with a minimum theoretical bias.

Spectra A Galactic supernova will allow us to observe electron antineutrinos with large statistics through the IBD, allowing to measure their spectrum. The neutral current processes discussed above will also have some limited spectral information. The electron neutrino spectrum is more difficult to determine, but this could become possible either with infrequent processes in conventional detectors (e.g. by the reaction $\nu_e + {}^{12}C \rightarrow e + {}^{12}N^*$ followed by the β^+ decay of ${}^{12}N^*$), or using detectors based on argon, such as DUNE, through $\nu_e + Ar \rightarrow e + K^*$. Also the elastic neutrino-electron reaction, that depends upon all types of neutrinos, will be observed.

Note that the observed spectra depend both on the astrophysics of the emission and on the oscillation patterns. The detailed time distribution of the events, and in particular of their energy distribution, will also be a very important diagnostic tool to understand the underlying astrophysical processes.

Neutrinos and the gravitational wave burst Gravitational waves from compact binary mergers are by now routinely measured, since the detection of the first one in 2016, and this emphasizes the importance of searching also for a gravitational wave signal from a supernova explosion, something which has been appreciated for a long time. The expectations are however unclear and may vary by orders of magnitude, depending on the details of the matter distribution in the star and requiring a rapid change in the quadrupolar component of the mass distribution. The observable signal could be a brief burst, with duration of a few tens of ms, strictly correlated to the re-bounce after the collapse, followed eventually by a later signal during the phase of accretion, or perhaps a late signal in the case of black-hole formation. Neutrinos could be quite valuable for this search, since they can determine the time of the re-bounce with a precision of about 10 ms [Pa09b; Ha09], thereby providing an external trigger for the gravitational wave detectors.

Neutrinos could also be emitted in the catastrophic astrophysical events associated to the mergers of compact stellar objects, such as those observed in gravitational waves. In particular, very-high energy neutrinos, with energies possibly extending beyond a PeV, are expected to be produced in the binary neutron star mergers that lead to short gamma ray bursts. They result from the interactions of the accelerated cosmic rays with the ambient gas and radiation. No neutrinos were however detected in association with the first binary neutron star merger observed in gravitational waves, but this non-observation was consistent with the inferred distance to the source and with the fact that the GRB jet in this event was not aligned with the line of sight [Al17].

7.6 Diffuse supernova neutrino background

Besides searching for the flux from individual supernovae, one may also consider the integral flux of neutrinos resulting from all the core collapse supernovae that took place in the Universe, which is referred to as the diffuse supernova neutrino background (DSNB). This flux can be estimated as

$$\Phi_{\nu_\alpha}(E) = \int_{M_0}^{M_m} dM \int_0^{z_m} dz \, c \left| \frac{dt}{dz} \right| \frac{dE_g}{dE} \frac{d^2\dot{n}_{\text{CCSN}}}{dz \, dM}(z, M) F_{\nu_\alpha}(E_g), \quad (7.17)$$

where the energy of the neutrino when it was generated in the SN explosion at redshift z is $E_g = E(1+z)$, with E its present day energy. The minimum initial mass leading to a CCSN is $M_0 \simeq 8\,M_\odot$, while the maximum mass M_m may exceed $100\,M_\odot$. The rate of CCSN explosions with original mass M, $d^2\dot{n}_{\text{CCSN}}/(dz\,dM)$, is expected to be proportional to the corresponding star formation rate (SFR). The differential rate of CCSN is observed to increase steeply with redshift, approximately as $(1+z)^{3.4}$ up to redshifts $z \simeq 1$. This is indeed similar to the evolution of the SFR, which has also been determined at higher redshifts where the CCSN rate is poorly known, and where it is seen to remain approximately constant up to $z \simeq 4$ to then decrease steeply. One may hence assume that a similar behavior holds for the rate of CCSN for $z > 1$. To perform the integral in the previous expression one can also use that for the high masses considered the mass dependence of the SFR approximately follows the Salpeter mass function, $dN_s/dM \propto M^{-2.35}$. One should note however that the detailed dependence of the neutrino fluxes with the star masses is poorly known. Moreover, some massive stars may fail to explode, hence remaining optically dim.

Others may collapse into black holes, leading to an abrupt termination of the neutrino flux in less than a second, what would result into a harder average neutrino spectrum.

Adopting for definiteness a similar reference neutrino flux $\bar{F}_{\nu_\alpha}$ for all stellar masses, one obtains

$$\Phi_{\nu_\alpha}(E) \simeq \frac{c}{H_0} \int_0^{z_m} dz \frac{1}{\sqrt{\Omega_m(1+z)^3 + \Omega_\Lambda}} \frac{d\dot{n}_{CCSN}}{dz} \bar{F}_{\nu_\alpha}\left(E(1+z))\right), \quad (7.18)$$

where we used that $dt/dz = -[H_0(1+z)\sqrt{\Omega_m(1+z)^3 + \Omega_\Lambda}]^{-1}$, with $H_0 \simeq 70\,\mathrm{km\,s^{-1}\,Mpc^{-1}}$ being the present day Hubble constant while $\Omega_m \simeq 0.3$ and $\Omega_\Lambda \simeq 0.7$ are the present fractional contributions from the matter and cosmological constant to the critical density. A reasonable approximation is to adopt $z_m = 4$ and consider that

$$\frac{d\dot{n}_{CCSN}}{dz} \simeq \min\left[(1+z)^{3.4}, 2^{3.4}\right] \frac{2 \times 10^{-4}}{\mathrm{Mpc}^3\,\mathrm{yr}}. \quad (7.19)$$

Note that the fluence from a SN at distance D is $F_\nu = N_\nu/4\pi D^2$, where N_ν is the total number of emitted neutrinos, and one may adopt an average neutrino spectrum similar to the one inferred from observations of SN1987A, which is also in reasonable agreement with typical results from detailed SN simulations.

Focusing on the electron antineutrinos, which are the relevant ones for the detection by means of the IBD process using water Cherenkov or scintillator detectors, the DSNB may be detected only above ~ 10–$20\,\mathrm{MeV}$, due to the large background from reactor antineutrinos which is present at lower energies. On the other hand, the DSNB is expected to exceed the direct atmospheric $\bar{\nu}_e$ background only for energies below $\sim 30\,\mathrm{MeV}$. However, below $\sim 50\,\mathrm{MeV}$ the predominant background for this search results from higher energy (up to $250\,\mathrm{MeV}$) atmospheric ν_μ CC interactions in the air, in which the muons produced are below the Cherenkov threshold and cannot be directly observed, but they get stopped and decay, producing a bump of electrons with energies centered at $\sim 40\,\mathrm{MeV}$. The electron background from these invisible muons can be reduced by using neutron tagging to identify the IBD signals from $\bar{\nu}_e$ interactions, and the tagging efficiency could be significantly improved by diluting Gd in the water [Ho09]. This should also reduce the background from solar ν_e, which could otherwise be problematic below $\sim 18\,\mathrm{MeV}$.

As a result, one typically expects that the DSNB should give rise to about 2 IBD events per year in Super-Kamiokande in the range $[10, 30]\,\mathrm{MeV}$, while only about 0.5 events per year are expected between

20 and 30 MeV. The present bounds are still a factor of a few above the DSNB predictions, but it is likely that in the next decade these neutrinos will be observed, and eventually studied in greater detail thanks to the improved performance of the Gd phase of Super-Kamiokande or by means of the future Hyper-Kamiokande detector, which will be about ten times larger. Their observation could shed light on the redshift evolution of the CCSN rate, on the average neutrino spectrum from past SNe and on the relative frequency of production of black holes and neutron stars in the core collapses.

7.7   Pre-supernova neutrinos

If one were lucky enough to observe a SN happening very closeby, within a few hundred pc, it may also be possible to observe the neutrinos emitted a few hours, or even days, before the core collapse [Od04; Pa17]. This may be the case if for instance the supergiant star Betelgeuse, lying at about 200 pc from us, were to explode soon.

While the Sun will burn H slowly for about 10^{10} yr, stars with much larger masses can burn H much faster, in only $\sim 10^7$ yr, to then continue the energy production by burning He for about 10^6 yr and then C for another $\sim 10^3$ yr. For initial stellar masses larger than about $10\,M_\odot$, the Ne burning will be ignited and then O will burn for few years to end up with Si burning in just a week in the core, and for a few hours in a shell, to produce the Fe core that finally collapses in the SN explosion. During all these stages the temperature of the star progressively increases, from few$\times 10^7$K up to more than 10^9K. Thermal processes that produce neutrinos become then increasingly important, being actually the main source of stellar energy losses after the He burning phase, and essentially determining the duration of all the subsequent burning stages.

The main neutrino producing thermal processes are the plasmon decay $\gamma^* \to \nu_\alpha \bar\nu_\alpha$, the photo-neutrino process $\gamma e^\pm \to \nu_\alpha \bar\nu_\alpha e^\pm$, the bremsstrahlung one $\gamma A \to \nu_\alpha \bar\nu_\alpha A$ and the pair process $e^+ e^- \to \nu_\alpha \bar\nu_\alpha$. Their relative importance depends on the temperature and density of the medium, being the plasmon decay the dominant one during the He burning phase, while the pair process is the most relevant one in the later stages when $T > 10^9$K. The pair process can proceed via NC, producing all neutrino flavors, or through W exchange, implying that the emission of electron flavor neutrinos is larger. Note that the neutrinos from the fusion processes themselves end up being subdominant. In the case of main sequence stars, they account for about 7% of the energy in the H fusion processes via the CNO cycle (while only for about 3% of the energy in the pp-chain), but they are not significant during the He burning phases since the C and O final products have the same proportion of neutrons and protons as the starting He nuclei. In addition, β processes in the medium take place, such as

$$(Z, A) \to (Z + 1, A^*) + e + \bar{\nu}_e \text{ or } (Z, A) \to (Z - 1, A^*) + e^+ + \nu_e \quad (7.20)$$

and

$$(Z, A) + e^+ \to (Z + 1, A^*) + \bar{\nu}_e \text{ or } (Z, A) + e \to (Z - 1, A^*) + \nu_e. \quad (7.21)$$

These processes can be exothermic and can lead to ν_e and $\bar{\nu}_e$ with energies of several MeV, becoming quite important in the latest Si burning stages. In particular, the $\bar{\nu}_e$ from the Si burning stage of a star at $\sim 200\,\text{pc}$, such as Betelgeuse, could lead to about 10^3 IBD interactions per day in Super-Kamiokande. These interactions could be detected provided n-tagging is used and a sufficiently low threshold ($\sim 3\,\text{MeV}$) is achieved, so as to be able to become sensitive to the high-energy tail of the distribution. Also scintillators, such as KamLAND, SNO+ or JUNO, may have a chance to detect them just above the threshold for the IBD reaction. Given that the $\bar{\nu}_e$ signal is almost isotropic, and that the scintillation light is emitted isotropically, there are no chances of getting directional information from it, but the candidate stars that could explode as SN within few hundred pc are just a few, and they can be monitored in detail once a rising neutrino signal is observed. The information that could be gathered by combining the pre-supernova neutrinos with the final SN neutrino burst, which for such a nearby SN could amount to $\sim 10^7$ events in Super-Kamiokande, together with the observation of the subsequent luminous explosion, would provide a precise picture of the star evolution starting from the Si burning phase until the formation of the compact remnant. Note that there are a few candidate stars within few hundred pc that could be in the C burning phase, and being the duration of this phase of $\sim 10^3\,\text{yr}$ there is a chance that one of them may explode sometime within the next century.[8] On the other hand, a nearby SN explosion may be harmful for terrestrial life only if it happens at less than about 10 pc, and hence the detection of an event like that from Betelgeuse could provide knowledge that would remain useful.

---

[8]On the other hand, given that one expects a couple of SN per century in the whole Galaxy, the chances that one would happen within few hundred parsecs would seem a priori very low.

Suggested exercises:

- Suppose that the galactic supernova frequency is $R = 1.63 \pm 0.43\,\text{CCSN/century}$, as reported in the text. Calculate the time between two such events and the chance to detect one Galactic supernova with a neutrino telescope being sensitive to the entire Milky Way, for observation times of 20, 30 or 40 years.
- Estimate the number of neutrinos and antineutrinos from a supernova and compare these numbers with the number of electrons originally present in the stellar core.
- Consider the reaction $\nu_\ell + p \to \nu_\ell + p$ and discuss the possibility to observe it in supernova neutrino detectors.
- Estimate the annual rate of IBD events expected in Super-Kamiokande from the DSNB in the visible energy ranges $E_e = [10, 30]\,\text{MeV}$ and $[20, 30]\,\text{MeV}$. Assume an average neutrino luminosity similar to that of SN1987A, with $\langle T \rangle = 4\,\text{MeV}$, $\langle \alpha \rangle = 3$ and $\langle \varepsilon_{\bar{\nu}_e} \rangle = 5 \times 10^{52}\,\text{erg}$.

Recommended reading:

- *The evolution and explosion of massive stars*, S.E. Woosley, A. Heger and T.A. Weaver, Rev. Mod. Phys. 74 (2002) 1015
- *Handbook of Supernovae*, A.W. Alsabti and P. Murdin Eds., Springer International Publishing AG (2017)

Chapter 8

Atmospheric Neutrinos

8.1 The oscillation of atmospheric neutrinos

When a cosmic-ray (CR) particle, such as a proton or a heavier nucleus, enters the atmosphere and knocks an air nucleus at a typical height of few tens of km above ground, an air shower gets initiated. The number of particles in the shower then grows exponentially through the successive interactions. Most of the secondary particles in the hadronic interactions are pions and, at very-high energies, there are comparable amounts of π^+, π^- and π^0, although heavier mesons (K, η, ρ, ...) as well as heavy unstable baryons also get produced. It is through the weak decays of these secondary particles that copious amounts of neutrinos get produced, the so-called atmospheric neutrinos. Note that the neutral pions almost immediately decay into two photons, feeding the electromagnetic component of the shower. These photons then cascade down by the pair production $\gamma + A \rightarrow e^+ + e^- + A$ and bremsstrahlung $e + A \rightarrow e + \gamma + A$ processes, with A representing here an air nucleus (typically 78% N, 21% O and 1% Ar).

The charged pion decays are the main source of atmospheric neutrinos via $\pi^+ \rightarrow \mu^+ + \nu_\mu$, as well as the charge conjugate process, and for sufficiently low energies the muons may also decay via $\mu^+ \rightarrow e^+ + \nu_e + \bar{\nu}_\mu$, further contributing to the neutrino fluxes. Since the muons get typically produced at heights $h \simeq 10$–20 km and their lifetime satisfies $c\tau_\mu \simeq 659$ m, if their energies are larger than few GeV they can actually reach ground level before decaying, with the condition for this to happen being that the dilated decay length $\Gamma c\tau_\mu$ be larger than the production height h, with $\Gamma = E/m_\mu$ being the Lorentz factor.[1] One then expects that at energies

---

[1]Note also that the muon energy losses due to ionization, which are characterized by a loss of about 2 MeV for every $\mathrm{g\,cm}^{-2}$ of air column density traversed, are actually non-negligible for muons with GeV energies.

below few GeV there will be about twice as many muon-type neutrinos than electron-type neutrinos, while at energies $E_\nu \gg$ GeV the parent muons will reach ground level and be stopped before decaying, so that the expected ratio $R \equiv (\nu_\mu + \bar{\nu}_\mu)/(\nu_e + \bar{\nu}_e)$ should become larger than two. Some excess of neutrinos with respect to anti-neutrinos is also expected, given that the positive charges of the CRs and of the air nuclei tend to favor the production of positively charged pions.

The first observation of atmospheric neutrinos was achieved back in the sixties with experiments located in deep underground gold mines in South Africa [Re65] and in India [Ac65], where the rock overburden allowed to largely suppress the background due to the muons that are also produced in the CR atmospheric showers. These experiments were able to detect the muons produced by the atmospheric muon neutrinos that interacted in the rocks surrounding the detectors. At GeV energies these neutrinos are essentially unattenuated by the Earth and hence arrive almost isotropically to the detector. Although for directions close to the vertical the muon fluxes were still dominated by the atmospheric muons, at zenith angles larger than about 50° most of the muons observed were produced by the neutrino interactions in the nearby rock.

During the eighties and nineties the atmospheric neutrinos were studied in detail using larger underground facilities, such as those hosting the IMB, Kamiokande, Soudan-2, MACRO or Super-Kamiokande detectors. Many of those experiments were focused in the search for proton decay, in which the atmospheric neutrinos represented an unwanted background, whose study led however to major discoveries. In particular, a significant deficit of muon-type atmospheric neutrinos was found, with the average value of the muon to electron neutrino flavor ratio that was observed at GeV energies being $R_{\rm obs} \simeq 0.6 R_{\rm MC}$, where $R_{\rm MC}$ is the expected value obtained in Monte-Carlo simulations that assume that neutrinos are massless. A natural explanation for this suppression was suggested to be the oscillations of muon neutrinos into another flavor, something which becomes possible in the presence of neutrino masses and flavor mixing.

More remarkably, the Super-Kamiokande experiment [Fu98] observed a zenith angle dependence of this ratio. This indicated that neutrinos coming from above, with typical path-lengths $d \simeq 10$ to 20 km, had not enough time to oscillate (especially in the multi-GeV sample for which the neutrino oscillation length is larger), while those arriving from below, with $d \simeq 13,000$ km, had already oscillated significantly (see Fig. 8.1). The most plausible explanation for these effects is that they are due to an oscillation

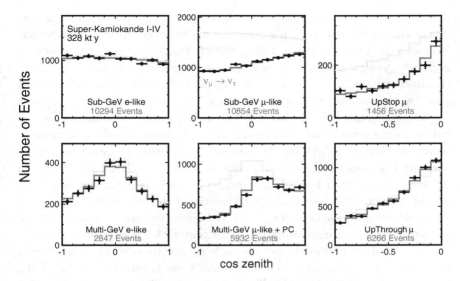

Fig. 8.1   Distribution of the different event samples versus the cosine of the zenith angle ($\cos\theta = -1$ corresponding to up-going neutrinos, while $+1$ corresponding to the down-going direction) measured by Super-Kamiokande (from [PDG]). The light-blue line corresponds to the expectations with no oscillations, while the red line is for the best fit neutrino oscillations.

$\nu_\mu \rightarrow \nu_\tau$ with almost maximal mixing, $\theta_{23} \simeq 45°$, and a mass squared difference $|\Delta m_{32}^2| \simeq 2.5 \times 10^{-3}\,\mathrm{eV}^2$, for which the associated oscillation length is $L_{\mathrm{osc}} \equiv 4\pi E/\Delta m^2 \simeq 10^3 E[\mathrm{GeV}]\,\mathrm{km}$. As also shown in Fig. 8.1, the resulting fit to the zenith angle dependence of the rates observed by Super-Kamiokande is in excellent agreement with the oscillation hypothesis.

Since the observed electron neutrino flux shape is in good agreement with the theoretical predictions in the absence of neutrino oscillations, the oscillations $\nu_\mu \rightarrow \nu_e$ can not provide a satisfactory explanation for the deficit of muon neutrinos. On the other hand, when crossing the Earth the ν_μ and ν_τ are equally affected by neutral current interactions, and hence the oscillations among them are not affected by matter effects. If the ν_μ were instead to oscillate into a new hypothetical sterile state not feeling the weak interactions, the oscillations would be affected by matter effects. In such a scenario, the zenith angle dependence of the oscillations would be modified in a way which is not supported by observations, what disfavors an explanation in terms of oscillations into sterile states. The oscillations into active states, like ν_τ, is also favored by observables that depend on the neutral current interactions in the detector, such as the production of π^0, which can not occur for sterile states. Studies with Super-Kamiokande have also found indications of charged-current interactions of high-energy atmospheric tau neutrinos leading to tau leptons, at a rate consistent with what would be expected from the oscillations of atmospheric muon neutrinos into tau neutrinos [Ab13].

An important different kind of experiment, which confirmed the oscillation solution to the atmospheric neutrino anomaly using man-made neutrinos, was K2K [Ah06]. It consisted of a beam of muon neutrinos, with typical energies just below a GeV, sent from the KEK accelerator in Tsukuba to the Super-Kamiokande detector, which are separated by a baseline of 250 km. The results obtained indicated that there was a deficit of muon neutrinos at the detector (158.1 ± 9 events expected with only 112 observed). This rate turned out to be consistent with the expectations based on the oscillation solution to the atmospheric neutrino observations. Newer long-baseline experiments, such as the one from Tokai to Kamioka (T2K, with a baseline of 295 km) [Ab17], that from Fermilab to the Soudan mine in Minnesota (MINOS, with a baseline of 734 km) [Ad13] or that from Fermilab to Ash River (NOνA experiment, with 810 km baseline) [Ac19], have further constrained the mixing angle and mass squared difference involved (see Fig. 8.2). Also the OPERA experiment at the Gran Sasso, receiving neutrinos from CERN, was able to observe the appearance of ten ν_τ events from a ν_μ beam [Ag18b], in agreement with the expectations from $\nu_\mu \to \nu_\tau$ oscillations.

Many of the long-baseline experiments aim the neutrino beam slightly off-axis from the detector, so as to have a neutrino energy distribution which is narrower and centered at lower energies. This approach makes it possible to improve the sensitivity to the oscillations, in spite of the reduction in the flux that results when observing a few degrees away from the beam axis. Suppressing the high-energy tail of the neutrino distribution also allows to enhance the impact of the quasi-elastic interactions, which provide a clear flavor tagging, with respect to the inelastic ones.

The long-baseline experiments also allow to study the appearance of electron-type neutrinos, which is sensitive to the small angle θ_{13}, and by combining neutrino and anti-neutrino beams they are sensitive also to the CP-violating phase δ. Additional observations of atmospheric neutrinos have been done with the IceCube DeepCore sub-array [Aa18], which can achieve threshold energies of about 6 GeV for which the oscillation length is of the order of the radius of the Earth, allowing then to explore the effects

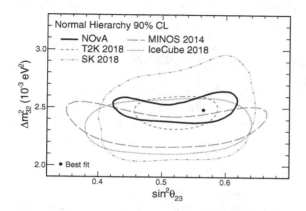

Fig. 8.2   Constraints on the Δm^2_{32}–$\sin^2\theta_{23}$ plane from different long-baseline experiments. Results correspond to normal ordering of the masses, but for inverted ordering ($\Delta m^2_{32} < 0$) the contours would be very similar since the associated matter effects are small. From [Ac19] (https://doi.org/10.1103/PhysRevLett.123.151803).

of oscillations of atmospheric neutrinos. Moreover, for energies near this threshold the matter effects are amplified for neutrinos crossing the central parts of the Earth, so that also these effects can be explored.

It is remarkable that the mixing angle involved in the $\nu_\mu \to \nu_\tau$ oscillations seems to be close to maximal, i.e. $\theta_{23} \simeq 45°$. This, together with the large mixing angle $\theta_{12} \simeq 33°$ that is required in the solar sector to explain the solar neutrino deficit, indicates that the neutrino mixing pattern is quite different from the one that is observed in the quark sector, where one had that $\theta_C \simeq 13°$, with the remaining mixing angles being much smaller. This provides a fundamental information that should help to understand the new physics underlying the origin of the neutrino masses.

The mass squared difference inferred from the atmospheric neutrino oscillations also indicates that at least one of the neutrinos has to be heavier than $\sqrt{|\Delta m^2_{32}|} \simeq 0.05\,\mathrm{eV}$. This is of potential relevance for cosmology and for the structure formation in the Universe, since the resulting contribution to the mass density from the relic neutrinos left over from the Big Bang turns out to affect the detailed outcome of the distribution of structures on galactic and cluster scales.

Recent global analyses of the neutrino oscillation data now favor, at about the 3σ level, the normal ordering corresponding to $\Delta m^2_{32} > 0$. This mostly results from the matter effects on the ν_e appearance in long-baseline experiments and also from the matter effects upon the atmospheric neutrinos.

8.2   Oscillations inside the Earth and the oscillograms

An interesting way to visualize the potential of atmospheric neutrinos, and eventually also of those from very-long-baseline experiments, to study the matter effects on neutrino oscillations is by means of the so-called oscillograms. These are plots depicting the neutrino flavor conversion probabilities as a function of the energy and of the nadir angle η, which is just the supplement of the zenith, so that $\eta = 0$ for vertically upcoming neutrinos and $\eta = 90°$ for horizontal directions.

Different nadir angles correspond to neutrinos traveling through different path lengths L across the Earth, with $L \simeq 2R_\oplus \cos\eta$, and hence going through different amounts of matter and crossing different density profiles. A simplified model of the Earth density profile would consist of a Fe and Ni core, having an inner solid part with a density of about $13\,\mathrm{g\,cm^{-3}}$ inside a radius 1,229 km and an outer molten part with a density of 11 to $12\,\mathrm{g\,cm^{-3}}$ extending up to a radius of 3,480 km. At larger radii there is the mantle, consisting mostly of O, Mg and Si with a typical density of about $5\,\mathrm{g\,cm^{-3}}$ and extending essentially up to $R_\oplus = 6,380\,\mathrm{km}$, with only the outer few tens of km being the less dense and colder crust. For detailed predictions one uses the Preliminary Earth Reference Model (PREM) [Dz81], which provides a more complete description of the Earth density profile as well as of its composition, so that for instance also the electron abundance per nucleon Y_e can be accurately obtained.

In order to derive the neutrino flavor conversion probabilities one needs then to integrate the neutrino evolution equations in a varying density profile. The results are shown in Fig. 8.3, where the oscillograms giving the probabilities $P(\nu_\mu \to \nu_e)$, $P(\nu_\mu \to \nu_\mu)$ and $P(\nu_\mu \to \nu_\tau)$ are shown. They were obtained using the code NuCraft [Wa15], and adopting the central values of the measured mixing angles and mass squared differences and considering the experimentally favored case of normal ordering, for which resonant matter effects appear always for neutrinos rather than antineutrinos. We also assumed no CP phase, i.e. $\delta = 0$, although the results have only a minor dependence on this quantity.

The main background pattern observed in the plots is that of the vacuum oscillations, which lead to a regular modulation of the probabilities, but there are also important pronounced modulations related to the matter

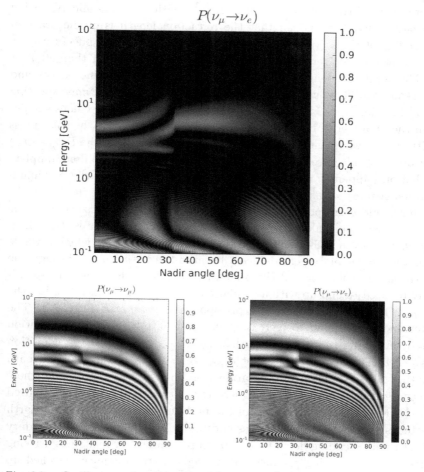

Fig. 8.3   Oscillograms describing the $P(\nu_\mu \rightarrow \nu_e)$, $P(\nu_\mu \rightarrow \nu_\mu)$ and $P(\nu_\mu \rightarrow \nu_\tau)$ probabilities of atmospheric neutrinos as a function of nadir angle and neutrino energy, considering the normal mass ordering case.

effects. To understand them it is useful to recall that the oscillation length in vacuum is given by

$$L_{\mathrm{osc}} = \frac{4\pi E}{\Delta m^2} \simeq 1{,}000 \, \mathrm{km} \frac{E/\mathrm{GeV}}{\Delta m^2/2.5 \times 10^{-3} \, \mathrm{eV}^2}, \tag{8.1}$$

and the refraction length of electron neutrinos in matter is

$$L_m \equiv \frac{2\pi}{\sqrt{2}G_{\mathrm{F}} N_e} \simeq 7{,}600 \, \mathrm{km} \frac{5 \, \mathrm{g} \, \mathrm{cm}^{-3}}{\rho}, \tag{8.2}$$

where we used that $N_e = Y_e N_A \rho/(\mathrm{g\,cm}^{-3})$, with $Y_e \simeq 0.5$ and N_A being Avogadro's number. Given that the refraction length is of the order of the radius of the Earth, it is to be expected that matter effects can be significant only for very-large baselines (nadir angles smaller than 80°).

The oscillation length in vacuum depends on the neutrino energy and mass squared difference, and if one considers the atmospheric mass splitting $|\Delta m_{31}^2| \simeq |\Delta m_{32}^2| \simeq 2.5 \times 10^{-3}\,\mathrm{eV}^2$, the oscillation length becomes smaller than the diameter of the Earth for $E_\nu < 12\,\mathrm{GeV}$ (while for the solar mass splitting, this would happen for $E_\nu < 400\,\mathrm{MeV}$). Looking at the $P(\nu_\mu \to \nu_\tau)$ plot one can indeed see that along the vertical direction the first complete oscillation happens for $E_\nu \simeq 12\,\mathrm{GeV}$. Along this direction, the maximum conversion into ν_τ takes place at $E_\nu \simeq 24\,\mathrm{GeV}$, for which the Earth diameter would correspond to half an oscillation length. These conversions have a large amplitude because the associated mixing angle is θ_{23}, which is close to maximal. For larger nadir angles, the energy for which a whole oscillation takes place gets reduced, because the path length through the Earth becomes smaller and the oscillation length needs to be correspondingly reduced to end up with a similar effect. The upper black band in the $P(\nu_\mu \to \nu_\tau)$ plot approximately corresponds to $\cos\eta \simeq E/(12\,\mathrm{GeV})$. The lower ones correspond to increasing integer multiples n of the oscillation length matching the neutrino path length, i.e. roughly to the condition $\cos\eta \simeq nE/(12\,\mathrm{GeV})$. Note that close to the horizon the neutrino path length, which extends from the production point in the atmosphere where the charged pions decay until the detector's location, is still a few hundred km. Hence, even if the fraction of the path length that crosses the Earth matter is smaller, the dark stripes end up crossing the $\eta \simeq 90°$ boundary rather than extending down to $E = 0$. In particular, for neutrinos arriving horizontally and being produced at a height h, the distance travelled up to the detector is $d \simeq \sqrt{2hR_\oplus} \simeq 500\,\mathrm{km}\sqrt{h/20\,\mathrm{km}}$, which is just half the oscillation length of neutrinos with $E \simeq 1\,\mathrm{GeV}$, explaining the maximum in the conversion probability observed at this energy for $\eta = 90°$.

The suppression of the $P(\nu_\mu \to \nu_\mu)$ survival probability taking place for $1\,\mathrm{GeV} < E < 30\,\mathrm{GeV}$ is what provided the first evidence of the oscillations of atmospheric neutrinos. In particular, the angular dependence of the oscillations, averaged above the corresponding detector thresholds, allowed to establish the corresponding neutrino mixing and mass squared splitting even if the detailed patterns of the oscillograms had not been determined.

Looking at the $P(\nu_\mu \to \nu_e)$ plot, one can see that at large nadir angles there is also a similar oscillation pattern related to the mass difference Δm_{31}^2, which is very close to Δm_{32}^2, although the amplitude of the oscillation is much smaller in this case since the associated mixing angle, $\theta_{13} \simeq 8°$, is small [Ak07]. Moreover, at energies below a few hundred MeV one can appreciate the oscillations related to the mass splitting $\Delta m_{21}^2 \simeq 7.5 \times 10^{-5} \, \mathrm{eV}^2$, for which the oscillation length in vacuum would be $L_{\mathrm{osc}} \simeq 3,300 \, \mathrm{km}(E/0.1 \, \mathrm{GeV})$. When the amount of matter traversed is large, the oscillations can be significantly affected by matter effects, as is also clearly seen in the plot.

When discussing the matter effects it is convenient to exploit the fact that in different energy regimes the three flavor neutrino oscillations approximately reduce to two flavor oscillations. In particular, at energies above one GeV the oscillations related to the mass splitting Δm_{21}^2 can be ignored, since their oscillation length becomes much larger than the radius of the Earth. One finds in this case that the oscillations driven by Δm_{31}^2 can be resonantly enhanced for the normal ordering case being considered. This is apparent in particular from the very large transition probability observed at $E \simeq 6 \, \mathrm{GeV}$ in the mantle region ($\eta \simeq 30°\text{–}70°$), which corresponds to the resonance condition $L_m \cos 2\theta_{13} = L_{\mathrm{osc}}$. Note that when the neutrinos are at the resonance the oscillation length in matter is $L_{\mathrm{osc}}^m|_{\mathrm{R}} \equiv 4\pi E/\Delta \mu^2 \simeq L_{\mathrm{osc}}/\sin 2\theta = L_m/\tan 2\theta$. Given that $\tan 2\theta_{13} \simeq 0.3$, the conversion turns out to be large for $\eta < 70°$. Even more striking is the behavior of the neutrinos crossing the Earth core, i.e. for $\eta < 30°$, in which case few ridges of matter enhanced oscillations are apparent. The main one connects the resonance in the mantle, at $E \simeq 6 \, \mathrm{GeV}$ for $\eta = 30°$, with the resonance that takes place in the higher density core for lower energies, i.e. at $E \simeq 3 \, \mathrm{GeV}$ for $\eta = 0$. There is also a region of enhanced resonance corresponding to the horizontal band near $3 \, \mathrm{GeV}$ for which the matter enhanced oscillations in the mantle region give a small effect and most of the flavor conversion is produced inside the core. There are two more regions at higher energies where the combined oscillations in the core and in the mantle can add-up coherently to produce a significant enhancement of the transition probabilities, something that can be interpreted analytically as due to a parametric enhancement of the non-resonant matter effects in regions of different densities (mantle and core), see e.g. [Ak99].

For energies from $100 \, \mathrm{MeV}$ up to $800 \, \mathrm{MeV}$ one can see instead the resonant enhancement of the $\nu_\mu \to \nu_e$ oscillations driven by Δm_{21}^2, which are associated to the mixing angle θ_{12}. The matter effects related to Δm_{31}^2 are negligible in this energy regime. Given the large value of the mixing angle θ_{12}, the matter oscillation length at the resonance, $L_{\mathrm{osc}}^m|_{\mathrm{R}} = L_m/\tan 2\theta_{12}$, is smaller than in the case associated to θ_{13} that we discussed before. As a consequence, the matter effects can lead to large enhancements up to larger nadir angles, i.e. for values $\eta < 80°$. One can indeed appreciate that there are four regions of enhanced transition probabilities at these energies. These correspond to resonant oscillations with a change in phase of $\pi/2$ (for the smaller path length at $\eta \simeq 80°$), $3\pi/2$, $5\pi/2$ and also $7\pi/2$ (for the largest path length crossing through the core, at $\eta \simeq 0$–$30°$).

If one goes back to the plots for the $P(\nu_\mu \to \nu_\mu)$ or $P(\nu_\mu \to \nu_\tau)$ transition probabilities, one can see that in the region of the parameter space in which the matter effects enhance the $\nu_\mu \to \nu_e$ conversions, one has as a side effect that the probabilities of conversion into ν_μ or ν_τ get suppressed. This results from the fact that the three probabilities satisfy the unitarity relation $P(\nu_\mu \to \nu_e) + P(\nu_\mu \to \nu_\mu) + P(\nu_\mu \to \nu_\tau) = 1$.

In order to be able to observe these features, it is important for the detectors to have a good energy resolution as well as low thresholds. The IceCube DeepCore, and in the future its lower threshold enhancement, or the ORCA component of the Mediterranean neutrino observatory KM3NeT, will go in this direction. New data from Super-Kamiokande and from the future Hyper-Kamiokande detector will also improve the results. Moreover, a baseline of 1,300 km, such as that of the long-baseline future experiment from Fermilab to the Deep Underground Neutrino Experiment (DUNE), corresponds to a nadir angle of $\eta \simeq 84°$. In this case the matter effects are moderate, although they have a significant impact on the ν_e appearance probability. All this should allow to determine the neutrino mass hierarchy with high significance. The long-baseline accelerator experiments will also be able to study the CP violation using separate neutrino and antineutrino beams, for which the impact of matter effects need to be taken into account.

8.3 The high-energy atmospheric neutrino fluxes

Making detailed estimates of the atmospheric neutrino fluxes is a very complex task, with some of the standard computations being those of the Bartol group [Ba04] or those of the group of Honda [Ho07] (see [Ga02] for a review). At energies below 10 GeV one needs to take into account that the CR spectrum, which is mostly of Galactic origin, gets suppressed and modulated by the effects of the solar wind. Moreover, the effects of the CR deflections by the geomagnetic field introduce a rigidity cutoff below which the CR spectrum gets strongly suppressed.[2] This cutoff is higher closer to the Equator and gives rise to the so-called latitude effect, which is the increase in the low-energy CR flux that is observed at higher latitudes. As a consequence, the CR flux predictions turn out to depend on the geographic location of the detector that is considered. For rigidities close to the geomagnetic cutoff, the CRs arriving from the East get more suppressed than those from the West, due to the shadowing by the Earth of the curved CR trajectories. The direction of this asymmetry actually allowed to establish that the CRs were positively charged particles. The CR asymmetry also reflects into an asymmetry in the resulting low-energy atmospheric neutrino fluxes, which was indeed observed with the Super-Kamiokande detector [Fu99]. At higher energies these complications are not relevant, but many other features contribute to shaping the atmospheric neutrino fluxes.

The decays of the charged pions that get produced in the CR hadronic interactions in the air provide the main source of the atmospheric neutrinos. However, these pions may live long enough so as to interact with air nuclei before decaying. Whether the pions interact or not is relevant to determine the slope of the resulting neutrino spectrum. Note that the pion interaction length, measured in terms of the associated column density, is $\lambda_{\pi \text{air}} = \rho_{\text{air}}/(n_{\text{air}}\sigma_{\pi \text{air}}) \simeq 120\,\text{g}\,\text{cm}^{-2}$, given that $\sigma_{\pi \text{air}} \simeq 200\,\text{mb}$. On the other hand, the dilated pion decay length is $L_\pi \equiv \Gamma c \tau_\pi$, with the lifetime satisfying $c\tau_\pi = 7.8\,\text{m}$. The requirement for the pion to decay before interacting is that $\rho_{\text{air}}\Gamma c\tau_\pi < \lambda_{\pi \text{air}}$ and hence, due to the Lorentz dilation of the pion lifetime, the competition between interactions and decays depends on the pion energy. It is only for $E_\pi \leq m_\pi \lambda_{\pi \text{air}}/(\rho_{\text{air}} c \tau_\pi) \equiv E_\pi^d$, with $E_\pi^d \simeq 200(10^{-4}\,\text{g}\,\text{cm}^{-3}/\rho_{\text{air}})\,\text{GeV}$, that the charged pions will be more likely to decay rather than to interact. When this happens, the ν_μ fluxes produced in the pion decays will have a spectral shape approximately following the shape of the CR spectrum, which is $\propto E^{-2.7}$ below PeV energies. On the other hand, for pion energies larger than E_π^d, the chances for the pions to decay before interacting become progressively small, approximately scaling as E_π^d/E, so that the resulting ν_μ fluxes get suppressed by an extra power of the energy, having then a spectrum scaling approximately as $E^{-3.7}$. Note that due to the degradation of the pion energy in each interaction step, combined with the steeply falling CR spectrum, the contribution to the neutrino fluxes arising from the decays of the pions that had suffered more than one hadronic interaction turns out in general to be sub-dominant.

---

[2]The rigidity R of a particle is just the momentum divided by the charge, $R \equiv |\vec{p}|/(eZ)$, and for relativistic particles it is just proportional to E/Z.

To get a more precise value of the energy E_π^d one needs to estimate the typical air density at which the pions decay. For this purpose one can adopt an exponential profile for the atmospheric density as a function of height h, $\rho_{\rm air} \simeq \rho_0 \exp(-h/h_0)$, with typical scale height $h_0 \simeq 10\,{\rm km}$. The column density traversed by the air shower since the primary CR entered the atmosphere with a zenith angle θ and until it reaches a height h is then $X \simeq \int_h^\infty {\rm d}z\, \rho_{\rm air}(z)/\cos\theta = \rho(h)h_0/\cos\theta$ (this is valid for $\theta < 80°$, since for more inclined showers one has to account for the curvature of the Earth). Hence, taking the simplified picture in which the CR interacts after traversing a typical proton-air interaction length of about $80\,{\rm g\,cm}^{-2}$ and considering that afterwards the pions traverse a column density $\lambda_{\pi\,{\rm air}}$ before decaying, as would be the case if their energy were E_π^d, the air density at the location where the pion decays would be $\rho_{\rm air} \simeq 2\times 10^{-4} \cos\theta (10\,{\rm km}/h_0)\,{\rm g\,cm}^{-3}$. This leads to $E_\pi^d \simeq 100\,{\rm GeV}/\cos\theta$. Since the typical energy of the neutrinos from the pion decay is about $E_\pi/4$, one would then expect that the ν_μ flux from pion decays will become steeper for energies above $\sim 25\,{\rm GeV}/\cos\theta$. Note that for inclined showers, which develop higher in the atmosphere where the air densities are lower, the spectral steepening takes place at higher energies than for vertical showers. This also implies that at the high energies for which the meson interactions become important the neutrino fluxes will get relatively enhanced near the horizon.

Regarding the flux of atmospheric electron neutrinos, which at low energies is dominated by those resulting from the muon decays, it will become strongly suppressed above GeV energies because the muons will reach ground level and be stopped before decaying. Given that the fraction of the muons that decay before reaching ground scales as E^{-1}, the associated ν_e fluxes will scale as $E^{-3.7}$, and at energies of order $100\,{\rm GeV}$ they become about a factor 20 smaller than the muon neutrino flux.

A quantity which is sometimes introduced to discuss the decay in the atmosphere of a particle of type i is the so-called critical energy ε_i, being that for which the dilated decay length equals the atmospheric scale height, i.e. $\varepsilon_i \equiv m_i h_0/(c\tau_i)$. We list in Table 8.1 the lifetimes, decay lengths and critical energies of the most relevant decaying particles.

As we discussed before, due to the meson interactions in the atmosphere the ν_μ flux from the charged pion decays get suppressed for $E_\nu \gg 25\,{\rm GeV}/\cos\theta$, scaling in this case as $\Phi_{\nu_\mu} \propto E^{-3.7}$. On the other hand, since charged kaons have a decay length much shorter than the pion one (see Table 8.1), they would preferentially decay rather than interact up

Table 8.1 Lifetime, decay length and critical energy for different particles contributing to the atmospheric neutrino fluxes.

Particle type	Lifetime $c\tau_i$	Decay length $L_i = \Gamma_i c\tau_i$	Critical energy $\varepsilon_i \equiv 10\,\mathrm{km}(m_i/c\tau_i)$
μ	659 m	$6.2\,\mathrm{km}(E/\mathrm{GeV})$	1.6 GeV
$\pi^{\pm}$	7.8 m	$5.6\,\mathrm{km}(E/100\,\mathrm{GeV})$	180 GeV
$K^{\pm}$	3.7 m	$7.5\,\mathrm{km}(E/\mathrm{TeV})$	1.3 TeV
K_{L}	15 m	$30\,\mathrm{km}(E/\mathrm{TeV})$	0.3 TeV
$D^{\pm}$	0.31 mm	$1.6\,\mathrm{km}(E/10\,\mathrm{PeV})$	60 PeV
D_s	0.15 mm	$7.6\,\mathrm{km}(E/100\,\mathrm{PeV})$	130 PeV

to higher energies, of order one TeV. Given that their dominant decay mode is $K^+ \to \mu^+ + \nu_\mu$, with branching ratio BR $\simeq 63\%$, this channel gives the major contribution to the muon neutrino fluxes above few hundred GeV. Kaons also provide the dominant contribution to the suppressed ν_e fluxes already above $\sim 100\,\mathrm{GeV}$, mostly from the neutral kaon semi-leptonic decay $K_{\mathrm{L}} \to \pi^{\pm} + e^{\mp} + \nu_e$, which has a large BR of about 40%. Since the K_{L} lifetime corresponds to $c\tau_{K_{\mathrm{L}}} \simeq 15\,\mathrm{m}$, the associated ν_e flux steepens to $\propto E^{-3.7}$ above $\sim 300\,\mathrm{GeV}$, and at TeV energies the charged kaon decays, which have a shorter lifetime, provide a comparable contribution to the ν_e fluxes through the channel $K^+ \to \pi^0 + e^+ + \nu_e$, which has a BR of 5%. Note that the much shorter lived K_{S}, with lifetime $c\tau_{K_{\mathrm{S}}} \simeq 2.7\,\mathrm{cm}$, promptly decays into two pions and can hence be considered just as an extra contribution to the pion production.

Above TeV energies, the fluxes of ν_μ and ν_e arising from π and K decays, i.e. the so-called conventional atmospheric neutrinos, become all suppressed due to the effects of the meson interactions in the air, with their spectra scaling approximately as $E_\nu^{-3.7}$. On the other hand, heavier mesons containing charm quarks, such as the D mesons consisting of $q\bar{c}$ (with $q = u,\ d,\ s$) or the charmed baryons $\Lambda_c \sim qqc$, can decay before having significant chances of interacting in the atmosphere up to energies of order $\varepsilon_c \simeq (10\,\mathrm{km}/0.1\,\mathrm{mm})m_c \simeq 10^8\,\mathrm{GeV}$ (see Table 8.1). These prompt decays, with typical picosecond lifetimes, give rise to a contribution to the neutrino fluxes having a spectrum that approximately scales as $E^{-2.7}$ and that hence becomes increasingly important for increasing energies. It turns out that the *prompt* atmospheric neutrino flux, which contributes similar amounts of ν_e and ν_μ, becomes dominant over the corresponding conventional fluxes for energies of few tens of TeV for ν_e and of few hundred TeV for ν_μ. This energy region provides indeed the best window to look for the prompt neutrino component [Ma19]. Also a small component of tau

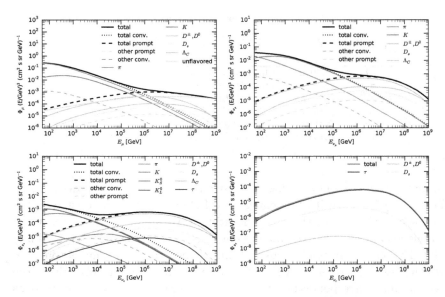

Fig. 8.4   Fluxes of atmospheric muons and neutrinos as a function of energy, from [Fe19] (https://doi.org/10.1103/PhysRevD.100.103018).

neutrinos are produced in the prompt meson decays, mostly from $D_s \rightarrow \tau + \nu_\tau$, in which the direct ν_τ has actually a small fraction of the energy, due to phase space limitations, while the dominant ν_τ flux is produced indirectly by the subsequent decay of the τ lepton. The different contributions to the atmospheric muon flux and to the fluxes of the three flavors of neutrinos and antineutrinos are depicted in Fig. 8.4, from [Fe19], where the features previously discussed can be appreciated.

Figure 8.5 shows different measurements of the atmospheric ν_μ and ν_e fluxes from the GeV up to several hundred TeV, as well as some theoretical estimates for the conventional and prompt neutrino fluxes.

The detailed computation of the prompt neutrino fluxes is not straightforward, since it relies on physics which has not yet been fully explored at colliders. In particular, the production of charmed quarks takes place mostly by gluon fusion, i.e. via $g + g \rightarrow c + \bar{c}$, and also through the next to leading order (NLO) contribution $g + g \rightarrow g + c + \bar{c}$, which is actually larger than the leading order. In the energy range where the prompt neutrinos are important, one has to deal with the interaction between the nucleons from the air nuclei and the nucleons N from the incident CRs, having energies $E_N \gg$ PeV. The relevant parton momentum in this

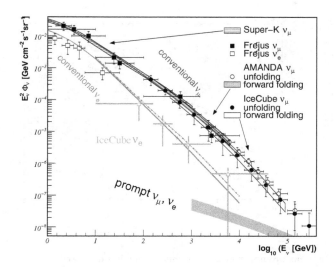

Fig. 8.5 Predicted conventional and prompt neutrino fluxes, compared with observations. Reprinted figure with permission from [Aa13], Copyright 2022 by the American Physical Society.

case can be a very small fraction of the nucleon's momentum, of order $x \sim m_c^2/(m_N E_N) \simeq 10^{-6}(\mathrm{PeV}/E_N)$. The parton distribution functions at such small values of x are however not well known and, although the gluon density tends to increase for decreasing x, a saturation is expected to take place. Hence, the predictions of charm production by perturbative QCD require to include NLO effects and to deal with the saturation of the gluon distribution, and as a consequence sizable uncertainties on the results still remain (see e.g. [Bh16]).

Fig. 8.6 displays the predictions for the prompt muon neutrino fluxes obtained by different authors [En08; Bh15; Ga15; Ga16b]. The upper line relies on the phenomenological dipole model to describe the interaction of the produced $c\bar{c}$ pairs with the nucleons, while the lower three models are based on perturbative QCD, with the predictions differing at the highest energies due mostly to differences in the parton distributions adopted for small values of x. The black solid line is the upper-bound obtained by the IceCube experiment [Aa16], which is not far from the model predictions, being already in some tension with the highest predictions based on the dipole model.

Another aspect which affects the predictions is the uncertain knowledge of the composition of the cosmic rays, in particular at energies beyond the

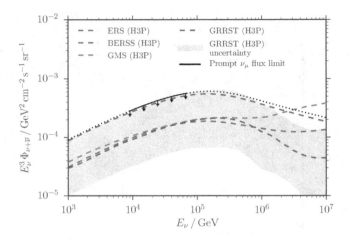

Fig. 8.6   Different prompt atmospheric muon neutrino flux predictions (dashed lines) and present upper-bounds from IceCube (black line with arrows), from [Aa16], reproduced by permission of the AAS.

knee of the CR spectrum that lies at $E_k \simeq 4\,\mathrm{PeV}$. At this energy there is a change from an overall spectrum scaling approximately as $E^{-2.7}$ below E_k to one scaling as E^{-3} above this energy. The CR composition in this regime is poorly constrained, although it is seen to become increasingly heavier above this energy. The precise estimates of the distribution of the different CR masses depend on the scenario that one adopts to account for the trends observed. For instance, a natural explanation for the CR spectral knee is that it could result from a rigidity dependent effect, such as from the less efficient CR acceleration at the sources above a certain rigidity or from a more efficient diffusive escape of the CRs from the Galaxy. In this case, the spectra of the CR nuclei with charge Z could become steeper at an energy ZE_k, scaling approximately as $E^{-(2.7+\Delta)}$ above this energy. In particular, for scenarios in which the CR diffusive escape from the Galaxy starts to be dominated above an energy ZE_k by the drift motions in the Galactic magnetic field, one typically expects values $\Delta \simeq 0.6$–0.7. In this way, the steepening of the spectrum of each charge component would actually be more pronounced than the overall average steepening observed in the total spectrum. Something qualitatively similar could also happen if for instance a limit on the acceleration power of the galactic CR sources were to give rise to an exponential suppression of the spectra above an energy ZE_k.

It is important to keep in mind that what is relevant for the computation

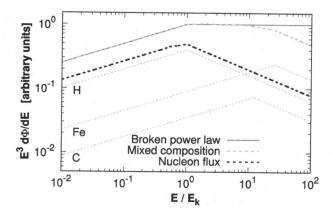

Fig. 8.7   Different component of the Galactic CR spectrum in a scenario explaining the knee as a progressive rigidity dependent steepening of the different mass components. Also shown is the spectrum of the nucleons, which is the relevant one for the neutrino production.

of the atmospheric neutrino fluxes is the spectrum as a function of the energy per nucleon E_N, rather than in terms of the total CR nucleus energy. Hence, one needs to know the composition and the spectra $d\Phi_Z(E)/dE$ of each nuclear species with charge Z and mass number A. Using that $E_N = E/A$, one should then have that

$$\frac{d\Phi_N}{d\ln E}(E_N) = \sum_A A \frac{d\Phi_A}{d\ln E}(E = AE_N). \qquad (8.3)$$

For example, if all the different CR nuclei were to have power-law spectra with a common spectral index α, and denoting with f_Z the fraction of the flux that is contributed at a given total energy by the CRs with charge Z, so that $d\Phi(E)/dE = \phi_0 \sum_Z f_Z(E/E_0)^{-\alpha}$, with E_0 an arbitrary reference energy, one would get

$$\frac{d\Phi_N}{dE}(E_N) = \phi_0 \sum_Z f_Z A^{2-\alpha} \left(\frac{E_N}{E_0}\right)^{-\alpha}. \qquad (8.4)$$

In Fig. 8.7 we show the results for the more realistic case mentioned above in which each CR component has a broken power-law spectrum, changing the shape from $E^{-2.7}$ to $E^{-3.4}$ at an energy ZE_k. We adopt for illustration a combination of several CR charges, with their fractions at energies below E_k taken as $f_H = 0.4$, $f_{He} = 0.25$, $f_C = 0.05$, $f_O = 0.08$, $f_{Ne} = 0.02$, $f_{Mg} = f_{Si} = 0.035$, $f_S = f_{Ar} = f_{Ca} = f_{Cr} = 0.01$

and $f_{\rm Fe} = 0.09$, which are typical values measured at TeV energies. The individual contributions from H, C and Fe are shown together with the total spectrum, which changes at E_k to a shape not very different than E^{-3}, which is also depicted for reference. At an energy $26E_k \simeq 100\,{\rm PeV}$, which is similar to the energy of the so-called second knee that is observed in the CR spectrum, the composition is dominated by Fe nuclei and the total spectrum becomes steeper, behaving as $E^{-3.4}$ beyond that energy. It is likely that an additional component of extragalactic origin, presumably dominated by protons, may start to emerge somewhere between 0.01 and $5\,{\rm EeV}$, but we do not include it here. One can see that in this example the spectrum in terms of the energy per nucleon, shown as a black dotted line, is quite different from the total spectrum as a function of the CR energy. In particular, the spectrum of the nucleons from nuclei heavier than hydrogen have a steepening at an energy $ZE_{\rm k}/A \simeq E_{\rm k}/2$. Hence, adopting realistic composition distributions will significantly suppress the atmospheric neutrino fluxes with respect to what would be obtained if the CR composition were all due to protons [Ca03]. As a consequence of all this, the associated atmospheric neutrino spectrum is expected to become steeper at $\sim 100\,{\rm TeV}$, which is just the range where the prompt contribution to the ν_μ flux should become dominant (and also where the astrophysical neutrino contribution emerges, as will be discussed in the next chapter).

8.4   The cascade equations

It is instructive to obtain approximate analytic expressions for the development of the different air-shower components, including the nuclei and the mesons, in order to derive neutrino fluxes reflecting the main properties that we described qualitatively before.

The transport equations for the flux ϕ_j of a given component j (where ϕ_j actually stands for the differential flux $d\Phi_j/dE$) is [Vo80; Li93]

$$\frac{d\phi_j}{dX} = -\frac{\phi_j}{\lambda_j} - \frac{\phi_j}{\lambda_j^d} + \sum_k S_{kj}, \qquad (8.5)$$

with X denoting the slant-depth (i.e. the amount of air traversed measured in g cm^{-2}), $\lambda_j = \rho_{\rm air}/(n_{\rm air}\sigma_{j\,{\rm air}})$ being the interaction length (which usually has a very mild logarithmic dependence with energy) and $\lambda_j^d = \rho_{\rm air}\Gamma_j c\tau_j$ being the grammage associated to the decay length (which, due to the Lorentz factor Γ_j, is proportional to the particle energy). The last term corresponds to the production or regeneration of the particle j, and is given by

$$S_{kj}(E, X) = \int_E^\infty dE' \, \frac{\phi_k(E', X)}{\lambda_k(E')} \frac{1}{\sigma_{k\,\text{air}}(E)} \frac{d\sigma_{k\,\text{air}\to j}(E, E')}{dE}. \tag{8.6}$$

This term couples the transport equations of different components. For instance, if j denotes the charged pions, the first term in Eq. (8.5) would correspond to the pion-air interactions that degrade their energy, the second term accounts for pion decays while the last term would describe the pion production by interactions of nucleons with air or the regeneration of pions in meson-air interactions, which are actually dominated by the interactions of the pions themselves. Since the energies involved in the collisions between CRs and atmospheric nuclei are much larger than the nuclear binding energies, only nucleon-nucleon interactions are relevant in this context and it is hence convenient to consider the nucleon flux, denoted as ϕ_N, adding up all the neutrons and protons that are present in the air showers. The unstable particles that eventually produce neutrinos in their decay ($\pi^\pm$, $K^\pm$, K_L, D^0, $D^\pm$, D_s, Λ_c) are generically denoted as M, for mesons. Note that although Λ_c is a baryon, it also gets included in the 'meson' component M. If one were interested in the low-energy neutrinos, the muons would certainly need to be included as well. One usually neglects the nucleons produced in meson interactions ($S_{MN} \simeq 0$), keeping only the regeneration terms S_{NN} or S_{MM} as well as the meson production from nucleons, S_{NM}.

If the initial CR spectrum is a power law and one neglects the energy dependence of the interaction lengths, it is a good approximation to adopt a separation of variables of the form $\phi_k(E, X) = g_k(X)E^{-\gamma}$. One has then that

$$S_{kj} = \frac{\phi_k(E, X)}{\lambda_k} Z_{kj}^\gamma(E), \tag{8.7}$$

where the production/regeneration moments are

$$Z_{kj}^\gamma(E) \equiv \int_0^1 dx \, x^{\gamma-1} \frac{1}{\sigma_{k\,\text{air}}(E)} \frac{d\sigma_{k\,\text{air}\to j}(E, x)}{dx}, \tag{8.8}$$

with $x \equiv E/E'$. If one further assumes that scaling holds, i.e. that $d\sigma/dx$ only depends on x, the different moments turn out to be constants that just depend on the process considered and on the spectral index γ, allowing for an analytic solution of the equations.

In particular, taking for the initial CR nucleon flux a single power law

$$\phi_N(E, X = 0) = \phi_{0N} E^{-\gamma}, \tag{8.9}$$

and assuming that the nucleon flux develops independently from the secondary meson fluxes (so that $S_{MN} = 0$), one gets that

$$\phi_N(E, X) = \exp(-X/\Lambda_N)\phi_N(E, X = 0), \tag{8.10}$$

where the effective nucleon attenuation length is

$$\Lambda_N = \frac{\lambda_N}{1 - Z_{NN}^\gamma}. \tag{8.11}$$

The factor Λ_N accounts for the nucleon losses by interactions as well as for their regeneration. One can then see that, under the assumption of scaling, the nucleon flux in the air shower remains a power law with the same spectral index as the incident CR flux, and that due to the interactions with the air it gets exponentially attenuated for increasing slant depth.

Concerning the meson cascade equations, there are qualitatively different solutions at the high energies (H) for which the decays can be neglected and at the low energies (L) for which the mesons tend to decay before interacting. The high-energy solution to the coupled nucleon and meson equations leads to

$$\phi_M^{\rm H}(E, X) \simeq \frac{Z_{NM}^\gamma}{1 - Z_{NN}^\gamma} \frac{\exp(-X/\Lambda_M) - \exp(-X/\Lambda_N)}{1 - \Lambda_N/\Lambda_M}\phi_{0N}E^{-\gamma}, \tag{8.12}$$

with $\Lambda_M = \lambda_M/(1 - Z_{MM}^\gamma)$. On the other hand, at low energies (where the meaning of 'low' depends on the meson being considered, being e.g. below tens of GeV for pions and below tens of PeV for charmed mesons), one has instead

$$\phi_M^{\rm L}(E, X) \simeq \frac{Z_{NM}^\gamma}{1 - Z_{NN}^\gamma} \frac{\lambda_M^d}{\Lambda_N} \exp(-X/\Lambda_N)\phi_{0N}E^{-\gamma}. \tag{8.13}$$

Since the decay length is proportional to the energy, one can see that at low energies the meson spectrum ends up scaling as $E^{-\gamma+1}$, being harder than the initial CR spectrum because the decaying mesons are more efficiently lost at lower energies.

The neutrino flux produced by the meson decays is obtained from

$$\frac{{\rm d}\phi_\nu}{{\rm d}X} = \sum_M S_{M\nu}, \tag{8.14}$$

where

$$S_{M\nu}(E, X) = \int_E^\infty {\rm d}E' \frac{\phi_M(E', X)}{\lambda_M^d(E')} \frac{1}{\Gamma_M(E)} \frac{{\rm d}\Gamma_{M\nu}(E, E')}{{\rm d}E}. \tag{8.15}$$

In the relativistic limit, the decay distribution has an approximate scaling relation satisfying

$$\frac{1}{\Gamma_M(E)}\frac{\mathrm{d}\Gamma_{M\nu}(E,E')}{\mathrm{d}E} \simeq B_{M\nu}\frac{F_{M\nu}(E/E')}{E'}, \qquad (8.16)$$

where $B_{M\nu}$ is the branching ratio for the meson M to decay into neutrinos, and the functions F describe the inclusive neutrino spectrum. For instance, for the pion decays one has

$$F_{\pi^+\to\mu^+}(x) = \theta(x - r_\pi)/(1 - r_\pi)$$
$$F_{\pi^+\to\nu_\mu}(x) = [1 - \theta(x - 1 + r_\pi)]/(1 - r_\pi), \qquad (8.17)$$

with $r_\pi \equiv (m_\mu/m_\pi)^2$. Analogous expressions hold for the other meson decays. One has then that

$$S_{M\nu}(E,X) = \frac{\phi_M(E,X)}{\lambda_M^d(E)} Z_{M\nu}^{\gamma+1}(E), \qquad (8.18)$$

where the decay moment is

$$Z_{M\nu}^\gamma(E) = B_{M\nu}\int_0^1 \mathrm{d}x\, x^{\gamma-1}F_{M\nu}(x). \qquad (8.19)$$

At the low energies for which the mesons decay promptly, one obtains that

$$\phi_\nu^{\mathrm{L}}(E,X) \simeq Z_{M\nu}^\gamma \frac{Z_{NM}^\gamma}{1 - Z_{NN}^\gamma}[1 - \exp(-X/\Lambda_N)]\phi_{0N}E^{-\gamma}. \qquad (8.20)$$

One then sees that in this case the neutrino flux develops quickly, since as soon as the mesons get produced on the scale of an hadronic interaction length they decay to produce neutrinos. At ground level ($X \gg \Lambda_N$) one then gets

$$\phi_\nu^{\mathrm{L}}(E) \simeq Z_{M\nu}^\gamma \frac{Z_{NM}^\gamma}{1 - Z_{NN}^\gamma}\phi_{0N}E^{-\gamma} \qquad (8.21)$$

and hence the neutrino flux ends up being proportional to the incoming CR nucleon flux.

On the other hand, at the high energies for which $\lambda_M^d \gg \Lambda_M$, the integration over the neutrino production at different heights leads, using in the expression for λ_M^d an exponential air-density profile with scale height h_0, to a neutrino flux at ground level equal to

$$\phi_\nu^{\mathrm{H}}(E) \simeq Z_{M\nu}^{\gamma+1} \frac{Z_{NM}^\gamma}{1 - Z_{NN}^\gamma} \frac{\ln(\Lambda_M/\Lambda_N)}{1 - \Lambda_N/\Lambda_M} \frac{\varepsilon_M}{\cos\theta}\phi_{0N}E^{-\gamma-1}, \qquad (8.22)$$

where the critical energy is $\varepsilon_M \equiv m_M h_0/(c\tau_M)$. One can see that in this case the neutrino spectrum is actually steeper by one additional power of

E with respect to the incoming CR spectrum. This comes out because, when the meson interactions are the limiting factor for the production of the neutrinos, the probability for a meson to decay before interacting is proportional to $\varepsilon_M/(E\cos\theta)$.

The discussion above considered the case of a CR spectrum with a single power-law, and in order to account for the spectral change in the CR spectrum at the knee one may use an interpolation of the neutrino fluxes obtained adopting the power-law nucleon fluxes which are present below and above the knee break. To obtain more precise results it becomes however necessary to account for the detailed CR spectrum and composition, to include the energy dependence of the cross sections and the scaling violations, as well as to eventually include nuclear effects in the CR air cross sections.

Suggested exercises:

- Calculate the path length ℓ of atmospheric neutrinos, from their height of production h (10 to 20 km) until an underground detector at a depth D (of 1 to 2 km), as a function of the zenith angle of their arrival direction. Estimate separately the path in the air and the one inside the Earth. Evaluate the solid angle covered by the core of the Earth.
- Derive Eqs. (8.3) and (8.4)
- Calculate the adimensional ratio between the vacuum term $\Delta m_{31}^2/(2E_\nu)$ and the matter term $\sqrt{2}G_F N_e$, and express it numerically for an isoscalar medium with density of $3\,\mathrm{g\,cm^{-3}}$. Find the energy at which the ratio is unity and discuss its meaning. Find the associated oscillation length.
- Derive Eqs. (8.10) and (8.12).

Recommended reading:

- *Cosmic Rays and Particle Physics,* T.K. Gaisser, R. Engel and E. Resconi, Cambridge University Press (2016)

Chapter 9

High-energy Astrophysical Neutrinos

In this chapter we present the main aspects of high-energy astrophysical neutrinos, an area that is developing at a fast pace after the detection, since 2013, of a flux of neutrinos of astrophysical origin with energies in the 1 TeV to 10 PeV range. These messengers are expected to be produced as secondaries in the interactions of cosmic rays, and since they travel straight and unattenuated they can help to identify the cosmic-ray sources and to understand the mechanism responsible for their acceleration. Studies of correlation between the neutrino arrival directions with various populations of celestial objects are in progress. The neutrino sources are also expected to be strong gamma-ray sources, so that there is an important connection between high-energy neutrino and gamma-ray astronomies. In particular, the first plausible identification of a high-energy neutrino source resulted from the observation of a neutrino with an energy of about 300 TeV from the direction of the Blazar TXS 0506+056, that was in a state of enhanced activity in gamma rays. Recent evidence of Galactic gamma-ray sources with energies as high as PeV is accumulating, and these are also potential sites for the production of PeV neutrinos. Even a connection with gravitational waves may exists if neutrinos get produced after the asymmetric collapse of compact astrophysical objects, and this kind of coincident signals are being actively searched for.

9.1 High-energy neutrino production

9.1.1 The cosmic-ray connection

It is widely believed that the astrophysical sources in which high-energy cosmic rays (CRs) are accelerated should also produce high-energy neutrinos. A simple motivation for this is the fact that the atmospheric neutrinos have been observed, and they originate in cosmic-ray interactions with the nuclei present in the atmosphere of the Earth. In an analogous way, if the sites where cosmic rays are accelerated, or the environment that surround them, have sufficient target material so as to allow for the conversion of a fraction of the cosmic-ray energy into secondary particles, they could naturally provide potentially observable sources of high-energy neutrinos.

The atmospheric neutrinos are mostly produced in the decays of mesons (pions, kaons or heavier ones). At very-high energies the mesons produced in the air showers that result from the cosmic-ray interactions with air molecules are strongly attenuated in the dense atmosphere of the Earth before they can decay, what strongly suppresses the fluxes of atmospheric neutrinos at high energies (see Chapter 8). On the other hand, if the astrophysical neutrinos are produced in sources where the gas or radiation targets have a density which is low enough so that the mesons have sufficient time to decay before they interact, the astrophysical neutrino flux could be less suppressed at high energies than the atmospheric neutrino flux. This is what may allow for the astrophysical neutrino fluxes to become observable above the atmospheric background at sufficiently high energies, typically above few tens of TeV. Given the connection between the high-energy neutrinos and the cosmic rays, we begin the discussion describing some relevant facts about these last (for a recent review see [Mo18]).

The spectrum of the cosmic rays observed at the Earth extends from GeV energies up to beyond 10^{20} eV. In these eleven decades of energy, the differential flux follows approximately a power law $d\Phi_{CR}/dE \sim E^{-\alpha}$, with $\alpha \simeq 3$, so that it drops by more than 30 orders of magnitude over this range. Some prominent features of the spectrum are associated with changes in the power-law spectral index α. The main ones are the so-called knee at an energy $E_k \simeq 4\,\text{PeV}$, where α changes from about 2.7 to 3; the second knee at $E_{sk} \simeq 100\,\text{PeV}$, where there is a further steepening to $\alpha \simeq 3.3$; the ankle at $E_a \simeq 5\,\text{EeV}$, where there is a hardening to $\alpha \simeq 2.7$ and a final suppression appears at $E_s \simeq 50\,\text{EeV}$, where the spectrum steepens to $\alpha \simeq 5$. Other features observed more recently involve a hardening at about 20 PeV, where the spectrum is found to actually change from a slope of 3.2 to about 3, and a steepening taking place at about 14 EeV, where it changes from about 2.5 to 3. The CR spectrum, multiplied by $E^{2.6}$ in order to better appreciate the features, is displayed in Fig. 9.1.

The observed changes in α may be related to changes in the CR acceleration properties, to changes in the CR diffusive propagation up to us, to changes in the CR composition or to changes due to the transition from a

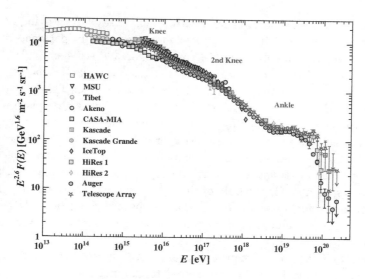

Fig. 9.1　Cosmic-ray spectrum measured by different experiments from 10 TeV up to beyond 100 EeV (from [PDG]).

Galactic to an extragalactic CR origin. On the other hand, the final suppression at the highest energies is probably related to a maximum energy achievable at the sources and/or to the CR attenuation caused by the interactions with the radiation backgrounds that they cross as they propagate up to us (the Greisen-Zatsepin-Kuzmin effect).

The CRs below the second knee are believed to be predominantly of Galactic origin, with the knee being related to the suppression of the light Galactic nuclei (H and He), while the second knee being probably associated to the suppression of the heavier Fe group Galactic elements. The CRs above the ankle are believed to be instead predominantly of extragalactic origin, but however the precise energy at which the transition from a Galactic to an extragalactic origin takes place is still unknown.

Note that the Fermi mechanism of diffusive shock acceleration, in which CRs get accelerated while crossing several times a shock-wave front, bouncing back and forth in the magnetic turbulence, naturally leads to a power-law spectrum, but with a typical spectral index at the source of $\alpha_s \simeq 2$ to 2.4. On the other hand, the Galactic CRs diffuse in the interstellar medium, which is permeated by magnetic fields, and remain confined inside the Galaxy for very long times, what enhances their fluxes. This residence time τ depends on the CR energy, with lower energy CRs staying confined for longer times, and its energy dependence is usually parameterized as $\tau \sim E^{-\delta}$, so that the observed CR spectrum should scale as $E^{-\alpha_s - \delta}$. One expects in particular that $\delta \simeq 1/3$ if the random Galactic magnetic field turbulence has a spectrum close to the Kolmogorov one. This may explain the values of $\alpha = \alpha_s + \delta \simeq 2.7$ that are observed below the spectral knee. Above the knee the steepening in the spectrum may be due either to a less efficient acceleration at the sources (larger α_s) or to a more efficient escape from the Galaxy (larger δ), or a combination of both effects. The emergence of CRs of extragalactic origin on top of the falling Galactic CR flux may be responsible for the bulk of the CRs observed above the second knee and up to the highest energies. The ankle feature could possibly reflect a change in the dominant source population contributing to the extragalactic CR fluxes.

Galactic CR sources are probably related to supernova remnants (SNR), since energetically it would be required to channel just about 10% of the kinetic energy of the supernova explosions into CR acceleration to account for the energy budget of the CRs observed below the knee [Gi64]. Moreover, the efficient acceleration of protons up to the knee energy may be possible in these sources if the magnetic fields get amplified near the shocks, as is expected to happen. Since the acceleration is an effect that depends on the rigidity of the particles, $R \equiv p/(eZ) \propto E/Z$, the maximum energy achievable for a nucleus should be proportional to its charge Z. In particular, if Galactic H nuclei get accelerated efficiently up to the knee energy, Fe nuclei could be accelerated by the same sources up to the second-knee energy. The extragalactic cosmic rays that dominate at the highest energies should instead be accelerated in more powerful sources, such as in the jets of active galactic nuclei (AGNs), those in gamma-ray bursts (GRBs), in tidal disruption events (TDE), in clusters of galaxies, in galaxy collisions, in starburst and star-forming galaxies, etc., but their actual sources still remain unknown [Me17; Ah18].

9.1.2   *The pp and pγ mechanisms of neutrino production*

We will then focus on the hypothesis that most of the observed high-energy neutrinos of non-atmospheric origin are *astrophysical neutrinos*, produced in CR collisions with the gas or with the radiation present in the environment of the sources where the CRs get accelerated. These two mechanisms for high-energy neutrino production are called the *pp* mechanism and the

$p\gamma$ mechanism respectively, depending on the nature of the target involved. As examples, the neutrino production in SNR is expected to be mostly due to the pp mechanism, taking place when the accelerated CRs hit the surrounding gas clouds, while the neutrino production in GRBs or in the inner jets of AGNs are expected to be dominated by the $p\gamma$ mechanism, since the radiation fields in these environments are very strong, mostly from synchrotron radiation of co-accelerated electrons or from thermal backgrounds. The pp mechanism could also contribute if these jets collide with gas, as could be the case in the lobes of radiogalaxies. Other attractive sites for high-energy neutrino production are the so-called CR reservoirs, which are sites where CRs could remain magnetically confined for very long times, even of the order of the age of the Universe. This could for instance be the case in galaxy clusters, where μG magnetic fields are observed over scales of several Mpc, or in starburst galaxies that have in their cores much stronger magnetic fields. The large amount of gas present in those environments can make the neutrino production via the pp mechanism to be quite efficient.

Note that very-high-energy neutrinos may also eventually get produced as the CRs propagate to us from cosmologically distant sources and interact with the background radiation that is present in the Universe. The neutrinos in this case arise mostly from the decay of the charged pions produced in photopion interactions of the CR protons with the CMB photons [Be69]. The fluxes of these *cosmogenic neutrinos* typically peak around few EeV, given the threshold for pion production from protons interacting with the CMB, which corresponds to proton energies of about 50 EeV. The flux of cosmogenic neutrinos may become significant if the primary CRs include a sizeable component of protons extending up to the highest energies, and it could be particularly enhanced if the sources of those CR protons were more intense at high redshift than what they are at present (see top panel of Fig. 9.2). If instead the CRs become predominantly heavy above the ankle of the spectrum, as is actually supported by the results obtained at the Pierre Auger Observatory, the flux of cosmogenic neutrinos with EeV energies resulting from the CR interactions with the CMB may end up being quite suppressed [Al11; Ro14]. The most relevant contribution in this case would arise from the CR interactions with the extragalactic background light (UV/IR backgrounds), which due to their higher energy could lead to photopion production involving lower-energy protons. In this case, the contribution to the neutrino fluxes would peak in the 10 PeV to 100 PeV range (see bottom panel of Fig. 9.2).

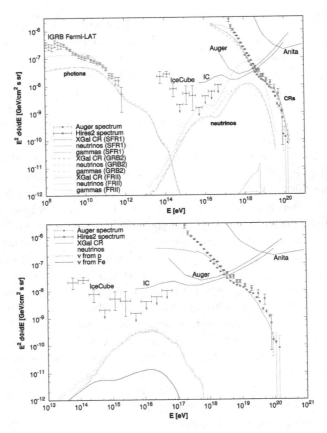

Fig. 9.2 Expected all-flavor cosmogenic neutrino fluxes as a function of energy (adapted from [Ro14]). Also shown are the adopted extragalactic CR flux (green) and the fluxes measured by Auger and HiRes. The flux of astrophysical neutrinos determined by IceCube is indicated, as well as the upper bounds form Auger, Anita and IceCube (90% CL bound per energy decade). Top panel: scenario with CR protons having a maximum energy $E_{max} = 200$ EeV, adopting different cosmological source evolutions. Also the resulting photon flux and the Fermi determination of the isotropic gamma-ray background (IGRB) are displayed. Bottom panel: scenario with a low-rigidity cutoff ($E_{max} = 5Z$ EeV), with a mixture of protons and iron CR primaries.

The pp mechanism: To study the production of astrophysical neutrinos in the environments of the CR sources, consider first the case of the pp mechanism in which a very-high-energy proton collides with a proton at rest (or with a nucleus of mass number A, which may be approximately described as an ensemble of A nucleons). This collision will lead to the production of a large number of pions and, to a smaller extent, also to some heavier mesons. The experimental observations show that most of the pions are produced in similar amounts for the different pion charges and that they carry a small fraction of the primary proton energy. For instance, in pp collisions at the Large Hadron Collider, which are detected in the center of mass system, a large pion multiplicity is observed in the *central* region away from the beam direction, having typically small transverse momenta ($\sim \Lambda_{\rm QCD}$) and resulting mostly from the interactions among the gluons from the two colliding protons. Some high-energy pions are also produced in the forward *fragmentation* region of the collision, carrying a significant fraction of the proton energy and showing an excess of π^+ over π^-, as results from the interactions that involve valence quarks. The subsequent decay of the pions will eventually lead to high-energy gamma rays and neutrinos through

$$\pi^0 \to \gamma + \gamma \ \text{ and } \ \pi^\pm \to \mu^\pm + \overset{(-)}{\nu_\mu} \ , \text{ followed e.g. by } \mu^+ \to e^+ + \nu_e + \bar{\nu}_\mu.$$

The kinematics of these decays is such that, in the rest frame of the pion, each gamma ray from the decay of a neutral meson π^0 carries $1/2$ of the initial energy and, likewise, in the decay chain of the charged pions each of the four light (anti)leptons carries away approximately $1/4$ of the initial pion energy, with the energies of the neutrinos from the muon decay being continuously distributed, while that from the pion decay being monochromatic. The photon and neutrino distributions in the laboratory frame can be obtained through the associated Lorentz transformations. For instance, one gets that the photon energy E_γ resulting from the decays of a π^0 with energy E_π has a uniform distribution $\mathrm{d}N_\gamma/\mathrm{d}E_\gamma \simeq 2E_\gamma/p_\pi$, covering the range $\sqrt{(1-\beta)/(1+\beta)}\,m_\pi/2 < E_\gamma < \sqrt{(1+\beta)/(1-\beta)}\,m_\pi/2$, with $\beta = p_\pi/E_\pi$. In this way, the photon spectrum can be obtained through a convolution of this distribution with the neutral pion spectrum, which in turn is obtained from the convolution of the pp cross section and the associated pion yield. The pion yield is however not known analytically, due to the non-perturbative nature of the hadronic interactions, and its details have to be worked out performing Montecarlo simulations based on specific hadronic models that describe the high-energy inelastic pp interactions.

The neutrino fluxes can be computed treating separately the muon neutrinos resulting from the two-body pion decays ($\nu_\mu^{(1)}$) and the electron and muon neutrinos from the three-body muon decay (ν_e and $\nu_\mu^{(2)}$). In this last case, one has also to take into account the fact that the muon produced in the weak pion decay is polarised, since for instance in the decay $\pi^- \to \mu^- \bar{\nu}_\mu$ the antineutrino is right handed, and hence the muon spin helicity in the

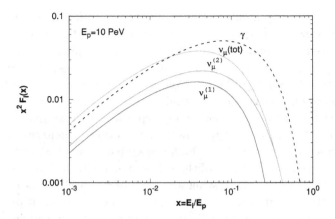

Fig. 9.3   Yields of neutrinos and photons, $x^2 F_i(x, E_p)$ vs. x, for an incident proton energy $E_p = 10 \, \mathrm{PeV}$ (from [Ro21b]). The spectrum of ν_e is very similar to that of the $\nu_\mu^{(2)}$ produced in the μ decays, while $\nu_\mu^{(1)}$ are the neutrinos from the pion decay $\pi \to \nu_\mu \mu$.

pion frame is positive. This implies that the muon decay products are on average not isotropically distributed in the frame of the decaying muon.[1]

If one assumes that the pions and muons do not lose energy before decaying, neither by synchrotron emission in the presence of magnetic fields nor by interactions with the medium, one can obtain the differential neutrino emissivity (number of emitted neutrinos per unit time and energy) from a source producing CR protons at a differential rate $q_p(E_p)$, as

$$q_{\nu_i}(E_\nu) = N_N \int_{E_\nu}^{\infty} \frac{dE_p}{E_p} \sigma_{pp} F_{\nu_i}(x_\nu, E_p) q_p(E_p), \qquad (9.1)$$

where N_N is the column density of nucleons traversed by the emitted CRs as they exit from the source, which is essentially that of hydrogen atoms plus four times that of He atoms. The adimensional functions $F_{\nu_i}(x_\nu, E_p)$ describe the yield of neutrinos with energies $E_\nu = x_\nu E_p$ from the interaction of a proton with energy E_p with the gas target. These functions have been parameterized in [Ke06] from the results of simulations of pp interactions and they are plotted in Fig. 9.3, adopting $E_p = 10 \, \mathrm{PeV}$, for the different neutrino flavors as well as for photons, for which an expression analogous to that in Eq. (9.1) holds in terms of a distribution F_γ.

---

[1]Remember that the fact that the electron tends to be emitted in the direction opposite to the muon spin was actually one of the proofs that parity was violated in weak interactions [Ga57].

One can see from Fig. 9.3 that the spectrum of the secondaries is quite broad and it extends down to energies well below E_p, while an often used simplifying assumption is to adopt instead $E_\nu \simeq E_\pi/4 \simeq E_p/20$. Note that the average value of x_ν in the interaction of a proton of a certain energy may be about 10^{-2}. However, if the spectrum of the CR protons is steep, the tail of the neutrinos produced with small values of x_ν could be buried below the neutrinos produced with higher values of x_ν from the more abundant lower energy protons. Hence, the average value of x_ν associated to the observed neutrinos will be larger than 10^{-2}, and closer to the usually adopted value of $1/20$, although it actually depends on the spectral shape of the CRs and may be significantly smaller than this value if the spectrum is hard [Ro21b].

The inelastic pp cross section σ_{pp} has a mild logarithmic energy dependence, which is approximately given by $\sigma_{pp} \simeq (34.9 + 1.985L + 0.18L^2)$ mb, with $L = \ln(E_p/\text{TeV})$ [Ka14], and this could also have a slight impact on the resulting shape of the neutrino spectrum. Note that we have considered in Eq. (9.1) that the target was thin, so that the probability for the CRs to interact before leaving the source is much smaller than unity. This corresponds to the assumption that $N_N \sigma_{pp} \ll 1$, which is satisfied as long as $N_N < 10^{25} \text{cm}^{-2}$.

In the case of interactions of heavier CR nuclei of mass number A with a hydrogen target, one would have that the associated cross section approximately satisfies $\sigma_{pA} \simeq A^a \sigma_{pp}$, where the exponent a is expected to be somewhere between $2/3$ and 1. The value $a = 1$ corresponds to the so-called superposition model, in which the different nucleons are assumed to interact independently, while smaller values of a may result as a consequence of nuclear shadowing effects.

If one considers a proton source with a power-law spectrum, emitting at a rate per unit time and differential in energy $q_p(E_p) = A_p E_p^{-\alpha}$, the neutrino emissivity will be

$$q_{\nu_i}(E_\nu) = \langle N_N A_p \rangle \int_{E_\nu}^{\infty} \sigma_{pp}(E_p)\, F_{\nu_i}(x_\nu, E_p) E_p^{-\alpha-1} \mathrm{d}E_p. \qquad (9.2)$$

There is a very important property of the hadronic interactions, called scaling, which implies in particular that the yield of pions in a pp collision mainly depends on the fraction of the nucleon energy going into the pion, $x_\pi = E_\pi/E_p$, and not on each energy separately. As a consequence of this, together with the mild growth of σ_{pp} and of the pion multiplicity with increasing energy, the neutrino spectrum will have in this case an approximate power-law shape, with a spectral index just slightly harder than that of the original proton spectrum. This is illustrated in the left

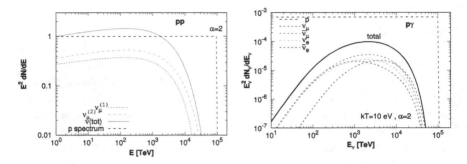

Fig. 9.4 Total ν spectrum (from all flavors), as well as the individual contributions from $\nu_\mu^{(1)}$ (the one from π decay) and $\nu_\mu^{(2)}$ (the one from μ decay), in pp scenarios (left panel) and in $p\gamma$ scenarios with a thermal background of photons with $kT = 10$ eV (right panel). We considered a power-law proton spectrum with $\alpha = 2$ and a sharp cutoff at $E_c = 100$ PeV (black dashed line, arbitrarily normalized). Adapted from [Ro21b].

panel of Fig. 9.4, where the spectrum of the different flavors of neutrinos resulting from a proton source with a spectral index $\alpha = 2$ and having a sharp cutoff at $E_c = 100$ PeV are displayed. Besides the slight spectral hardening, one can also see that the neutrino spectrum in this example starts to become suppressed above approximately $E_c/100 = 1$ PeV and, as a consequence of the broad distribution of neutrino energies resulting from the pp interactions, the suppression is much softer than that adopted for the proton spectrum.

The $p\gamma$ mechanism: Turning now to the $p\gamma$ scenarios, in which the target consists of energetic photons (UV, X-rays or γ-rays), the $p\gamma$ cross section is often dominated by the resonant production of the Δ baryon,

$$p + \gamma \rightarrow \Delta^+ \rightarrow n + \pi^+ \text{ or } p + \pi^0.$$

This is the largest contribution to the $p\gamma$ cross section when the proton energy is not much larger than the threshold for the production of the Δ resonance, with some subdominant contributions arising from higher resonances such as Δ' and from non-resonant channels such as the t-channel charged pion exchange. For increasing energies the multiple pion production becomes allowed, and it eventually becomes dominant at much higher energies. The final neutrino spectrum will not only depend on the spectrum of the CR protons but also on the target photon spectrum, and is generally not expected to be distributed as a power law. Note that if the target photon spectrum were very steep, the pion production at high energies could still be dominated by the Δ-resonance production from the very abundant low-energy photons, even if the photon energies extend to high enough values for which the multipion production is kinematically allowed.

In the resonant Δ production process, the pions carry on average about 20% of the proton energy, and hence one expects that the average energy of the photons produced in the π^0 decays satisfies $\langle E_\gamma \rangle \simeq \langle E_\pi \rangle / 2 \simeq E_p/10$, while that of the neutrinos from the charged pion decays would be $\langle E_\nu \rangle \simeq \langle E_\pi \rangle / 4 \simeq E_p/20$. Note that in this case the observed astrophysical neutrinos with energies $E_\nu \sim 100$ TeV $- 10$ PeV would correspond to primary proton energies $E_p \sim 2$ PeV $- 200$ PeV, i.e. to CR nucleons with typical energies in between those of the knee and the second knee of the CR spectrum. At these energies the observed CR spectrum is however likely dominated by heavy nuclei from the Galactic contribution, while on the other hand the astrophysical neutrinos are mostly produced by extragalactic sources, whose CRs may not even reach us due to their slow diffusive propagation through the intergalactic magnetic fields. Astrophysical neutrinos can hence give us information about the cosmic-ray fluxes at their production site, even if the fluxes of those CRs are not directly observable from the Earth. However, this information is intertwined with the type of target the cosmic rays collide with and with the nature of the sources. This makes the connection between the neutrino and CR fluxes model-dependent and requires theoretical input for a proper interpretation.

The detailed energy distribution of the neutrino (and photon) fluxes from the decays of mesons produced in the $p\gamma$ interactions can be obtained from the yields derived from Montecarlo simulations of these interactions, using codes such as SOPHIA [Mu00], and making the convolution with the proton and photon spectra. One usually performs the computation in the reference frame where the photons are isotropic, and we will denote the quantities in this frame with a prime. Considering that the muons and pions do not suffer energy losses before they decay, one obtains [Ke08]

$$q_i(E_i') = \int \frac{dE_p'}{E_p'} \, d\varepsilon' \, q_p(E_p') \frac{dn_{\text{ph}}}{d\varepsilon'}(\varepsilon') \Phi_i(\eta, x_i), \qquad (9.3)$$

where ε' is the energy of the isotropic target photons. The variable $\eta \equiv 4\varepsilon' E_p'/m_p^2$ characterizes the center of mass total energy squared of the interaction and $x_i = E_i'/E_p'$ is the fraction of the proton energy carried by the secondary, with i describing the (anti)neutrino type or the photons. The different functions $\Phi_i(\eta, x_i)$ were conveniently parameterized in [Ke08]. As an example, we show in the right panel of Fig. 9.3 the resulting neutrino and photon spectra for the case of CR protons accelerated with $\alpha = 2$

up to maximum energy of 100 PeV and interacting with a thermal photon background with $kT = 10\,\mathrm{eV}$.

If the neutrino production takes place in relativistic jets, such as in GRBs or blazars, the frame associated to the isotropic photon background will be the shock rest frame (SRF). The energy in the comoving frame will hence typically appear boosted with respect to the energy E' in the SRF by the Lorentz factor Γ of the jet, which can be O(10) for AGNs or O(100–1000) for GRBs. In the observer's frame on Earth, the energy should also appear redshifted by the cosmological expansion, so that $E \simeq \Gamma E'/(1+z)$, with z being the source redshift. Note that in GRBs the target photon spectrum is usually considered to be a broken power-law, with $dn_{\mathrm{ph}}/d\varepsilon' \propto \varepsilon'^{-\beta}$, with $\beta = 1$ for $\varepsilon' < \varepsilon'_{\mathrm{b}} \simeq 1\,\mathrm{keV}$ while $\beta = 2$ for larger energies. In this case the predicted neutrino spectrum will also have an approximate broken power-law shape, with an eventual suppression at very-high energies depending on the cutoff of the proton spectrum or eventually depending on the synchrotron and interaction losses suffered by the muons and pions before decaying.

Differences between the pp and $p\gamma$ mechanisms: Let us examine now some of the differences between the pp and $p\gamma$ mechanisms. The main ones are related to the resulting spectra of the secondaries:

- Unlike the pp mechanism, the $p\gamma$ mechanism is a process with a high threshold for the proton energy, because to produce the Δ resonance (with $m_\Delta = 1.232\,\mathrm{GeV}$), at which the cross section gets largely enhanced, one needs that

$$E'_p > \frac{m_\Delta^2 - m_p^2}{4\varepsilon'_\gamma} = 1.6 \left(\frac{100\ \mathrm{eV}}{\varepsilon'_\gamma}\right)\ \mathrm{PeV}. \qquad (9.4)$$

  In particular, if one has a photon target in the UV/X-ray band, such as those around supermassive black holes, with typical energies $\varepsilon' \sim 0.1\,\mathrm{keV}$, the neutrinos produced will be very suppressed below an energy of about 100 TeV, while the fluxes produced by the pp mechanism can instead extend down to much lower energies with no suppression, as is apparent in Fig. 9.3.

- In the case of the $p\gamma$ mechanism, the resulting neutrino (and very-high-energy gamma ray) spectra will reflect to a large extent the shape of the spectrum of the target photons. Instead, a characteristic feature of the pp mechanism is that the secondary particle spectra will follow closely the distribution of the primary protons, as was discussed before. In particular, if the cosmic rays are power-law distributed, in a pp scenario also the neutrinos and the very-high-energy gamma rays produced at the source will have a distribution close to a power law, with almost the same slope.

Other differences between the pp mechanism and $p\gamma$ mechanism concern the relative proportion of the neutrino and gamma ray fluxes, because one expects a larger amount of neutral pions, with respect to the charged pions, to be produced in the $p\gamma$ mechanism in comparison to the pp mechanism. In particular, if we consider only the pion production through the Δ resonance we would expect that $\text{BR}(p\gamma \to p\pi^0) = 2/3$ and $\text{BR}(p\gamma \to n\pi^+) = 1/3$, due to isospin selection rules. On the other hand, for the pp mechanism one has that, to a good approximation, the π^+, π^0 and π^- are all produced in similar amounts. Hence, the $(\pi^+ + \pi^-)/\pi^0$ ratio is about 0.5 for the $p\gamma$ mechanism when the Δ resonance dominates, while it is about 2 in the pp mechanism. Note however that in the $p\gamma$ mechanism at energies beyond the Δ resonance, for which the multipion production becomes relevant, this ratio increases and typically tends to become closer to unity.

Another difference between the two mechanisms concerns the production of electron antineutrinos, which might be detected through the W-resonance process in interactions with electrons. In the $p\gamma$ mechanism no $\bar{\nu}_e$ result from the decay chain of the positive pion, $\pi^+ \to \nu_\mu e^+ \nu_e \bar{\nu}_\mu$, that is produced at the Δ resonance. Electron antineutrinos could however reach us as a consequence of the oscillations of the $\bar{\nu}_\mu$ produced at the source, but in this case a relative shortage of $\bar{\nu}_e$ would still persist at the Earth in comparison with the neutrino flavors expected from the pp mechanism, for which $\bar{\nu}_e$ are produced via the π^- decays. Moreover, if the Δ resonance dominates the $p\gamma$ process the all flavor antineutrino fluxes will be $1/3$ of the total (neutrino plus antineutrino) fluxes, while for the pp process they amount to about half of the total fluxes. Electron antineutrinos may also be eventually produced at the sources via the $p\gamma$ mechanism at energies beyond that of the Δ resonance, through the contribution from multi-pion production, and this could make the ratio of neutrinos and antineutrinos more similar in both mechanisms. Note also that the $\bar{\nu}_e$ resulting from the decays of the neutrons produced in association with the pions have a much lower energy, of order $10^{-3} E_n$, than those from pion decays, and can hence be neglected.

If the magnetic fields are large in the region where pions are produced, typically for $B > 10^3$ G, the muons may lose a significant amount of their energy by synchrotron radiation before decaying. In this hypothetical case, above a certain critical energy the neutrino fluxes at the source will be dominated by the $\nu_\mu^{(1)}$ component from the direct pion decay, with the $\nu_\mu^{(2)}$ and ν_e neutrinos from the μ decay being strongly suppressed. This critical energy can be estimated equating the muon decay time, $t_{\text{dec}}^\mu = (E_\mu/m_\mu)\tau_\mu \simeq 20(E_\mu/\text{PeV})$ s, with the muon synchrotron loss time, $t_{\text{sync}}^\mu = (9/4)m_\mu^4/(e^4B^2E_\mu) \simeq 3 \times 10^7$ s/$[(B/\text{G})^2(E_\mu/\text{PeV})]$, and is $E_\mu \simeq \text{PeV}/(B/\text{kG})$, with the associated neutrino energy being a factor of about 3 smaller. These kind of scenarios, known as muon-damped sources, produce an almost pure muon flavor composition at the source, and could take place for instance above PeV energies if the magnetic fields in the interaction region are larger than few kG. At energies about 20 times larger, the pion themselves will lose their energy by synchrotron emission before they can decay, and hence a strong suppression in the total neutrino flux will result above the corresponding neutrino energies if the magnetic fields are strong. The neutrino spectrum in the pion-damped regime would become steeper by two extra powers of the energy, given that the fraction of the pions that decay before losing significant amounts of energy decreases as E^{-2}, until eventually the neutrinos from kaon decays would become the dominant ones [Ra98; Wa00; Ka05].

The non-observation of a strong suppression in the astrophysical neutrino fluxes starting at or below PeV energies hence suggests that in the pp scenarios the magnetic fields in the interaction region at the source are not much larger than a kG. In the case of the $p\gamma$ mechanism, which usually takes place in highly relativistic jets, accounting for the Lorentz boost Γ typically requires that the magnetic field in the shock rest frame should not exceed about $100\,\text{kG}(\Gamma/100)$ in order that the neutrino flux not be suppressed below observed energies of PeV. One should keep in mind however that the superposition of sources with different magnetic fields, or even the emission of neutrinos from different regions of a source having different magnetic field values, could soften the suppression effect in the observed neutrino fluxes associated to the muon and pion damped scenarios.

9.1.3 *Connection between neutrino and gamma-ray astronomies*

As discussed above, high-energy neutrinos and photons are both produced in cosmic-ray collisions. Let us denote K_π the ratio between charged and neutral pions produced in a CR collision, so that for instance $K_\pi \simeq 0.5$

for the $p\gamma$ process if the Δ resonance dominates, $K_\pi \simeq 1$ including the non-resonant channels while $K_\pi \simeq 2$ for the multipion production, which is the dominant process in particular for the pp mechanism and can also contribute sizeably to the $p\gamma$ mechanism at high energies. If the muons are not damped, so that the neutrino plus antineutrino flavor ratio at the source is approximately that from the pion-decay chain $(\nu_e : \nu_\mu : \nu_\tau) \simeq (1 : 2 : 0)$, one finds that the neutrino plus antineutrino source emissivity per flavor can be related to the photon emissivity as

$$\frac{1}{3}\sum_\alpha q_{\nu_\alpha}(E_\nu) \simeq q_{\pi^\pm}(4E_\nu)\frac{\mathrm{d}E_\pi}{\mathrm{d}E_\nu} \simeq 4K_\pi q_{\pi^0}(4E_\nu)$$

$$\simeq 2K_\pi q_\gamma(2E_\nu)\frac{\mathrm{d}E_\gamma}{\mathrm{d}E_\pi} \simeq K_\pi q_\gamma(2E_\nu). \tag{9.5}$$

This leads to a relation between the energies emitted in neutrinos and photons, per logarithmic energy interval, which reads

$$\frac{1}{3}\sum_\alpha \left[E_\nu^2 q_{\nu_\alpha}(E_\nu)\right] \simeq \frac{K_\pi}{4}\left[E_\gamma^2 q_\gamma(E_\gamma)\right]_{E_\gamma = 2E_\nu}. \tag{9.6}$$

Note also that, due to oscillations, the initial $(1 : 2 : 0)$ neutrino flavor ratio will be converted to an approximate $(1 : 1 : 1)$ value when the neutrinos arrive to the Earth.

The connection between neutrino and photon fluxes is useful, and in some cases it may be probed observationally, but one should keep in mind that gamma rays can also be produced by accelerated electrons via synchrotron and inverse Compton processes, without any associated neutrinos. In this case, the gamma rays are said to be of *leptonic* origin, in contrast with those produced in CR interactions which are said to be of *hadronic* origin. On the other hand, gamma rays can be readily absorbed if the target is thick, while neutrinos are not, and if this happens no direct relation between the neutrino and the gamma ray fluxes may be established.

Another important aspect is that the Universe becomes opaque to high-energy photons coming from far-away extragalactic sources. In fact, when photons travel to us they can produce e^+e^- pairs by interactions with the background photons of the CMB or with the extragalactic background light (EBL), producing electromagnetic showers that dissipate their energy by inverse Compton and pair production processes. This would produce an electromagnetic cascade down to energies below a TeV, for which the pair production process goes below threshold even for optical/UV target photons. Note that for background photons with energies ε_b, the high-energy gamma rays will be above the threshold of pair production for energies

$\varepsilon > m_e^2/\varepsilon_{\rm b} \simeq 0.26({\rm eV}/\varepsilon_{\rm b})\,{\rm TeV}$. The attenuation due to the pair production processes with the CMB background (for which $\varepsilon_{\rm b} \sim 10^{-3}\,{\rm eV}$) is then very pronounced for PeV photons, for which the attenuation length can be as small as few tens of kpc [Pr96]. On the other hand, the extragalactic background light of IR, optical and UV photons ($\varepsilon_{\rm b} \sim 0.01$ to $1\,{\rm eV}$) dominates the gamma-ray attenuation in the range below few hundred TeV, with the associated attenuation length becoming for instance of few hundred Mpc at TeV energies. For a given energy, the sources lying at distances larger than the corresponding photon attenuation length will contribute neutrinos but no photons at these energies. In particular, at PeV energies no photons can reach us from outside the Milky Way, and at TeV energies no photons can reach us from sources beyond few hundred Mpc. Only photons with much lower energies, resulting from the interaction of the high-energy photons and the subsequent cascading process, are observable, and hence the connection between the high-energy photon and neutrino fluxes becomes quite indirect. In particular, the overall diffuse fluxes of astrophysical neutrinos with energies between $\sim 10\,{\rm TeV}$ and $10\,{\rm PeV}$, whose sources are expected to be extragalactic and far away, can only be related to a contribution to the diffuse fluxes of gamma rays below few TeV (in a similar way as happens with the photons associated to the cosmogenic neutrinos, which are produced with EeV energies but show up at the Earth with energies below $10\,{\rm TeV}$, as was displayed in Fig. 9.2). On the other hand, this allows to use the upper bounds on the diffuse fluxes of GeV to TeV gamma rays obtained by the Fermi satellite to constrain the astrophysical neutrino fluxes below $100\,{\rm TeV}$, by comparing their associated photon production with the Fermi bounds on the diffuse radiation [Mu13]. These bounds apply if the high-energy neutrino sources are not opaque to photons, and lead to some tension with pp scenarios involving steep CR source spectra ($\alpha > 2.3$) extending well below $100\,{\rm TeV}$, since in this case a strong associated GeV to TeV photon flux would be expected but is not observed.

A very remarkable feature is that the overall power associated to the astrophysical neutrino flux observed by IceCube in the $10\,{\rm TeV}$ to $10\,{\rm PeV}$ range turns out to be comparable to that in gamma rays observed by the Fermi satellite in the GeV to TeV range, and also to that in CRs at energies above $1\,{\rm EeV}$, as is apparent in Fig. 9.2. This could suggest that some deep connection between them may be at work, although their similarity could also be just a chance coincidence.

Let us also note that for Galactic CR sources, such as the one that could be accelerating CRs to PeV energies near the supermassive black hole at the Galactic center [Ab16b] or the many sources being now observed by the LHAASO observatory [Ca21], the star light and the IR emission of the Galaxy itself can contribute to the attenuation of the high-energy gamma rays during their propagation to us [Ve16]. In particular, these attenuation effects have to be taken into account in order to relate the TeV–PeV gamma-ray emission that was observed from Galactic sources with the possible associated neutrino fluxes that could potentially be observed at neutrino telescopes if the photons are of hadronic origin [Mo06; Ce17]. In the case of Galactic CRs accelerated in sources within few kpc, such as nearby young supernova remnants, microquasars or X-ray binaries, the attenuation effects on the gamma rays should instead be negligible, and hence for these sources the connection between the gamma rays and neutrinos would be more direct.

Given that the regions where core collapse supernovae explode are in general sites of intense stellar formation activity, it often happens that they are surrounded by large amounts of target material that can lead to the production of gamma rays and neutrinos. This is the case for instance for the supernova remnant RX J1713.7-3946, which is just at 1 kpc from the Earth, making it a promising source of high-energy neutrinos. The maximum neutrino signal from this source can be predicted thanks to the gamma rays that have been observed with energies up to ~ 40 TeV with the HESS telescope. Since this source is in the southern hemisphere, at a declination of -39°, it could become observable for a neutrino detector in the northern hemisphere looking for up-going muons produced by neutrino interactions near the detector. If the observed gamma rays are of hadronic origin, one expects to observe from it of order one event per km^2 yr of exposure. More in general, for these kind of Galactic sources one may observe in a neutrino telescope a signal of this size as long as the γ-ray flux satisfies $I_\gamma(> 10 \text{ TeV}) > 10^{-13} \text{ cm}^{-2} \text{ s}^{-1}$, which may be achieved in only very few specific Galactic sources [Vi11; Ha17].

Besides the production of neutrinos in individual Galactic sources or in high-density molecular clouds, also a diffuse flux of neutrinos is expected from the CRs interacting with the gas present across the Galactic disk [St79; Be93]. In particular, the associated photon production from π^0 decays has been observed in the GeV range with satellites, and it should in principle extend up to at least several hundred TeV with a spectral slope comparable to that of the CRs. A similar emission in neutrinos from the charged pion decays should exist, and its flux may be detectable on top of the more isotropic atmospheric neutrino background, whose spectrum is steeper. In particular, the next generation of neutrino detectors, having areas in excess of a km^2, may have good chances of observing this diffuse flux. The expectations depend on the details of the CR composition changes above the knee energy [Ca03], on the possible hardening of the CR spectra or the enhancement of the CR density in the inner Galaxy regions, as well as on the actual profile of the Galactic gas density [Be93; Ca05; Ya16].

9.1.4   *Connection between neutrino and cosmic-ray fluxes*

Since the high-energy astrophysical neutrinos are expected to be produced in the interactions of cosmic-ray nuclei with target material at the sources, a relation between the neutrino fluxes and the CR fluxes is expected to hold. The neutrino fluxes should indeed be proportional to the CR emissivity of the sources and to the probability for the accelerated CRs to interact at their sources to produce neutrinos. This probability is proportional to the column density of the target material (either photons or gas) that the CRs traverse before exiting the source region. On the other hand, for the CR production to be efficient one expects that, at least at very-high energies, the sources should be *thin*, so that the chances for the CRs to escape the sources without being attenuated by interactions be significant. The maximum neutrino flux resulting from thin sources, known as the Waxman-Bahcall (WB) flux limit [Wa99; Wa01], is obtained when the probability for the accelerated CRs to interact at the sources is set to unity, and considering that the same sources are also the ones responsible for the observed CR flux at the highest energies. This flux level has been used as a guide to estimate the astrophysical neutrino fluxes that could be explored with neutrino observatories, such as IceCube. Remarkably, the fluxes of astrophysical neutrinos that were observed [Aa14; Aa16; Ab21] are not far from the WB neutrino flux bound, which is roughly at the level of $E_\nu^2 d\Phi_\nu/dE_\nu \leq 10^{-8}\,\mathrm{GeV\,cm^{-2}s^{-1}sr^{-1}}$. This suggested that the CRs producing the astrophysical neutrinos in the 100 TeV to few PeV range had indeed a high probability to interact with target material while exiting their sources.

The original derivation of the WB flux level was obtained considering that most of the CRs above 10 EeV were protons of extragalactic origin, and using the observed fluxes above those energies to normalize the associated CR production rate (taking also into account the attenuation of the proton fluxes due to the interactions with the CMB to infer the CR source emissivities). This rate was then extrapolated to lower energies assuming a constant energy production per logarithmic bin, as results from the E^{-2} spectrum expected from diffusive shock acceleration. It was these extrapolated CR emissivities at energies below $100\,\text{PeV}$ which were assumed to be responsible for the production of the astrophysical neutrinos, leading to the flux level quoted above. This computation also assumed that below the spectral ankle feature at $\sim 5\,\text{EeV}$, the observed CRs were predominantly of Galactic origin [Wa99] (or eventually considering that below the ankle the extragalactic protons contributed at most about 10% of the observed CR flux [Wa01]). However, some of these hypothesis are now known to be not valid. In particular, the measurements obtained with the Pierre Auger Observatory suggest that the CR composition becomes increasingly heavier above the ankle, and do not support the presence of a significant component of protons above $5\,\text{EeV}$ [Aa17], what is in tension with the assumption underlying the WB limit. On the other hand, the Galactic component may well fade away just above the second knee, and hence the presence of an extragalactic component dominating the CR flux above $0.1\,\text{EeV}$ is quite likely [Mo19]. We note that the extragalactic component dominating the flux below a few EeV, which is the one relevant for the production of the astrophysical neutrinos below $10\,\text{PeV}$, may arise from a different source population than the one dominating the flux at energies above the ankle, and hence to use the latter to normalize the flux of the lower energy extragalactic component may not be justified. Taking these facts into account, the detailed computation of the neutrino fluxes being produced in scenarios in which the observed CR fluxes down to the second knee of the spectrum are predominantly of extragalactic origin shows that the level of neutrino fluxes observed are actually consistent with them being produced in sources which are thin to the escaping CRs [Ro21c]. This implies that only a small fraction of the CRs (of order 1 to 10%, depending on the actual extragalactic source emissivities) are required to interact in their way out of the sources in order to produce the observed neutrino fluxes.

One has to also keep in mind that there may be some sources of neutrinos from which the CRs cannot exit at all, in particular if the target material is so dense that the CRs get strongly attenuated. The neutrino fluxes from those *hidden* sources would not be directly constrained by the observed CR fluxes, which would then need to be produced in other types of sources.

9.2   The search for the astrophysical neutrinos

Huge efforts have been made over the last decades to try to observe the small flux of high-energy astrophysical neutrinos. Note that typical expectations for the level of these fluxes in the 100 TeV to 10 PeV range, as could result for instance from GRBs or AGNs, is that the flux per flavor could be in the ballpark of

$$E_\nu^2 \frac{d\Phi_\nu}{dE_\nu} \simeq 10^{-8} \frac{\text{GeV}}{\text{cm}^2 \, \text{s} \, \text{sr}}, \qquad (9.7)$$

which by the way coincides with the WB bound discussed above. Equivalently, this flux can be expressed as

$$\frac{d\Phi_\nu}{d \ln E_\nu} \simeq \frac{\text{PeV}}{E_\nu} \frac{3 \times 10^3}{\text{km}^2 \, \text{yr} \, \text{sr}}. \qquad (9.8)$$

This kind of fluxes would exceed the atmospheric muon neutrino fluxes above about 100 TeV, and exceed the atmospheric ν_e fluxes at somewhat smaller energies. Given that at PeV energies the neutrino nucleon interaction cross section is at the level of $\sigma_{\nu N} \simeq \text{nb} = 10^{-33} \, \text{cm}^2$, one has that the probability for a PeV neutrino to interact when crossing a nucleon column density N of one km of water is of order $P = N\sigma \simeq (1 \, \text{g} \, \text{cm}^{-3}) (N_A \, g^{-1}) \, 1 \, \text{km} \, \sigma_{\nu N} \simeq 6 \times 10^{-5}$. Hence, one could expect to observe a few to a few tens of neutrino events per year above 100 TeV in a km^3 detector sensitive to neutrinos from a significant fraction of the sky. Note that this crude estimate does not account for the actual energy dependence of the neutrino flux nor that of the neutrino nucleon cross section, for the fiducial volume of the detector in the analysis considered or the effective volume which is relevant when neutrinos interacting outside the detector can also be observed, nor for their attenuation in the Earth, etc. Anyway, this estimate gives a reasonable first order approximation, indicating that the size of the detector which is required to observe the astrophysical neutrino fluxes is in the kilometer scale.

At present, the IceCube observatory at the South Pole has reached the 1 km^3 scale, relying on the experience gained with the previous smaller Amanda detector. This large volume of clear ice, reaching a depth of 2.5 km, is instrumented with strings of photomultiplier tubes (PMTs) which can detect the Cherenkov light emitted by relativistic charged secondary particles produced in the neutrino interactions. This huge size has indeed allowed to discover and to start to study in some detail the astrophysical neutrinos. In the northern hemisphere, the Antares observatory in the Mediterranean and the giant volume detector (GVD) in the lake Baikal in Russia have been deployed over the last decades. Now, the ARCA detector, at a site near Sicily with a depth of 3,400 m, is aiming to reach the km^3 scale to be able to study the astrophysical neutrinos, while the ORCA detector, near France, aims to a smaller but more densely instrumented volume to study the oscillations of GeV atmospheric neutrinos.

Note that the deep ice is quite transparent, so that the long attenuation length allows to put the PMT strings at more than 100 m separation between themselves, but it has however a significant light scattering due to the presence of frozen micro-bubbles in it. On the other hand, the longer scattering length of deep ocean water allows a better timing of the signals and has hence some advantages for the reconstruction of the incoming neutrino directions, which could lead to an angular resolution improved by up to an order of magnitude with respect to the one achieved in the ice (and thus to an improvement by about two orders of magnitude in the solid angle relevant for the associated background when point sources are searched for).

The main background in the search for astrophysical neutrinos arises from the atmospheric neutrinos, which were discussed at length in Chapter 8. There is also a very large flux of atmospheric muons, which can still reach a depth of few km in water and which give rise to a rate of order 10^3 Hz in IceCube, compared to 10^{-3} Hz from atmospheric neutrinos and 10^{-6} Hz from astrophysical neutrinos. This requires to develop different strategies to discriminate these backgrounds, such as looking for the upgoing muon signals from below the horizon, which have no atmospheric muon background, to look at energies above tens of TeV for which the atmospheric neutrino fluxes get strongly suppressed (given that their spectrum is steeper than that of astrophysical neutrinos), look at the characteristics of different flavors of neutrinos, etc.

Note that at GeV energies the atmospheric neutrinos arise mostly from the pion decays, and their spectral slope is comparable to the CR spectral slope of $\gamma \simeq 2.7$. Beyond 100 GeV, the attenuation of the pions in the atmosphere leads to a neutrino spectral slope steeper by an extra power of E, so that their flux falls approximately as $E^{-3.7}$. This flux is largely dominated by the ν_μ flavor, given that the high-energy muons produced in the pion decays generally reach ground level and are slowed down before they decay, leading hence to a suppressed ν_e flux. At few TeV, the kaons give the main contribution to the atmospheric neutrino fluxes, and the ratio of ν_e to ν_μ fluxes is typically 1/30. At higher energies, above few tens of TeV for ν_e and few hundred TeV for ν_μ, the dominant contribution should come from the decays of charmed hadrons (such as D mesons or Λ_c baryons), which lead to comparable amounts of ν_e and ν_μ fluxes with a slope following that of the CR spectrum. It is just in this regime, in which the theoretical predictions for the atmospheric neutrino fluxes are more uncertain, that the astrophysical neutrino fluxes become actually dominant.

9.3   The event topologies

9.3.1   *The throughgoing muons*

The original method considered to search for high-energy neutrinos, already exploited with the first neutrino telescopes, is to search for throughgoing muons. These muons get produced by ν_μ or $\bar{\nu}_\mu$ interacting in the rock around the detector and they then pass through it. Given the large range of the muons at high energies, this enlarges considerably the effective volume of the detector with respect to the tracks starting inside the detector (which are of course also recorded, together with those stopping in it). The reconstruction of the rectilinear muon tracks allows to achieve a very good angular resolution for these events, typically better than one degree at TeV energies. However, only part of the muon track is reconstructed and, moreover, the cascade associated to the nuclear recoil in the first interaction (whose energy depends on the inelasticity of the process) is not registered, and hence the reconstruction of the neutrino energy is much more uncertain than when the process is fully contained inside the detector.

The muon energy loss in matter can be approximated as

$$\frac{\mathrm{d}E_\mu}{\mathrm{d}X} \simeq -\alpha - \beta E_\mu, \tag{9.9}$$

where $\mathrm{d}X \equiv \rho\,\mathrm{d}x$ is the matter column density traversed in a distance $\mathrm{d}x$. The coefficient $\alpha \simeq 2 \times 10^{-6}\,\mathrm{TeV\,cm^2\,g^{-1}}$ accounts for the fact that low-energy muons lose by ionization about $2\,\mathrm{MeV}$ per cm in water, behaving as minimum ionizing particles (MIPs). The second term, involving the parameter $\beta \simeq 4 \times 10^{-6}\,\mathrm{cm^2\,g^{-1}}$, accounts for the fact that at energies larger than a GeV the losses become *catastrophic*, due to the pair creation, bremsstrahlung and photo-nuclear interactions (which actually have a more stochastic nature than the almost continuous ionization losses). This implies that the distance d travelled by a muon with original energy E_μ until

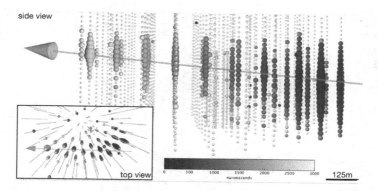

Fig. 9.5 Signals detected in the different PMTs of the IceCube detector, associated to a $\sim 300\,\mathrm{TeV}$ neutrino arriving from the direction of the blazar TXS 0506+056 (from [Aa18c]). The color scale indicates time, with bluer colors corresponding to earlier hits. The size of the circles depend on the detected signal in each PMT.

it reaches the threshold energy E_{th} is

$$d(E_\mu, E_{\mathrm{th}}) \approx D \times \ln\left(\frac{1 + E_\mu/\varepsilon}{1 + E_{\mathrm{th}}/\varepsilon}\right), \text{ with } \begin{cases} D = \dfrac{\rho_{\mathrm{ice}}}{\beta} \simeq 2 \text{ km} \\[2mm] \varepsilon = \dfrac{\alpha}{\beta} \simeq 0.5 \text{ TeV} \end{cases}. \qquad (9.10)$$

This shows that above TeV energies the muon range becomes larger than the km scale. Note that the throughgoing events are useful to search for neutrinos arriving from below the horizon, since otherwise the background from downgoing atmospheric muons can be very large. On the other hand, for energies above few tens of TeV the Earth becomes increasingly opaque to the neutrinos, and hence above few hundred TeV the sample of muon tracks relevant for the astrophysical neutrino studies gets restricted to those arriving from directions near or just slightly below the horizon [Ab21c].

An event of this kind is shown in Fig. 9.5. This specific event has been particularly important because, having an energy of about 300 TeV, it pointed towards the direction of the blazar TXS 0506+056, which was seen in gamma rays to be in a flaring state. This provided the first likely identification of a very-high-energy neutrino source [Aa18c].

9.3.2 The cascades

In the CC interaction of an electron or a tau neutrino, or in the NC interaction of any of the three neutrino flavors, one should observe instead a

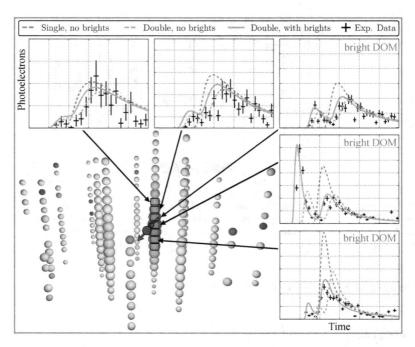

Fig. 9.6   Double-bang event due to the interaction of a ν_τ observed by IceCube (from [Ab20]). Reddish colors correspond to earlier hits.

much more localized signal resulting from the recoil of the nuclear target and of the shower generated by the outgoing electron or by the decay of the tau lepton. The energy of these showers gets deposited within a few meters in the water (or ice), with the associated light reaching a large number of PMTs around it, essentially in all directions. These kind of events are then named *cascades*. The energy of the original neutrino can be reconstructed reasonably well, modulo the inelasticity of the interaction in the NC events, or the energy carried away by the ν_τ in the decay of the tau lepton produced in the CC interaction of a tau neutrino. However, the angular resolution achieved, typically of about $10°$ in IceCube, is much poorer than that of the muon tracks discussed before.

9.3.3   *Double bangs and double pulses*

A particularly interesting case of cascades is that of the *double bangs* resulting when the two cascades produced by a ν_τ, i.e. that of the initial nuclear recoil and that from the subsequent tau decay products, get sufficiently separated so as to become distinguishable. This would allow to tag the tau neutrino flavor, what is especially interesting given that no significant ν_τ fluxes are expected from the atmospheric neutrino background while tau neutrinos are instead expected to appear in the astrophysical neutrino fluxes as a consequence of flavor oscillations. The decay length of a tau lepton is $L_\tau \simeq (E_\tau/\text{PeV})50\,\text{m}$, and hence the double-bang signature may be identified for ν_τ energies above few hundred TeV. Moreover, the detailed study of the time distribution of the pulses generated by the events in individual PMTs may allow to identify a *double pulse* signal even if the two cascades are separated by less than 10 m and cannot be resolved, allowing for the ν_τ identification down to energies of about 100 TeV. Figure 9.6 shows one of the first events of this kind detected by the IceCube observatory [Ab20].

9.3.4 *The starting events*

A special search performed by IceCube including events with different topologies is that of high-energy starting events (HESE) [Aa21b]. These are events, either tracks or cascades, which are produced inside an inner fiducial volume of the detector, with the outer part of it being used as a veto for the atmospheric muons as well as for the atmospheric neutrinos, since these last usually have also muons associated to the same atmospheric shower which arrive simultaneously. It has been indeed through the analysis of this kind of events that the first evidence in favor of the astrophysical neutrino fluxes was obtained.

Figure 9.7 shows a map, in Equatorial coordinates, of the arrival directions of the neutrinos detected by IceCube. It includes HESE events with energies above 30 TeV and throughgoing muon tracks with estimated energies above 200 TeV. The HESE events from tracks and cascades arrive preferentially from the southern hemisphere, given that at these energies there is a significant absorption by the Earth of the upgoing neutrinos (which are those arriving from the north). The throughgoing tracks are even more attenuated by the Earth, given the higher threshold energy considered, and to reduce background their arrival directions are restricted to be below the horizon (which for IceCube corresponds to being slightly above the Equator). Shades of blue indicate the absorption by the Earth for 100 TeV neutrinos, which screens about 90% of the original flux near the north pole. The arrival directions are broadly consistent with an isotropic distribution.

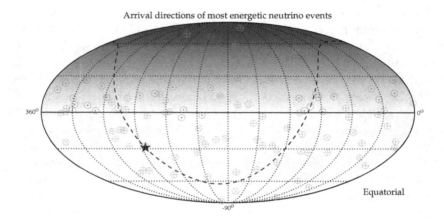

Fig. 9.7   Map of HESE events with deposited energy above 30 TeV ($\oplus$ are cascades while $\otimes$ are tracks) and troughgoing muon-track events with $E > 200$ TeV ($\odot$) detected by IceCube. The dashed line is the Galactic plane, with a star indicating the Galactic center location (courtesy of Markus Ahlers).

9.3.5   *The Glashow resonance*

A particular type of event is that produced by an electron antineutrino interacting with an atomic electron, a process which becomes resonant when an on-shell W boson gets produced. This happens for an energy

$$E_{\rm WR} = \frac{M_W^2}{2m_e} \simeq 6.3\,{\rm PeV}. \tag{9.11}$$

The produced W-boson decays into hadrons with a branching ratio of about 68%, and in this case all the energy of the initial neutrino gets deposited into the cascade. Note that although the cross section at the peak of the resonance is about 360 times larger than the CC neutrino nucleon cross section at the same energy, the resonance is narrow, having a width of $(\Gamma_W/M_W)E_{\rm WR} \simeq 0.17\,{\rm PeV}$. Also the number of electrons in the water is smaller than the number of nucleons ($n_e/n_N = 5/9$) and the resonant process only involves $\bar\nu_e$. If all flavors of neutrinos and antineutrinos were present in similar amounts, one expects from these considerations that about half of the events within 2.4 PeV of $E_{\rm WR}$ will be due to the Glashow resonance, while the resonance events would dominate the rate by an order of magnitude for energies within 10% of $E_{\rm WR}$. The discovery [Aa21] of one cascade event with a reconstructed energy of ~ 6 PeV has provided the first solid evidence for this kind of process, more than 50 years after its existence had been proposed [Gl60].

9.4 The measured astrophysical neutrino spectrum

The first results of IceCube showing the existence of astrophysical neutrinos concerned just a couple of HESE events with energies above 1 PeV. The HESE sample was then enlarged incorporating events down to 60 TeV (at a rate of about a dozen per year), including all flavors and from all directions [Aa21b]. Evidence for astrophysical neutrinos was later found in the dataset of throughgoing events from ν_μ upgoing neutrinos with energies above 40 TeV [Ab21c]. Also a sample of cascade events, dominated by ν_e and ν_τ flavors and with energies down to 17 TeV (exploiting the lower atmospheric backgrounds for these flavors) was used to infer the astrophysical neutrino spectrum [Aa20]. Astrophysical neutrino oscillations lead to expect that all classes of events have approximately the same spectrum, and the simplest assumption one can adopt to fit the results is the power-law distribution

$$\frac{\mathrm{d}\Phi_\nu}{\mathrm{d}E_\nu} = \Phi_{\mathrm{astro}} \left(\frac{E_\nu}{100\,\mathrm{TeV}} \right)^{-\gamma_{\mathrm{astro}}}. \qquad (9.12)$$

Remember that this is the approximate shape expected if the primary CRs are distributed as a power law and the pp mechanism for neutrino production applies, or it may approximately describe the spectrum just in a limited energy range if the production mechanism is different. The normalization obtained for the per flavor flux at 100 TeV from the different analyses performed is quite similar, of order $\Phi_{\mathrm{astro}} = (1.6$–$1.9) \times 10^{-18} \mathrm{GeV}^{-1}\,\mathrm{cm}^{-2}\mathrm{s}^{-1}\,\mathrm{sr}^{-1}$ (which is actually similar to the estimate adopted in Eq. (9.8)). However, the different analyses obtained different values for the power-law slope γ_{astro}, ranging from 2.89 ± 0.2 from the HESE sample, 2.53 ± 0.07 from the cascades and 2.28 ± 0.08 from the throughgoing muons. One has to keep in mind however that each analysis involves different energy ranges and different regions of the sky, that the accumulated statistics gathered up to now is still quite limited and that no sample is completely free from background contamination.

9.5 Neutrino attenuation by the Earth

Neutrinos coming from directions below the horizon traverse large amounts of terrestrial matter, and their flux may then be significantly attenuated

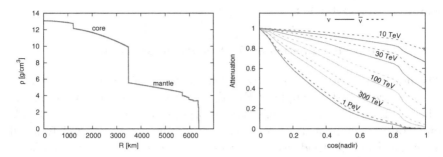

Fig. 9.8   Left panel: Earth density according to the PREM model. Right panel: neutrino (solid) and antineutrino (dashed) attenuation while crossing the Earth, as a function of the cosine of the nadir angle and for different neutrino energies.

by interactions if their energy is high enough, i.e. for $E \gg 10\,\mathrm{TeV}$, which is just the range relevant for the study of astrophysical neutrinos.

The neutrino flux reaching a detector from a given direction after accounting for the interactions in the Earth can be obtained by multiplying the original flux by the attenuation factor $A = \exp(-\sigma_{\mathrm{abs}}(E) \times N)$, with σ_{abs} being the interaction cross section with nucleons (from CC and NC) and N being the column density of nucleons along the direction of the incoming neutrinos. We have neglected here regeneration processes, such as those arising from the fact that in a NC interaction the scattered neutrino still contributes to the flux at lower energies, since given the steepness of the neutrino spectrum the impact of these effects turns out to be small. Similarly, in CC interactions the tau neutrinos produce a tau lepton, which may decay before loosing much energy to give rise to a lower energy ν_τ, whose contribution to the flux is small and may also be neglected if the spectrum is steep.

The column density traversed across the Earth by a neutrino incident with a nadir angle η is

$$N \simeq 2N_{\mathrm{A}} \int_0^{R_\oplus \cos\eta} \rho\left(\sqrt{x^2 + (R_\oplus \sin\eta)^2}\right) \mathrm{d}x, \qquad (9.13)$$

where $R_\oplus = 6371$ km is the average Earth radius, N_{A} is Avogadro's number, x is the coordinate along the neutrino path inside the Earth and we neglected for simplicity the depth of the observatory, which is just a few km at most. The Earth density ρ is usually described using the PREM model [Dz81], which accounts for the density changes across the crust, mantle and core of the Earth. This density profile is plotted in the left panel of Fig. 9.8.

In the right panel of the figure we show the resulting attenuation factor of the neutrino and antineutrino fluxes for different energies, as a function of the nadir angle. It is apparent that for energies above a few tens of TeV the attenuation of the neutrinos crossing the core of the Earth is quite significant, and at PeV energies it is almost complete, so that only neutrinos incident near the horizon or coming from the sky above the detector may be observed at the highest energies. This attenuation is indeed apparent in the map of arrival directions shown in Fig. 9.7.

The measurement of the flux of the atmospheric and astrophysical neutrinos as a function of the nadir angle has actually been used by the IceCube collaboration to determine the attenuation by the Earth, and in this way infer the average neutrino plus antineutrino cross section in the 10 TeV to PeV energy range [Ab21b]. These are energies well beyond those tested in accelerator experiments, and the inferred cross section turns out to be in broad agreement with the predictions of the Standard Model.

9.6 Effects of astrophysical neutrino oscillations and the flavor triangle

The phases appearing in the flavor oscillation probabilities associated to the propagation of the astrophysical neutrinos are quite large:

$$\varphi = \frac{\Delta m^2 \, L}{4E_\nu} = 2.8 \times 10^4 \, \frac{\Delta m^2}{7.4 \times 10^{-5} \, \mathrm{eV}^2} \, \frac{100 \, \mathrm{TeV}}{E_\nu} \, \frac{L}{\mathrm{pc}}, \qquad (9.14)$$

with L being the distance traveled, which would be of order 1 to 10 kpc for Galactic sources and larger than a Mpc for extragalactic sources. This means that for sure flavor oscillations affect the neutrinos propagating over cosmic distances. Moreover, the probabilities for the neutrino flavor to change, considering that the detection is performed in finite energy bins, that neutrinos arrive from sources at different distances and also due to the quantum decoherence of the flavor states into an incoherent superposition of mass eigenstates during their propagation, will be given by the averaged oscillations expression

$$P_{\ell \to \ell'} = \sum_{i=1}^{3} |U_{\ell i}^2| \, |U_{\ell' i}^2|. \qquad (9.15)$$

Using the present best fit values of the mixing angles from Table 4.1, the resulting approximate values of the oscillation probabilities (for the NO

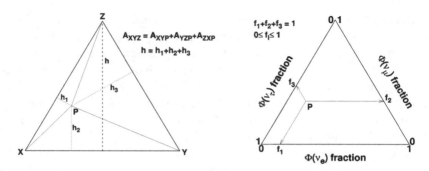

Fig. 9.9   Illustration of Viviani's theorem (left panel) and of the usage of the triangular plot for the flavor fractions, which are obtained as shown in the right panel.

case) are

$$\text{matrix}(P_{\ell \to \ell'}) \simeq \begin{pmatrix} 0.552 & 0.226 & 0.222 \\ 0.226 & 0.395 & 0.379 \\ 0.222 & 0.379 & 0.399 \end{pmatrix} \text{ with } \ell, \ell' = e, \mu, \tau. \qquad (9.16)$$

Many neutrino properties related to their flavor content can be represented by means of an equilateral triangle. This makes use of Viviani's theorem, which states that for any point inside an equilateral triangle the sum of the distances from the point to the three sides is a constant. To prove this theorem, consider an equilateral triangle whose sides have length a and height $h = a\sqrt{3}/2$, being its area $A = ah/2$. If we take any point P internal to the triangle and join it to the three vertices, we delimit in this way three triangles with corresponding heights h_1, h_2 and h_3 (see left panel of Fig. 9.9). The sum of their areas, $A_1 + A_2 + A_3 = a(h_1 + h_2 + h_3)/2$, equals the total area A, and thus the sum of the heights satisfies $h_1 + h_2 + h_3 = h$. Note that the fractions $f_i \equiv h_i/h$, with $0 \le f_i \le 1$, can be easily identified in a triangle with $a = 1$ by projecting the point P up to one of the sides along a line parallel to the base of the corresponding triangle (see right panel of the figure). One has then that for all points inside the triangle the relation $\sum f_i = 1$ should hold. These fractions are then said to form a triad. The theorem may also be generalized for a point external to the triangle if one considers heights with negative sign.

This theorem has been widely used in particle physics to visualize various quantities. In particular, one can exploit it to display the allowed regions of the Mandelstam variables (with signs) in a $2 \to 2$ scattering reaction, which satisfy

$$s + t + u = \sum_{i=1}^{4} m_i^2. \tag{9.17}$$

The same theorem has also several applications in neutrino physics. For instance, it was used [Fo95] to display the regions compatible with the observations on the mixing elements of mass states in the electron neutrino ν_e, or the flavor composition of the mass state ν_3 that dominates the atmospheric neutrino oscillation, exploiting the unitarity constraints

$$\sum_{i=1,2,3} |U_{ei}^2| = 1 \text{ or } \sum_{\ell=e,\mu,\tau} |U_{\ell 3}^2| = 1. \tag{9.18}$$

It is also possible to use it to depict the minimum value of the parameter $m_{\beta\beta}$ which is probed in the neutrinoless double-beta decay [Vi99].

This representation is particularly useful to describe the flavor content of the astrophysical neutrinos, referring to it in this case as the *flavor triangle*. The probabilities of averaged neutrino oscillations satisfy the constraint

$$\sum_{\ell'=e,\mu,\tau} P_{\ell\to\ell'} = 1, \tag{9.19}$$

and the flux fractions $f_\ell \equiv \Phi_\ell/\Phi_{\text{tot}}$ of the different flavors of astrophysical neutrinos, either at the sources (f^0) or at the Earth after oscillations (f), can be displayed in a triangle exploiting that [At00]

$$\sum_{\ell=e,\mu,\tau} f_\ell^{\,0} = 1 \text{ or } \sum_{\ell=e,\mu,\tau} f_\ell = 1. \tag{9.20}$$

In this case, the fluxes Φ_ℓ include the sum of neutrinos and antineutrinos, and one considers that they all have, up to a normalization factor, the same energy distribution, so that the flavor ratios are independent of energy.

To get acquainted with the usage of this triangle, let us examine the expectations for the flavor fraction in different scenarios. Given the initial flavor fraction (at the source) f_ℓ^0, one calculates the final flavor fraction at Earth as,

$$f_\ell = \sum_{\ell'=e,\mu,\tau} P_{\ell\to\ell'}\, f_{\ell'}^0. \tag{9.21}$$

The associated points in the flavor triangle can be identified using the mapping into the Cartesian plane, considering as origin the leftmost vertex with $f_e = f_\mu = 0$ and using that $x = f_e + f_\mu \sin 30°$ and $y = f_\mu \cos 30°$. A reasonable condition on the neutrino production mechanism is that the ν_τ component at the source is negligible, corresponding to $f_\tau^0 = 0$. This would

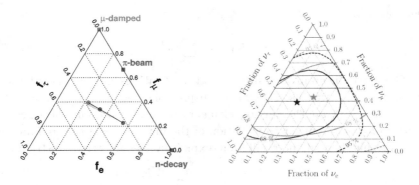

Fig. 9.10   Left panel: flavor fractions for the μ-damped, π-decay and n-decay scenarios (squares are fractions at the source, circles those at the Earth). The best fit neutrino mixing parameters are adopted. The line is obtained in the absence of tau neutrinos at the production and with generic values of f_e^0, while the narrow gray triangle encloses the most general case. Right panel: constraints on the flavor fractions obtained in two analyses by the IceCube collaboration [Ab20].

correspond to considering the initial neutrino flavor along the right edge of the triangle associated to the source fractions (see left panel of Fig. 9.10).

A specific example of neutrino production scenario is that of the pion decay chain, with original flavor ratios $(1 : 2 : 0)$, corresponding to fractions $(f_e^0 : f_\mu^0 : f_\tau^0) = (1/3 : 2/3 : 0)$, which are transformed by oscillations into a ratio at the Earth of about $(0.335 : 0.339 : 0.326)$, which by the way is not very different from the usual assumption that all flavors have similar fluxes.[2] Another possible scenario is the one in which the muons get damped at the sources, for which the source ratio $(0 : 1 : 0)$ gets mapped into $(0.226 : 0.395 : 0.379)$. In the case of sources in which the neutron decay is the main source of neutrinos, such as in the case in which there is a strong photodisintegration of heavy nuclei and a negligible pion production, the initial ratio of $(1 : 0 : 0)$ gets mapped into $(0.552 : 0.226 : 0.222)$. These different cases are illustrated in the left panel of Fig. 9.10, where the squares along the right edge indicate the fractions at the sources while the circles inside the triangle are the corresponding fractions at the Earth.

The more general case of a source fraction of the form $(f_e^0 : 1 - f_e^0 : 0)$

---

[2]For the effects of including non-pionic channels, see e.g. [Vi08].

would correspond, after oscillations, to fractions at the Earth given by

$$f_e = P_{e\mu} + (P_{ee} - P_{e\mu})f_e^0 \simeq 0.226 + 0.325 f_e^0,$$
$$f_\mu = P_{\mu\mu} + (P_{\mu e} - P_{\mu\mu})f_e^0 \simeq 0.395 - 0.169 f_e^0, \qquad (9.22)$$
$$f_\tau = P_{\tau\mu} + (P_{\tau e} - P_{\tau\mu})f_e^0 \simeq 0.379 - 0.157 f_e^0.$$

Note that the associated locations in the flavor triangle should lie along the segment joining the muon-damped and neutron decay cases depicted in the figure. In a more general hypothetical (and non-realistic) case in which the ν_τ fraction at the source is allowed to be sizeable, one anyway has that the final flavor fractions will lie inside the very narrow gray triangle that is also indicated in the figure. The vertices of this triangle are obtained from the fractions resulting from the propagation of the three vertices of the original triangle at the sources, i.e. the flavor admixtures corresponding to $(f_e^0 : f_\mu^0 : f_\tau^0) = (1 : 0 : 0)$ of the neutron decay sources, $(0 : 1 : 0)$ of the muon-damped sources, and $(0 : 0 : 1)$ of a pure ν_τ source (this last being mapped to $(f_e : f_\mu : f_\tau) \simeq (0.221 : 0.379 : 0.399)$). One can also appreciate that, even in the absence of a ν_τ component at the source, the fraction of ν_τ at the Earth turns out to be quite similar to that of ν_μ. Indeed, both become identical in the limit of $\theta_{13} \simeq 0$ and $\theta_{23} \simeq 45°$. Let us also mention that, due to the experimental uncertainties of the measured mixing angles, the predictions for the final flavor fractions have actually some spread around those depicted in the figure, which considered for simplicity just the present central values of the mixing angles.

The right panel of Fig. 9.10 shows the observational constraints obtained by the IceCube collaboration through the study of different event topologies (tracks, cascades and double pulses) [Ab20]. These results are consistent with all the possibilities, but in the long term one should be able, with more statistics and improved analyses, to better discriminate between the different scenarios.

9.7 Other searches and outlook

Many other searches of high-energy neutrinos have been performed. In particular, the cosmogenic neutrinos, with energies above a PeV and up to 10 EeV, have been searched by IceCube looking for extremely high energy neutrinos, either tracks or cascades, that could contribute on top of the astrophysical 'background' [Aa18b]. Also the Auger Observatory has searched for these energetic neutrinos, with the best sensitivity being achieved at energies close to few EeV, by looking for Earth skimming tau neutrinos producing tau leptons while interacting in the Earth crust, which could then produce an observable horizontal shower if these tau leptons exit from ground and decay in the atmosphere near the detector [Aa19]. None of these searches obtained positive results, and the bounds derived just start to constrain models in which CRs are predominantly protons up to the highest energies and their sources have a strong cosmological evolution. More realistic models in which the CR composition becomes heavier beyond the ankle predict however significantly smaller fluxes, as was illustrated in Fig. 9.2.

Another interesting recent search performed by IceCube, Antares and Auger [Al17] has been to look for very-high-energy neutrinos in coincidence with the neutron star merger detected in gravitational waves by the LIGO-Virgo Collaborations (and also observed in electromagnetic radiation by many other experiments). No neutrinos were detected in this case, and the constraints derived are not very far from some optimistic model predictions for the case in which the jet produced in this relatively nearby merger would have been pointing towards us, which was however not the case. The future observation of neutrinos in association with gravitational waves would certainly be an important milestone in multimessenger astronomy.

The field of very-high energy neutrino astronomy, which is just at its dawn at present, is expected to be significantly boosted by the detectors coming online, such as ARCA and GVD, and later on with the construction of new detectors, such as the IceCube Gen-2 (with an order of magnitude larger volume) [Aa21c], the proposed Pacific Ocean Neutrino Experiment in the ocean just west of Canada (P-ONE, with a size of several km^3) [Ag20e], and the giant radio array GRAND (covering an area of order $10^5\,km^2$) [Al20]. One hence expects that in this way we will be able to further address the many remaining open issues in the near future.

Suggested exercises:

- Demonstrate that for the energy of interest for astrophysical neutrinos the atmospheric neutrinos do not oscillate, neither in vacuum nor in matter. Are there direct channels for the production of tau neutrinos? If yes, try to estimate their relative contribution to the atmospheric neutrino flux.

- Quantify the effect of uncertainties in the parameter θ_{23} and in the CP violating phase δ on the oscillation probabilities of cosmic neutrinos. Discuss whether it is realistic to imagine the possibility of probing these parameter values by measuring precisely cosmic neutrino fluxes.

- The isospin of the nucleon doublet (p, n) is $1/2$, that of the pion triplet (π^+, π^0, π^-) is 1 and that of the delta multiplet $(\Delta^{++}, \Delta^+, \Delta^0, \Delta^-)$ is $3/2$. Calculate the ratio $\langle \pi^+ n | H_s | \Delta^+ \rangle / \langle \pi^0 p | H_s | \Delta^+ \rangle$, where H_s is the strong Hamiltonian responsible for the decay of the Δ, which is invariant under isospin transformations. Hint: compare the isospin Clebsch-Gordan coefficients appearing in the matrix element of each process.

Chapter 10

Neutrinos in Cosmology

Neutrinos are being continuously produced in a wide variety of astrophysical environments, such as from the Earth radioactivity, the beta processes associated to nuclear fusion reactions in stars and the strong thermal production in the late stages of stellar evolution, with the supernova explosions providing the spectacular emission associated to the final stellar collapses. Neutrinos are also produced through the interactions of high-energy cosmic rays with background radiation or gas present around their sources, during their propagation through intergalactic space or in the atmosphere of the Earth. In addition to all these different sources of astrophysical neutrinos, neutrinos were also abundantly produced in the early hot stages of the Universe, remaining today as a remnant background somewhat analogous to the CMB photons. These are the lowest energy neutrinos known to exist, and although we have verified their existence in various ways, we have not yet been able to detect them directly in the laboratory. These cosmic neutrinos played a relevant role in many different processes, as will be discussed in the present chapter, and they allow us to make important and unique inferences about the Universe.

10.1   The neutrino decoupling

When the Universe was younger than a second, having temperatures higher than an MeV, neutrinos were in equilibrium via pair annihilations with electrons and positrons, which in turn were in equilibrium with photons. The distribution of the particles which were in equilibrium in the hot primeval plasma at temperature T was given by the Fermi-Dirac (for fermions) or Bose-Einstein (for bosons) distributions, with the energy density of a species

i being

$$\rho_{\rm F,B} = g_i \int \frac{{\rm d}^3 p}{(2\pi)^3} \frac{E}{\exp(E/T) \pm 1}, \qquad (10.1)$$

with $E^2 = p^2 + m^2$ and g_i being the associated number of degrees of freedom. Considering the relativistic limit, one has that

$$\rho_\gamma = g_\gamma \frac{\pi^2}{30} T^4 \quad \text{and} \quad \rho_\nu = \frac{7}{8} g_\nu \frac{\pi^2}{30} T^4, \qquad (10.2)$$

where $g_\gamma = 2$ accounts for the two photon polarisations while $g_\nu = 2 N_\nu$ considering that $N_\nu = 3$ families of left-handed neutrinos and right-handed antineutrinos were in equilibrium through weak interactions. A similar expression holds for electrons, with $g_e = 4$ given that in this case the four components of the Dirac fermion were in equilibrium. This leads to the general expression

$$\rho = g_* \frac{\pi^2}{30} T^4, \qquad (10.3)$$

with

$$g_* \equiv \sum_B g_i + \sum_F \frac{7}{8} g_i \qquad (10.4)$$

being the effective number of relativistic degrees of freedom in equilibrium.

At $T \sim$ MeV the weak interactions became however no longer effective to change the number of neutrinos, so that those neutrinos of cosmic origin decoupled from the rest of the plasma and still remain around us today. The temperature $T_{\rm d}$ at which the decoupling took place can be obtained by equating the neutrino interaction rate $\Gamma \sim G_{\rm F}^2 T^5$ with the Hubble expansion rate $H = \sqrt{8\pi G_{\rm N}\rho/3}$, with Newton's constant being $G_{\rm N} \propto M_{\rm Pl}^{-2}$. This gives $T_{\rm d} \simeq (g_*/G_F^4 M_{\rm Pl}^2)^{1/6}$, and including the exact numerical factors it corresponds to about $2\,{\rm MeV}$ for the electron neutrino flavor and about $3\,{\rm MeV}$ for the less interacting muon and tau neutrino flavors (which just couple through NC at these energies). Note that there are also beta processes with the much smaller amount of neutrons and protons present, such as $p + e \Longleftrightarrow n + \nu_e$, which remain in equilibrium down to $T \simeq 0.8\,{\rm MeV}$.

Slightly after the neutrino decoupling, at $T \simeq m_e \simeq 0.5\,{\rm MeV}$, the electrons became non-relativistic and their annihilation into photons was no longer compensated by the inverse process of pair creation. Hence, all electron-positron pairs essentially disappeared into radiation, effectively increasing the temperature of the photons in relation to that of the neutrinos. One can obtain the relation between these temperatures exploiting that the

Universe expands adiabatically, and hence the entropy that was initially into the photons and electrons, which were at the same temperature as the neutrinos, T_ν, was transferred just to the photons which acquired a temperature T_γ (this is the so-called instantaneous reheating approximation, but actually the photons just cooled down more slowly than the neutrinos, leading to the same final relation between these temperatures). The entropy density is $s = (P + \rho)/T$, where for a relativistic gas the pressure is $P \simeq \rho/3$, and hence one gets that

$$s = g_s \frac{2\pi^2}{45} T^3 \quad , \text{ with } \quad g_s \equiv \sum_B g_i \left(\frac{T_i}{T} \right)^3 + \sum_F \frac{7}{8} g_i \left(\frac{T_i}{T} \right)^3 , \qquad (10.5)$$

where we allowed for decoupled species to be at different temperatures T_i. Equating the entropy of the original photons and electron-positron pairs to that of the 'reheated photons', one gets

$$\left(2 + \frac{7}{8} 4 \right) T_\nu^3 = 2 T_\gamma^3 \Rightarrow T_\nu = \left(\frac{4}{11} \right)^{1/3} T_\gamma. \qquad (10.6)$$

This relation is still valid up to the present times, and since we know that by now the CMB temperature is $T_{\rm CMB} = 2.725$K, this implies that the cosmic neutrino background (CνB) present temperature is $T_{\rm C\nu B} \simeq 1.945$K $\simeq 0.17$ meV. The different flavors of neutrinos were initially in equal proportions, and today they will be equally distributed among the different mass eigenstates i. Let us note that there is actually a slight residual reheating of the neutrinos when electrons and positrons annihilate,[1] and this translates into the fact that the precise ratio between the neutrino and photon energy densities after the reheating is

$$\frac{\rho_\nu}{\rho_\gamma} = \frac{7}{8} N_{\rm eff} \left(\frac{4}{11} \right)^{4/3} , \qquad (10.7)$$

with the effective number of degrees of freedom associated to the neutrinos being slightly larger than three, with $N_{\rm eff} \simeq 3.045$ [Do92; Sa16].

The meaning of the neutrino temperature is that it describes the momentum distribution at different times, with the density of each type of neutrino (or antineutrino) being

$$\frac{{\rm d}n_\nu}{{\rm d}p} = \frac{p^2}{2\pi^2} \frac{1}{\exp(p/T_\nu) + 1}. \qquad (10.8)$$

The redshifting of the momenta of relativistic particles due to the expansion of the Universe just preserves the form of this distribution, with the

---

[1]Given the strong energy dependence of the weak cross sections, these additional neutrinos are actually enhanced at high energies with respect to a thermal distribution.

temperature being scaled as $T_\nu = (1 + z)T_{C\nu B}$ in terms of the redshift z. Upon integration one obtains $n_\nu = 0.75(\zeta(3)/\pi^2)T_\nu^3$ for each helicity degree of freedom. The present density of neutrinos plus antineutrinos for each mass eigenstate is hence $n_{\nu_i} + n_{\bar{\nu}_i} = 112\,\mathrm{cm}^{-3}$, which summed over the three species is not very different from the CMB photon density of about $410\,\mathrm{cm}^{-3}$.

It has to be noted that the distribution of massive neutrinos as a function of the energy changes as soon as they become non-relativistic, i.e. when their average momentum $\langle p \rangle = 3.15\,T_\nu$ becomes smaller than their masses. This happens for redshifts $z < (m_{\nu_i}/(3.15\,T_{C\nu B})) - 1 \simeq 188(m_{\nu_i}/0.1\,\mathrm{eV})$. Using that $\mathrm{d}E/\mathrm{d}p = p/E$, one has that

$$\frac{\mathrm{d}n_{\nu_i}}{\mathrm{d}E} = \frac{E\sqrt{E^2 - m_i^2}}{2\pi^2} \frac{1}{\exp(\sqrt{E^2 - m_i^2}/T_\nu) + 1}. \tag{10.9}$$

In addition, massive neutrinos may at present be slightly clustered around galaxies, what may distort their momentum distribution and enhance their densities around large-scale structures, but this effect is expected to be small if $m_{\nu_i} < 0.1\,\mathrm{eV}$ [Ri04].

Another interesting aspect of the neutrino background is that in the early universe what get produced are the active species of left-handed neutrinos and right-handed antineutrinos of each flavor. As long as neutrinos are relativistic, these chiralities are equivalent to the corresponding helicities, and these last are preserved in the neutrino propagation (neglecting minor effects from gravitational clustering around large-scale structures). When neutrinos become non-relativistic, each helicity state will have essentially equal proportions of both chiralities, and hence a fundamental difference appears between the Majorana and Dirac neutrino cases. In the first case, both chiralities will correspond to active states under the weak interactions (left-handed neutrinos and right-handed antineutrinos, both being just the two different components of the Majorana neutrino). On the other hand, for the Dirac case half of the chirality states (right-handed neutrino and left-handed antineutrino) will not feel the weak interactions. This difference is relevant in the attempts to detect the relic background of neutrinos, since half of the neutrino background would be completely undetectable in the Dirac case.

In particular, the more realistic approach to achieve their detection was proposed long ago by Weinberg [We62], and consists of using as target unstable beta decaying nuclei, which can capture the very low-energy neutrinos from the background in an exothermic process, without having an

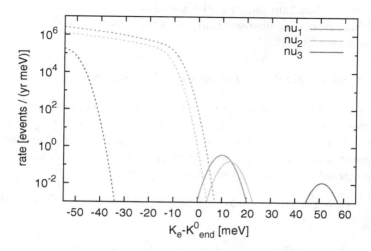

Fig. 10.1 Spectra of the electrons emitted by the capture of the CνB neutrinos, considering a target of 100 g of tritium. The dotted lines indicate the three components of the beta decay spectrum. The solid lines indicate the three components of the cosmic neutrino capture spectrum, assuming an energy resolution of 7 meV, for the case of normal ordering and a lighter neutrino mass of $m_1 = 10$ meV (from [Ro18]).

energy threshold. The electron emitted after the capture of the neutrino from the background will have an energy slightly above the endpoint of the normal beta decay spectrum of that nucleus, by an amount of about $2m_{\nu_i}$ if the neutrino is non-relativistic. On the other hand, the capture of each mass eigenstate will be proportional to $|U_{ei}|^2$, so that actually three different peaks with different strengths would be expected in the beta spectrum. The overall amplitude of the peaks will be proportional to the associated matrix element and to the neutrino relic density, and a factor of 1/2 will appear in the Dirac neutrino case due to the population of the sterile states [Co07; Lo14]. An ongoing attempt towards the relic neutrino detection is the PTOLEMY experiment at the Gran Sasso [Be19], aiming to use tritium as target nucleus, which has a half-life of 12.3 yr and a relatively low Q-value of 18.6 keV. The two most challenging issues that a future experiment will have to address are to achieve a target mass guaranteeing a reasonable number of observed events (e.g., 100 g of tritium corresponds to about 8 events per year at most) and to reach a sufficiently small energy resolution so as to be able to discern the tiny neutrino capture signal from the much larger beta decay background near the endpoint, as is illustrated in Fig. 10.1. Quantum uncertainties associated to the substrate on which the tritium atoms are deposited may also have an effect on the resolution of the detector [Ap22].

10.2 Cosmological bounds on neutrino masses

Given the non-vanishing neutrino mass squared differences inferred from oscillations, with $m_{\text{atm}} \equiv \sqrt{|\Delta m_{32}^2|} \simeq 50\,\text{meV}$ and $m_{\text{sol}} \equiv \sqrt{|\Delta m_{21}^2|} \simeq 8.6\,\text{meV}$, we see that even if one neutrino were massless the other two mass eigenstates would be non-relativistic at present. For the normal ordering case, one would have in general the mass spectrum

$$m_1 \quad , \quad m_2 = \sqrt{m_1^2 + m_{\text{sol}}^2} \quad , \quad m_3 = \sqrt{m_2^2 + m_{\text{atm}}^2} \quad \text{(NO)}, \quad (10.10)$$

so that

$$\sum_i m_i > m_{\text{sol}} + \sqrt{m_{\text{sol}}^2 + m_{\text{atm}}^2} \simeq 59\,\text{meV} \quad \text{(NO)}. \quad (10.11)$$

On the other hand, for the inverted ordering case the neutrino masses, ordered by increasing values, would be

$$m_3 \quad , \quad m_1 = \sqrt{m_3^2 + m_{\text{atm}}^2 - m_{\text{sol}}^2} \quad , \quad m_2 = \sqrt{m_3^2 + m_{\text{atm}}^2} \quad \text{(IO)}, \quad (10.12)$$

so that

$$\sum_i m_i > \sqrt{m_{\text{atm}}^2 - m_{\text{sol}}^2} + m_{\text{atm}} \simeq 99\,\text{meV} \quad \text{(IO)}. \quad (10.13)$$

Given the large number of relic neutrinos permeating the whole Universe, their contribution to the mass budget of the Universe turns out to be non-negligible. In particular, their density normalized to the critical density is

$$\Omega_\nu \equiv \frac{\rho_\nu}{\rho_c} \simeq 2 \times 10^{-3} \frac{\sum_i m_i}{100\,\text{meV}}, \quad (10.14)$$

where $\rho_c \equiv 3H^2/(8\pi G_N) \simeq 5\,\text{keV}\,\text{cm}^{-3}$ is the total energy density that would be required to have a flat Universe (i.e., such that $\Omega_{\text{tot}} = 1$). For comparison, the baryons contribute $\Omega_b \simeq 0.05$, the dark matter $\Omega_{\text{DM}} \simeq 0.26$ and the dark energy $\Omega_\Lambda \simeq 0.69$, so that the neutrinos contribute at least a few percent of what is contributed by the baryons.

The contribution of massive neutrinos to the cosmological density has some subtle relevant effects on the structure formation and on the expansion history, which can be used to set stringent bounds on the sum of their masses. Note that although the cosmology is not sensitive to the neutrino mixing angles nor to the individual masses, obtaining an upper bound on the sum of the masses below about $0.1\,\mathrm{eV}$ could already exclude the inverted ordering case, and a positive determination of the total neutrino masses, when combined with the known mass squared differences, would provide a measure of the individual neutrino masses.

A very important moment in the history of the Universe is the recombination time, corresponding to a temperature of about $0.3\,\mathrm{eV}$ (redshift $z_{\mathrm{rec}} \simeq 1100$), which is when electrons bind to protons to form neutral hydrogen. After this moment light can travel unhindered and the Universe becomes transparent. Neutrinos will be relativistic at the recombination time if they have masses smaller than $0.5\,\mathrm{eV}$, and this will be even more true at the previous times, such as at that of matter-radiation equality, which is when the inhomogeneities of matter start to grow (at redshift $z_{\mathrm{eq}} \simeq 3400$). Hence, the neutrino masses do not affect directly the generation of the primary CMB anisotropies, with the main effect of the neutrinos at this stage being related to the effective number of relativistic degrees of freedom N_{eff} that they contribute to.

Using the CMB observations to determine whether N_{eff} agrees with the standard value of 3.045 could then be of paramount importance to confirm our view of the early universe. Note that the parameter N_{eff} could differ from this value if additional neutrinos were present, such as sterile ones having some mixing with the active ones that could have equilibrated them in the early universe, or also if axions or new types of *dark* radiation contributed at early times. A larger N_{eff} could in particular shift the value of z_{eq} by delaying the time of matter-radiation equality. This would leave less time for the growth of the matter overdensities until recombination, suppressing the amplitudes of the peaks in the Fourier transform of the observed CMB temperature and polarisation two point correlation functions, which are the main quantities that can be measured in CMB observations. Note that given the many parameters present in the standard cosmological model, one may alternatively consider that the value of z_{eq} is kept fixed by increasing also the matter content while shifting instead the Hubble rate H_0, and because of this there is a correlation between these two important parameters. This degeneracy can be partially lifted by including in the analyses the measurements of the power spectrum of the large-scale matter distribution measured with galaxy surveys, which being an observable from the late universe is less affected by geometrical effects.

In particular, the baryon acoustic oscillations (BAO) taking place at decoupling, generated by the pressure of the photons fighting against the contraction of the baryons, leave an imprint at a characteristic scale in the galaxy power spectrum, which is affected if N_{eff} is modified. Since the neutrinos were distributed more uniformly than the photons at decoupling, increasing N_{eff} tends to reduce the BAO peaks and also slightly shifts them. Combining the different measurements of the Planck satellite (CMB temperature and polarization correlations and CMB lensing effects obtained from the non-gaussianities of the CMB anisotropies) with the BAO data gathered mostly from the Baryon Oscillation Spectroscopic Survey (BOSS), the Planck Collaboration obtained the constraint [Ag20]

$$N_{\text{eff}} = 2.99^{+0.34}_{-0.33}, \tag{10.15}$$

in perfect agreement with the expectations from three standard neutrinos.

Although the neutrino masses are not relevant before recombination, they indirectly have an impact on the observed CMB anisotropies through their effects after they become non-relativistic at $z < 188\, m_i/(0.1\,\text{eV})$. In particular, their late contribution to the matter density after they become non-relativistic affects, through their effect on the geometry, the angular distance at which the CMB anisotropies are observed. They can also affect the secondary anisotropies produced after the recombination, such as the late integrated Sachs Wolfe effect due to the changing gravitational potential of the structures traversed by the photons (so that the blue shifts resulting when they fall into a potential well is not completely compensated by the red shift when they exit from it), they can affect the redshift of matter-cosmological constant equality and most importantly they also affect the lensing of the CMB by galactic structures, which tends to smooth out the peaks at small angular scales. The main effect of the neutrinos on the galaxy power spectrum is related to their velocity dispersion, which is much larger than that of the dominant cold dark matter and allows them to free stream away from the small structures. They hence have the effect of suppressing the power on scales of galaxies and clusters. By combining all these observables, most notably the temperature and polarization correlations, the CMB lensing and BAO, the Planck Collaboration obtained the constraint [Ag20]

$$\sum m_i < 0.12\,\text{eV}\ (95\,\%\text{CL}), \tag{10.16}$$

which is actually the most stringent bound on the neutrino masses at present, being just within a factor of two of the minimum allowed value for the sum of the masses.

Analyses using the Planck results together with data from the Lyman-alpha forest power spectrum (instead of from galaxy survey data) obtained also very similar quantitative results [Ye17]. Measurements with improved sensitivities are expected to be able to infer the absolute scale of the neutrino masses in the near future, probably even before their more direct measurement is achieved.

10.3   Big Bang nucleosynthesis and neutrinos

Let us go back in time again to consider the first few minutes after the Big Bang, just after the neutrinos decoupled, the positrons annihilated and therefore, the photons heated up. A very important event in this epoch was the fusion of protons and neutrons which, in the process known as primordial nucleosynthesis, produced ^{4}He, and small proportions of D, ^{3}He and ^{7}Li [Ga46]. It is here that most of the ^{4}He present in the Universe was produced, and the exact amount of He produced was largely influenced by the contribution of the neutrinos to the radiation of the Universe, given the impact they had on the expansion rate.

As mentioned before, at MeV temperatures the neutrons and protons were in beta equilibrium but their interactions became inefficient and freezed-out at $T_{fo} \simeq 0.8\,\mathrm{MeV}$, leaving a neutron to proton relative abundance of

$$\left.\frac{n_n}{n_p}\right|_{fo} \simeq \exp\left(-\frac{m_n - m_p}{T_{fo}}\right) \simeq \frac{1}{5}. \tag{10.17}$$

Subsequent neutron decays led to $n_n/n_p \simeq 1/7$ by the time fusion reactions prevailed over photon dissociation and neutrons got efficiently trapped in nuclei, especially into ^{4}He due to its high binding energy. This happened after the so-called deuterium bottleneck, which corresponds to the fact that it was only when the temperature became smaller than about $0.1\,\mathrm{MeV}$ that the high-energy tail of the photon distribution was no longer able to dissociate the deuterium produced by the combination of neutrons and protons, so that the nuclear fusion could proceed to form heavier elements. Once D was able to survive from the photodisintegrations, it became possible to continue the nucleosynthesis through $D + n \rightarrow T + \gamma$, $T + p \rightarrow {}^4\mathrm{He} + \gamma$, $^3\mathrm{He} + n \rightarrow {}^4\mathrm{He} + \gamma$, $^3\mathrm{He} + D \rightarrow {}^4\mathrm{He} + p$, $^3\mathrm{He} + {}^4\mathrm{He} \rightarrow {}^7\mathrm{Be} + \gamma$ and $^4\mathrm{He} + T \rightarrow {}^7\mathrm{Li} + \gamma$. These were essentially all the reactions taking place, given that there are no stable nuclei with $A = 5$ or 8 which could have bridged the production of heavier elements, and the nucleosynthesis essentially ended at $T \simeq 0.01\,\mathrm{MeV}$.

It is important to emphasize the qualitative differences between the primordial nucleosynthesis and the nucleosynthesis taking place in the main-sequence stars, in which no free neutrons are present. In this last case, the deuterium production proceeds mainly through $p + p \to D + e^+ + \nu_e$, with the associated emission of the pp neutrinos. Also no tritium gets produced and most of the ^{7}Li gets produced by the EC in ^{7}Be from the abundant electrons present in the background. On the other hand, in the primordial universe all nuclei formed are completely ionized, and the relatively dilute medium implies that the electron capture does not take place until much later, only when the Be nuclei start to recombine. Given the larger binding energies of the electrons in Be, this happens at redshift $z \simeq 30000$, before the He recombination at $z \simeq 5000$ and the H recombination at $z \simeq 1100$. In the early universe there was clearly also no analog of the CNO cycle which happens in stars.

Most of the neutrons present when Big Bang nucleosynthesis started ended up into ^{4}He nuclei, so that the associated primordial mass fraction is

$$Y_{\rm p} \equiv \frac{\rho(^4{\rm He})}{\rho_b} \simeq \frac{4n_n/2}{n_p + n_n} = \frac{2(n_n/n_p)}{1 + n_n/n_p} \simeq 0.25. \qquad (10.18)$$

On the other hand, the primordial D and ^{3}He abundances are at the level of few 10^{-5} by number, and the final ^{7}Li/H abundance is at the level of 10^{-10}. All the fusion reactions depend on the density of baryons normalized to that of photons, $\eta_B \equiv (n_n + n_p)/n_\gamma$, and an agreement with the observed primordial element abundances is obtained only in the range $\eta_B \simeq (5.8$–$6.5) \times 10^{-10}$, which is also consistent with the baryon density inferred from fits to the observed CMB anisotropies. Note that a larger baryon density increases the D burning interactions, hence depleting the final D abundance. Also note that in the stars, given their high central densities all the D produced is quickly burned into ^{4}He, and as a consequence essentially all the deuterium in the Universe is of primordial origin.

Regarding the neutrinos, the actual He abundance $Y_{\rm p}$ is quite sensitive to the effective number of degrees of freedom contributing to the radiation at the time of the freezeout of the weak interactions. A larger g_* would imply a faster expansion and hence a higher $T_{\rm fo}$, with a consequently increased value of n_n/n_p and hence a higher $Y_{\rm p}$. This fact was already exploited back in 1977 to obtain the upper bound $N_\nu < 5$ on the number of neutrino families [St77], which was probably the first use of cosmology to constrain the properties of fundamental particles. With much improved measurements of ^{4}He and D abundances, one infers at present that $N_\nu < 3.4$ [Fi19].

The neutrinos that get produced during the primordial nucleosynthesis are those from the decays of neutrons and tritium (which are actually $\bar{\nu}_e$)

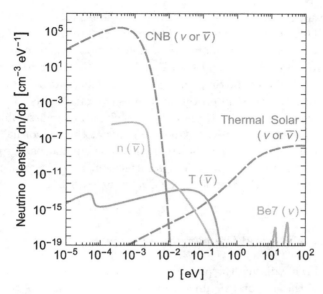

Fig. 10.2 Spectra of the low-energy neutrinos from primordial nucleosynthesis as well as the cosmic neutrino background and those produced in the Sun by thermal processes. Reprinted figure with permission from [Vi20], Copyright 2022 by the American Physical Society.

and the ν_e from the electron capture of ^{7}Be, and by now these neutrinos are distributed in the different mass eigenstates in proportion to $|U_{ei}|^2$. The neutrons have a half-life of about 10 min, and their decays contribute to the antineutrino fluxes between T_{fo} and the end of nucleosynthesis, which happens at redshift of about 10^8, so that at present they have typical energies of about 10^{-8} MeV $\sim$ 10 meV (with those decaying before the deuterium bottleneck giving an enhanced contribution at about 1 meV). The tritium nuclei have a half-life of 12.3 yr, and hence they decay at typical redshifts of few 10^5, and given their endpoint energy of 18.6 keV the present energies of these neutrinos are in the ballpark of 0.1 eV [Iv18]. The EC in ^{7}Be produces two neutrino lines, with energies of 385 keV in the transition to an excited state of ^{7}Li (10% of the time) and one of 826 keV in the transition to the ground state of ^{7}Li (90% of the time). These lines appear broadened due to the large associated period of Be recombination, and at present they are redshifted to energies of few tens of eV [Kh11]. The EC in ^{7}Be produce about 90% of the ^{7}Li of primordial origin, with just the remaining 10% being produced directly as ^{7}Li at the time of nucleosynthesis.

The resulting neutrino spectra from all these processes are shown in Fig. 10.2. This figure also includes the background from the decoupled cosmic neutrinos (CνB) at low momenta as well as the thermal solar neutrinos, which are relevant above about 0.1 eV and, given the values of the temperature in the interior of the Sun, they peak in the keV range. They arise by neutrino pair production in processes such as plasmon decay ($\gamma^* \to \bar{\nu} + \nu$), Compton processes ($\gamma + e \to e + \bar{\nu} + \nu$) or electron bremsstrahlung from nuclei ($A + e \to A + e + \bar{\nu} + \nu$). One can see that the primordial ^{7}Be neutrinos are buried deep under the thermal solar neutrino background, but those from tritium and neutron decays surface out at momenta $p_\nu \sim 10^{-2}$–10^{-1} eV, in between the tail of the CνB and the distribution of those from the Sun.

10.4   Neutrinos and the baryon asymmetry of the Universe

We finally briefly discuss the possible connection between the neutrinos and the origin of the baryon asymmetry of the Universe, which is the fact that the Universe we know is just made of matter, having negligible amounts of antimatter. The present amount of baryons with respect to the CMB photons, as determined by CMB observations [Ag20] (and consistently with BBN predictions), is

$$\eta_B \equiv \frac{n_B}{n_\gamma} = (6.12 \pm 0.04) \times 10^{-10}, \qquad (10.19)$$

while the density of antibaryons is much smaller, $n_{\bar{B}} \ll n_B$, so that also $(n_B - n_{\bar{B}})/n_\gamma \simeq \eta_B$. On the other hand, note that the present leptonic number asymmetry, which is due to the densities of electrons and the asymmetries between neutrinos and antineutrinos, is not known with a similar precision, although it is plausible that its value is of the order of η_B.

Antimatter is usually created together with matter in pair-creation processes, and when the Universe was hotter than 1 GeV the baryons and antibaryons (which were at that stage as quarks and antiquarks) had densities comparable to that of photons. However, at lower temperatures they hadronised and became non-relativistic, their equilibrium densities became Boltzmann suppressed and they annihilated very efficiently to almost completely disappear. The amount of baryons which survived these annihilations was the consequence of a slight imbalance, of about one extra baryon per 10^9 baryon-antibaryon pairs, pre-existing at earlier times. How this tiny baryon excess was generated is what the different theories of baryogenesis try to explain, and a huge amount of work has gone into developing them.

In the mid sixties it was realized by Sakharov [Sa67] that the generation of a baryon-antibaryon asymmetry in a Universe having originally no net baryon excess could be the consequence of particle interactions occurring at early times, and this dynamical generation of an asymmetry should be possible as long as three conditions are satisfied. These Sakharov conditions are:

- The interactions should violate the baryon number B, since otherwise the total baryon number would always remain equal to its initial vanishing value.
- The interactions should violate the C and CP symmetries, under which the baryon number B changes sign, since otherwise opposite asymmetries would be produced in a process and in the C (or CP) conjugate process, such as in the decay of a particle and that of the corresponding antiparticle, leading to no net final baryon number production.
- The baryon number violating interactions have to take place out of equilibrium, since otherwise any asymmetry generated will be immediately erased by the same interactions that produced it acting in the opposite direction.

Although the specific particle model considered originally by Sakharov was quite ad-hoc, after the introduction of the grand-unified theories (GUTs) in the mid seventies these theories became attractive candidates for baryogenesis [Yo78; Di78; We79]. The unified treatment of the quarks and leptons as members of larger multiplets, having interactions connecting them, gave rise to baryon (and lepton) number violation. Also some of the new heavy particles appearing at the GUT scale could naturally decay out of equilibrium when they became non-relativistic in the rapidly expanding early universe. Moreover, the interactions leading to their decay can contain C and CP violating couplings.

As a simple example, the $SU(5)$ GUTs combine the standard Higgs doublet H with a color triplet T into the five dimensional representation $\bar{5}_H$: $\{T, H\}$, and the Yukawa couplings with the fermions in the 10 : $\{Q, u^c, e^c\}$ and $\bar{5}$: $\{d^c, L\}$ representations are $\lambda_{ij} 10_i 10_j 5_H + \lambda'_{ij} 10_i \bar{5}_j \bar{5}_H$, with i and j labeling the generations. This implies that the scalar triplet T, which needs to have a mass at the GUT scale in order to avoid inducing a too rapid proton decay, can decay out of equilibrium through $T \to \bar{q}\bar{q}$ or $T \to q\ell$. The first channel has $B = -2/3$ while the second has $B = 1/3$, so that clearly

B is violated in the T decays. Note that however $B - L$ is not violated in $SU(5)$, and both final states have $B - L = -2/3$. The net baryon asymmetry produced in the decay of a $T \bar{T}$ pair into the different final states f, with baryon number B_f, is

$$\varepsilon = \frac{\sum_f B_f \left[\Gamma(T \to f) - \Gamma(\bar{T} \to \bar{f})\right]}{\Gamma_T}, \tag{10.20}$$

with the total width being just $\Gamma_T = \sum_f \Gamma(T \to f)$. Note that CP will be violated if the branching ratios of T and $\bar{T}$ into specific conjugate channels differ, so that for instance $\Gamma(T \to \bar{q}\bar{q}) \neq \Gamma(\bar{T} \to qq)$. These differences can arise at the one-loop level through the combined effects of the imaginary part of the 1-loop amplitude and the complex phases in the Yukawa couplings, as will be discussed in more detail below for the specific case of the mechanism of baryogenesis through leptogenesis. In order for the asymmetry to be non-vanishing, it turns out however to be necessary to consider an extension of the minimal $SU(5)$ having at least two different (non-degenerate) triplet fields, and hence two different scalar 5-plets, so that the products of the different Yukawa couplings lead to a non-trivial phase. Note that due to CPT the total width of particles and antiparticles coincide, $\Gamma_T = \Gamma_{\bar{T}}$, and this implies that a compensation between the branching ratios into the different final states should be at work, so that for instance $\left[\Gamma(T \to \bar{q}\bar{q}) - \Gamma(\bar{T} \to qq)\right] = -\left[\Gamma(T \to q\ell) - \Gamma(\bar{T} \to \bar{q}\bar{\ell})\right]$, but in any case the asymmetry ε can be non-zero due to the different baryon number associated to each of the final states.

The simplest scenario for the generation of the baryon asymmetry is that the triplet scalars were in equilibrium before becoming non-relativistic, thus having at that time a density similar to the one of photons, and that during their subsequent decays the inverse process that would produce the heavy triplets was largely suppressed, so that they went significantly out of equilibrium. The final asymmetry generated in this case would be

$$\eta_B \simeq \xi \frac{\varepsilon}{g_*}, \tag{10.21}$$

where the factor $g_* \simeq 10^2$ is the effective number of relativistic degrees of freedom which were in equilibrium at the time of the heavy particle decays. This factor takes into account the subsequent dilution of the asymmetry relative to the photons which would take place as these particles annihilated into radiation. The factor $\xi < 1$ takes into account the non-trivial effects of the incomplete departure from equilibrium during the decays, the possible non-complete initial equilibration as well as the eventual washout of the asymmetry by scattering processes, whose detailed computation requires the integration of the associated Boltzmann equations.

If the decaying particles were initially in equilibrium and the washouts processes are not important, so that $\xi \simeq 1$, one finds that to reproduce the observed baryon asymmetry it would be required to have an asymmetry per decay of order $\varepsilon \simeq 10^{-7}$, while this asymmetry would need instead to be much larger if the washouts are important or if the initial equilibration of the heavy particles was not complete.

Detailed investigations of GUT baryogenesis were then performed (see e.g. [Ko80]). It was also understood that baryon and lepton number violation effects can be present in the Standard Model through non-perturbative effects, even if they do not occur at the perturbative level [tH76]. Moreover, in the mid eighties it was actually realized that the non-perturbative processes induced by the non-trivial changes in the topology of the non-abelian $SU(2)_L$ gauge fields associated to the sphaleron configurations [Kl84], were in equilibrium at temperatures larger than the electroweak scale, and hence could strongly impact the baryon number generation [Ku85]. This phenomenon is related to the chiral anomaly affecting the baryon and lepton number currents, $J_B^\mu = \sum_i B_i \bar{\Psi}_i \gamma^\mu \Psi_i$ and similarly for J_L^μ, which implies that

$$\partial_\mu J_B^\mu = \partial_\mu J_L^\mu = n_F \frac{g^2}{32\pi^2} F_{\mu\nu}^a \tilde{F}^{a\mu\nu} + ..., \tag{10.22}$$

with $n_F = 3$ being the number of families, g is the $SU(2)_L$ coupling and $\tilde{F}^{a\mu\nu} = (1/2)\varepsilon^{\mu\nu\rho\sigma} F_{\rho\sigma}^a$ is the dual of the non-abelian $SU(2)_L$ field strength $F_{\mu\nu}^a$, with $a = 1, 2, 3$ (and we omitted the analogous hypercharge contribution for simplicity, since abelian fields do not affect the results).

The sphaleron is the gauge-Higgs configuration connecting two topologically inequivalent vacua of the gauge fields, in which $F_{\mu\nu}^a = 0$ although the gauge fields themselves, A_μ^a, do not vanish and are twisted in a non-trivial way. These transitions between different neighbouring gauge-Higgs vacua also have associated the production of all the fermion doublets of the three generations, hence violating baryon and lepton number [Ka93; Ru96]. To see this, note that the baryon number is

$$B = \int d^3x \, J_B^0, \tag{10.23}$$

and hence one gets

$$\frac{\partial B}{\partial t} = n_F \int d^3x \frac{g^2}{32\pi^2} F_{\mu\nu}^a \tilde{F}^{a\mu\nu}, \tag{10.24}$$

so that the variation of the baryon number over time is

$$B(t) - B(0) = n_F \int_0^t \mathrm{d}t' \int \mathrm{d}^3x \, \frac{g^2}{32\pi^2} F_{\mu\nu}^a \tilde{F}^{a\mu\nu}. \qquad (10.25)$$

The integrand in this equation is actually a total divergence of the form $\partial_\mu K^\mu$, with

$$K^\mu = \frac{g^2}{32\pi^2} \varepsilon^{\mu\nu\rho\sigma} \left(F_{\nu\rho}^a A_\sigma^a - \frac{1}{3} g \varepsilon^{abc} A_\nu^a A_\rho^b A_\sigma^c \right). \qquad (10.26)$$

One will then have that

$$\Delta B = \Delta L = n_F \Delta N_{\mathrm{CS}}, \qquad (10.27)$$

with ΔN_{CS} being the change in the Chern-Simons number

$$N_{\mathrm{CS}} = \int \mathrm{d}^3x \, K^0 = \frac{g^2}{32\pi^2} \int \mathrm{d}^3x \, \varepsilon^{ijk} \left(F_{ij}^a A_k^a - \frac{1}{3} g \varepsilon^{abc} A_i^a A_j^b A_k^c \right). \qquad (10.28)$$

Note that N_{CS} is a gauge dependent quantity, although ΔN_{CS} itself is gauge independent. If a transition between two topologically different vacua takes place, so that in the initial and final states A_μ^a is pure gauge with $F_{\mu\nu}^a = 0$, one finds that in the $A_0^a = 0$ temporal gauge N_{CS} is an integer, labelling the winding number of the gauge field configuration (i.e. how much the pure gauge field is twisted with respect to the trivial configuration $A_\mu^a = 0$). Hence, in a transition between neighbouring vacua with $\Delta N_{\mathrm{CS}} = 1$, the associated change in the baryon and lepton numbers will be $\Delta B = \Delta L = n_F$, corresponding to the creation of the quark and lepton doublets of all n_F generations. Given its origin related to the chiral anomaly, this baryon and lepton number violation is often called *anomalous*.

Note that there is a finite energy barrier between two inequivalent vacua, and at zero temperature a transition between them would require a tunneling process (mediated by an instanton), which has a negligible probability to occur [tH76]. However, at finite temperature it becomes possible to jump over the barrier by means of a sphaleron configuration, what will be unsuppressed at temperatures above the electroweak scale of about 10^2 GeV.

The realization that the B and L violating (but $B - L$ conserving) sphaleron transitions were unsuppressed at high temperatures had some major implications for the theories of baryogenesis. The main consequences were:

- The simplest GUT theories that were based on the $SU(5)$ scenarios, in which $B - L$ is conserved, became no longer viable for baryogenesis, since the baryon number generated at the GUT scale would be later completely erased by the anomalous Standard Model processes.

- GUT models based on $SO(10)$ or larger groups, in which $B - L$ can be violated, can still provide valid scenarios for baryogenesis.
- The presence of sphalerons in equilibrium implies that the final baryon and lepton numbers would be

$$n_B = C\, n_{B-L} \; ; \quad n_L = (C - 1) n_{B-L}, \qquad (10.29)$$

with the value of the constant C depending on the different fast processes (gauge interactions, weak and strong sphalerons as well as Yukawa couplings) that are in equilibrium at high temperatures. In particular, it is found [Ha90] that slightly above the electroweak phase transition

$$C = \frac{24 + 4N_H}{66 + 13N_H}, \qquad (10.30)$$

where the number of Higgs doublets in the Standard Model is just $N_H = 1$, while for instance in the minimal supersymmetric version one has $N_H = 2$. Hence, it becomes necessary to generate a non-vanishing $B - L$ asymmetry in the first place in order to be left with a non-vanishing B asymmetry at the end.

- The Standard Model anomalous B number generation attracted a lot of attention as a source of the baryon asymmetry, in the so-called electroweak baryogenesis scenarios. These could take place at relatively low temperatures when the sphalerons went out of equilibrium at the electroweak phase transition. However, the departure from equilibrium necessary for baryogenesis requires that this transition be first order, something which does not happen in the Standard Model, and also the CP violation arising from the CKM mixing proved to be insufficient. Extensions of the theory had then to be invoked, such as some supersymmetric scenarios with very specific characteristics, which are by now quite constrained (for a recent review see [Bo21]).
- Another very attractive possibility also opened up, which is that of generating initially a lepton number asymmetry that would then be reprocessed and partially converted into a baryon asymmetry by the sphalerons. A way to achieve this is through the out of equilibrium decays of the heavy Majorana neutrinos present in seesaw models, which are naturally present in GUT theories such as $SO(10)$ and allow to provide a simple explanation for the lightness of the known neutrinos. These models became known as *leptogenesis scenarios*, and they indeed provide a very natural possibility to explain the origin of the matter-antimatter asymmetry of the Universe, which is deeply linked with neutrino physics.

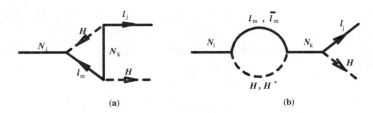

Fig. 10.3   One-loop diagrams contributing to the CP violating asymmetry in the decays of the heavy singlet neutrinos (from ref. [Co96]).

The leptogenesis paradigm was proposed by Fukugita and Yanagida [Fu86] and considers the singlet neutrinos N_i, in principle one per each generation, which have a large Majorana mass M_i and couple through a Yukawa interaction with the left-handed lepton doublets L_j and the Higgs doublet H as

$$-\mathcal{L} \supset \frac{1}{2} M_i \bar{N}_i^c N_i + h_{ji} \varepsilon_{\alpha\beta} \bar{L}_j^\alpha N_i H^\beta + \text{h.c.,} \qquad (10.31)$$

with α and β being $SU(2)$ indices while i and j label the generations. The heavy Majorana neutrinos can decay both into leptons and into anti-leptons, with

$$\Gamma_i = \Gamma(N_i \to LH) + \Gamma(N_i \to \bar{L}\bar{H}) = \frac{(h^\dagger h)_{ii}}{8\pi} M_i. \qquad (10.32)$$

The simplest scenarios assume that the three heavy neutrinos have hierarchical masses, $M_1 \ll M_2 < M_3$ and hence consider that by the time the lightest neutrino N_1 becomes non-relativistic and decays to produce a lepton asymmetry, the other two heavier neutrinos have already decayed and are hence no longer present in the background (see e.g. [Lu92] for some early work).

In order for the heavy neutrinos N_1 to decay out of equilibrium when they become non-relativistic, at $T \sim M_1$, it is necessary that the expansion rate $H \sim \sqrt{G_N \rho}$ be larger than the decay rate Γ_1, and hence that $M_1 > (h^\dagger h)_{11} \times 10^{16}$ GeV, clearly pointing to a GUT origin for the singlet neutrino masses, or eventually to a more intermediate scale if the couplings are small (such as $M_1 > 10^{10}$ GeV for $(h^\dagger h)_{11} \sim 10^{-6}$).

The CP violation which is required to generate a lepton asymmetry in these decays arises from the interference of the tree-level diagram with the one-loop contributions which are shown in Fig. 10.3, and is [Co96]

$$\varepsilon_i \equiv \frac{\Gamma(N_i \to LH) - \Gamma(N_i \to \bar{L}\bar{H})}{\Gamma(N_i \to LH) + \Gamma(N_i \to \bar{L}\bar{H})} = \varepsilon_i^{\text{vertex}} + \varepsilon_i^{\text{wave}}, \qquad (10.33)$$

where the *vertex* part arises from the interference of the tree-level amplitude with the first diagram in the figure while the *wave* part from its interference with the second diagram. One has in particular that

$$\varepsilon_i^{\text{vertex}} = \frac{1}{8\pi} \sum_k f(y_k) \mathcal{I}_{ik}, \tag{10.34}$$

where $y_k \equiv M_k^2/M_i^2$ and $f(x) = \sqrt{x}(1 - (1+x)\ln[(1+x)/x])$, and[2]

$$\mathcal{I}_{ik} = \frac{\text{Im}(h^\dagger h)_{ik}^2}{(h^\dagger h)_{ii}}. \tag{10.35}$$

For the wave-function piece one has

$$\varepsilon_i^{\text{wave}} = -\frac{1}{8\pi} \sum_{k \neq i} \frac{M_i M_k}{M_k^2 - M_i^2} \mathcal{I}_{ik}, \tag{10.36}$$

where we considered that the mass splittings are much larger than the decay widths ($|M_k - M_i| \gg \Gamma_k$). In the hierarchical case, in which $y_k \gg 1$, one finds that the wave-function contribution to ε is twice as large as the vertex contribution, with the total asymmetry from the decay of N_1 being

$$\varepsilon_1 \simeq -\frac{3}{16\pi} \sum_{k \neq 1} \frac{1}{\sqrt{y_k}} \mathcal{I}_{1k}. \tag{10.37}$$

Note that the CP violating asymmetry in N decays appears because there is an imaginary part in the one-loop diagrams (the absorptive part of the integral), which is the same in the decay into a given channel and into the conjugate channel, while the product of Yukawa couplings appearing in both decays are complex conjugated of each other, giving rise to a mismatch between the phases in the direct and conjugate decay channels.

The absorptive part of the loop integral can be obtained by direct computation or, alternatively, using the Cutkosky rule [Cu60], i.e. cutting the loop integral with a vertical line and setting the intermediate particles onshell, which is possible as long as the intermediate particles are lighter than the decaying one. In this case the absorptive part can be considered as resulting from a rescattering of the intermediate particles in the loop. A useful cross check for this is to consider the unitarity relation telling that the transition probability into all final states should be unity, $SS^\dagger = 1$, and writing the scattering matrix as $S = 1 + iT$ in terms of the transition matrix T_{if} between initial state i and final state f. One hence obtains that

$$T_{fi} = T_{if}^* + i \sum_n T_{ni} T_{nf}^*. \tag{10.38}$$

---

[2]Note that in [Co96] the Yukawa coupling was introduced as $\lambda_{ji}\varepsilon_{\alpha\beta}\bar{N}_i L_j^\alpha H^\beta + \text{h.c.}$, being the conjugate of that introduced here, $\lambda = h^*$, so that $(\lambda^\dagger\lambda)_{ij} = (h^\dagger h)_{ji}$.

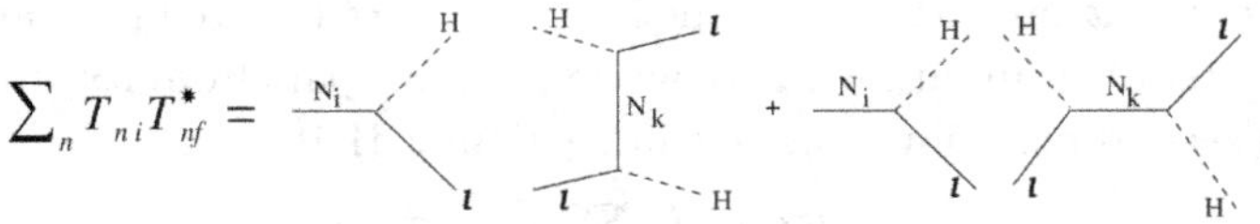

$$\sum_n T_{ni} T_{nf}^* =$$

Fig. 10.4   Unitarity relation and one-loop CP violation.

On the other hand, CPT implies that $T_{fi} = T_{\bar{i}\bar{f}}$, so that

$$\varepsilon \propto |T_{if}|^2 - |T_{\bar{i}\bar{f}}|^2 \simeq -2\,\mathrm{Im}\left[T_{if} \sum_n T_{ni} T_{nf}^*\right]. \qquad (10.39)$$

The above expression is just what is obtained from the interference between the tree-level decay amplitude T_{if} and what results from applying
the Cutkosky rule to obtain the absorptive part of the one-loop diagrams,
which is just the sum over all the possible intermediate states and transition
amplitudes, as is illustrated in Fig. 10.4. Note that the vertex contribution will correspond to the t-channel exchange of the heavy neutrino N_k in
the amplitude $T_{nf} = T(HL \to HL)$, while the wave contribution will be
associated to the s-channel exchange of N_k.

The quantity ε_1 quantifies the leptonic asymmetry produced in the
heavy Majorana neutrino decays, and it will then be partially reprocessed
into a baryonic asymmetry by sphaleron processes, leading in the simplest
scenarios to $\eta_B \simeq -(28/79)\varepsilon_1 \xi/g_*$ (see Eq. (10.30) with $N_H = 1$), and the
washout term ξ is obtained by solving the Boltzmann equations.

The expression for the wave contribution in Eq. (10.36) can get largely
enhanced if the masses of the different heavy neutrinos are close to each
other, and when their mass splittings are of the order of the decay widths
this gives rise to some new type of scenarios, known as *resonant leptogenesis* [Co97; Pi04]. The large enhancements in the decay asymmetries in
this case may allow for instance to achieve a successful generation of the
baryon asymmetry with lighter right-handed neutrinos, and hence at somewhat lower temperatures and even in situations where the washout processes
are strong.

In supersymmetric scenarios there are some additional contributions to
the generation of a lepton asymmetry, such as from the decays of the scalar
superpartners of the heavy singlet neutrinos, and one has to consider that
also the supersymmetric companions of the leptons and Higgs bosons run
in the loops, what leads however to qualitatively similar outcomes [Co96].

There are also possible new kinds of contributions arising from the super-symmetric soft breaking terms, what leads to the so-called *soft-leptogenesis* scenarios [Gr03; DA03; Gi04].

Other effects that could be relevant are those related to the flavor composition of the lepton produced in the N_1 decays. In particular, the leptonic Yukawa couplings which are in equilibrium at the time of these decays could affect the impact of the washout processes (i.e. the L violating scatterings which are active at the time of leptogenesis). This gave rise to the scenarios of *flavoured leptogenesis* [Ba00; Na06; Na06b; Ab06].

Leptogenesis has also been considered in the type II and type III seesaw scenarios involving heavy scalar or fermionic $SU(2)$ triplet fields.

Yet another possibility is the so-called *ARS leptogenesis* [Ak98; Dr18], based on the generation of a lepton number by the CP violating oscillations of relatively light (GeV) sterile neutrinos as they get produced and try to reach equilibrium. This scenario requires that the Yukawa interactions of at least one of the sterile states freeze-in before the electroweak phase transition, so that they don't get fully equilibrated (in contrast to the usual freeze-out of particles that were before in equilibrium). The same Yukawas are responsible for transferring these asymmetries into the lepton doublets, so that they then get partially transferred to the baryons by the sphalerons, but some leptonic asymmetry also survives in the singlets which remained out of equilibrium. The standard leptogenesis and the ARS mechanism may actually be viewed as limiting cases of a broader unified description of the leptogenesis scenarios [Kl21].

The possibilities for generating the baryon asymmetry through the decay of the heavy neutrinos are indeed plenty (see e.g. [Bo21] for a review), and it is quite amazing that the neutrinos may in this way be deeply related to the origin of the baryonic matter which constitutes our observed Universe, including the stars, the planets and even ourselves.

Suggested excercises:

- Assuming that the mass squared differences are perfectly measured and using the bound in Eq. (10.16), derive the limit on the mass of the lightest neutrino, assuming the mass spectrum has normal or inverted orderings.
- Compare the present contribution to the energy density of the photons and of a neutrino with mass $m = 50\,\text{meV}$. What was the value of this ratio at decoupling and when the temperature was $1\,\text{MeV}$?

- Considering that the standard leptogenesis scenario applies, are light neutrinos and antineutrinos expected to be distributed in exactly the same way, or is it likely that they store a leptonic asymmetry? In the second case, discuss whether it is feasible to observe it.
- Prove Eq. (10.39).

Recommended reading:

Neutrino cosmology, J. Lesgourgues et al., Cambridge University Press (2013)

Bibliography

[Aa13]   M.G. Aartsen et al. (IceCube Collaboration), Phys. Rev. Lett. 110 (2013) 151105

[Aa14]   M.G. Aartsen et al. (IceCube Collaboration), Phys. Rev. Lett. 113 (2014) 101101

[Aa16]   M.G. Aartsen et al. (IceCube Collaboration), Astrophys. J. 833 (2016) 3

[Aa17]   A. Aab et al. (Pierre Auger Collaboration), JCAP 04 (2017) 038

[Aa18]   M.G. Aarsten et al. (IceCube Collaboration), Phys. Rev. Lett. 120 (2018) 071801

[Aa18b] M.G. Aartsen et al. (IceCube Collaboration), Phys. Rev. D 98 (2018) 062003

[Aa18c] M.G. Aarsten et al., Science 361 (2018) eaat1378 [arXiv:1807.08816]

[Aa19]   A. Aab et al. (Pierre Auger Collaboration), JCAP 10 (2019) 022

[Aa20]   M.G. Aartsen et al. (IceCube Collaboration), Phys. Rev. Lett. 125 (2020) 121104

[Aa21]   M.G. Aartsen et al. (IceCube Collaboration), Nature 591 (2021) 220

[Aa21b] M.G. Aartsen et al. (IceCube Collaboration), Phys. Rev. D 104 (2021) 022002

[Aa21c] M.G. Aartsen et al. (IceCube Collaboration), J. Phys. G 48 (2021) 060501

[Ab06]   A. Abada et al., JCAP 04 (2006) 004

[Ab09]   J.N. Abdurashitov et al. (SAGE Collaboration), Phys. Rev. C 80 (2009) 015807

[Ab11]   S. Abe et al. (KamLAND Collaboration), Phys. Rev. C 84 (2011) 035804

[Ab13]   K. Abe et al. (Super-Kamiokande Collaboration), Phys. Rev. Lett. 110 (2013) 181802

[Ab16]   A. Abramowski et al. (HESS Collaboration), Nature 531 (2016) 476

[Ab16b] K. Abe et al. (Super-Kamiokande Collaboration), Phys. Rev. D 94 (2016) 052010

[Ab17]   K. Abe et al. (T2K Collaboration), Phys. Rev. Lett. 118 (2017) 151801

[Ab18]   K. Abe et al. (T2K Collaboration), Phys. Rev. Lett. 121 (2018) 171802

[Ab20]   R. Abbasi et al. (IceCube Collaboration), arXiv:2011.03561 (2020)

[Ab21]   R. Abbasi et al. (IceCube Collaboration), Phys. Rev. D 104 (2021) 022002

[Ab21b] R. Abbasi et al. (IceCube Collaboration), Phys. Rev. D 104 (2021) 022001

[Ab21c] R. Abbasi et al. (IceCube Collaboration), Astrophys. J. 928 (2022) 50

[Ac65]   C.V. Achar et al., Phys. Lett. 18 (1965) 196

[Ac19]   M.A. Acero et al. (NOνA Collaboration), *First measurement of neutrino oscillation parameters using neutrinos and antineutrinos by NOνA*, Phys. Rev. Lett. 123 (2019) 151803

[Ad11]   E.G. Adelberger et al., Rev. Mod. Phys. 83 (2011) 195

[Ad13]   P. Adamson et al. (MINOS Collaboration), Phys. Rev. Lett. 110 (2013) 251801

[Ad14]   P. Adamson et al. (MINOS Collaboration), Phys. Rev. Lett. 112 (2014) 191801

[Ag18]   M. Agostini et al. (Borexino Collaboration), Nature 562 (2018) 505

[Ag18b] N. Agafonova et al., Phys. Rev. Lett. 120 (2018) 211801

[Ag20]   N. Aghanim et al. (Planck Collaboration), Astrom. & Astrophys. 641 (2020) A6

[Ag20b] M. Agostini et al. (Borexino Collaboration), *Comprehensive geoneutrino analysis with Borexino*, Phys. Rev. D 101 (2020) 012009

[Ag20c] M. Agostini et al. (GERDA Collaboration), Phys. Rev. Lett. 125 (2020) 252502

[Ag20d] M. Agostini et al. (Borexino Collaboration), Nature 587 (2020) 577

[Ag20e] M. Agostini et al. (P-ONE Collaboration), Nature Astron. 4 (2020) 913

[Ag20f] M. Agostini et al. (Borexino Collaboration), The European Phys. J. C 80 (2020) 1091

[Ah06]   M.H. Ahn et al. (K2K Collaboration), Phys. Rev. D 74 (2006) 072003

[Ah12]   J.K. Ahn et al. (RENO Collaboration), Phys. Rev. Lett. 108 (2012) 191802

[Ah13]   B. Aharmim et al. (SNO Collaboration), Phys. Rev. C 88 (2013) 025501

[Ah18]   M. Ahlers and F. Halzen, Prog. Part. Nucl. Phys. 102 (2018) 73

[Ak98]   E.K. Akhmedov, V. A. Rubakov and A.Yu. Smirnov, Phys. Rev. Lett. 81 (1998) 1359

[Ak99]   E.K. Akhmedov, Nucl. Phys. B 538 (1999) 25

[Ak07]   E.K. Akhmedov, M. Maltoni and A.Yu. Smirnov, JHEP 05 (2007) 077

[Ak17]   D. Akimov et al. (COHERENT Collaboration), Science 357 (2017) 1123

[Ak19]   E. Akhmedov, arXiv:1901.05232

[Ak21]   D. Akimov et al. (COHERENT Collaboration), Phys. Rev. Lett. 126 (2021) 012002

[Ak22]   M. Aker et al. (KATRIN Collaboration), Nature Physics 18 (2022) 160

[Al88]   E.N. Alexeyev, L.N. Alexeyeva, I.V. Krivosheina and V.I. Volchenko (Baksan Collaboration), Phys. Lett. B 205 (1988) 209

[Al05]   M. Altmann et al. (GNO Collaboration), Phys. Lett. B 616 (2005) 174

[Al11]   R. Aloisio, V. Berezinsky and A. Gazizov, Astropart. Phys. 34 (2011) 620

[Al17]   A. Albert et al. (ANTARES and IceCube and Pierre Auger and LIGO

        Scientific and Virgo Collaborations), Astrophys. J. Lett. 850 (2017) L35

[Al20]   J. Alvarez-Muñiz et al. (GRAND Collaboration), Sci. China Phys. Mech. Astron. 63 (2020) 219501

[An04] P. Antonioli et al., New J. Phys. 6 (2004) 114

[An12] F.P. An et al. (Daya Bay Collaboration), Phys. Rev. Lett. 108 (2012) 171803

[An19] G. Anton et al. (EXO-200 Collaboration), Phys. Rev. Lett. 123 (2019) 161802

[Ap22] A. Apponi et al. (PTOLEMY Collaboration), arXiv:2203.11228

[Ar05] T. Araki et al. (KamLAND Collaboration), Nature 436 (2005) 499

[Ar05b] T. Araki et al. (KamLAND Collaboration), Phys. Rev. Lett. 94 (2005) 081801

[As62] G.A. Askaryan, JETP 14 (1962) 441

[As09] M. Asplund, N. Grevesse, A.J. Sauval and P. Scott, Annu. Rev. Astron. & Astroph. 47 (2009) 481

[At00] H. Athar, M. Jezabek and O. Yasuda, Phys. Rev. D 62 (2000) 103007

[Ba82] J.N. Bahcall et al., Rev. Mod. Phys. 54 (1982) 767

[Ba00] R. Barbieri, P. Creminelli, A. Strumia and N. Tetradis, Nucl. Phys. B 575 (2000) 61

[Ba02] J.N. Bahcall, Phys. Rev. C 65 (2002) 025801

[Ba04] G.D. Barr et al., Phys. Rev. D 70 (2004) 02300

[Ba05] J.N. Bahcall, A. M. Serenelli and S. Basu, Astrophys. J. 621 (2005) L85

[Be34] H. Bethe and R. Peierls, Nature 133 (1934) 532

[Be69] V. Berezinsky and G. Zatsepin, Phys. Lett. 28B (1969) 423

[Be85] H.A. Bethe and J.R. Wilson, Astrophys. J. 295 (1985) 14

[Be93] V.S. Berezinsky, T.K. Gaisser, F. Halzen and T. Stanev, Astropart. Phys. 1 (1993) 281

[Be04] J.F. Beacom and M.R. Vagins, Phys. Rev. Lett. 93 (2004) 171101

[Be10] G. Bellini et al. (Borexino Collaboration), Phys. Lett. B 687 (2010) 299

[Be19] M.G. Betti et al. (PTOLEMY Collaboration), JCAP 07 (2019) 047

[Be22] G. Bellini et al., Riv. Nuovo Cimento 45 (2022) 1

[Bh15] A. Bhattacharya et al., JHEP 06 (2015) 110

[Bh16] A. Bhattacharya et al., JHEP 11 (2016) 167

[Bi87] R.M. Bionta et al. (IMB Collaboration), Phys. Rev. Lett. 58 (1987) 1494

[Bo21] D. Bödeker and W. Buchmüller, Rev. Mod. Phys. 93 (2021) 3

[Ca64] N. Cabibbo, Phys. Rev. Lett. 10 (1963) 531

[Ca03] J. Candia and E. Roulet, JCAP 09 (2003) 005

[Ca04] F. Cavanna, M.L. Costantini, O. Palamara and F. Vissani, Surveys High Energ. Phys. 19 (2004) 35

[Ca05] J. Candia, JCAP 11 (2005) 002

[Ca21] Z. Cao et al. (LHAASO Collaboration), Nature 594 (2021) 33

[Ce17] S. Celli, A. Palladino and F. Vissani, Eur. Phys. J. C 77 (2017) 66

[Ch35] S. Chandrasekhar, MNRAS 95 (1935) 207

[Ch85] H.H. Chen, Phys. Rev. Lett. 55 (1985) 1534

[Ch93] J. Christensen-Dalsgaard, C.R. Proffitt and M.J. Thompson, Astrophys. J. Lett. 403 (1993) L75

[Ch21]   J. Christensen-Dalsgaard, Living Reviews in Solar Physics 18 (2021) 2

[Cl98]   B.T. Cleveland et al., Astrophys. J. 496 (1998) 505

[Co47]   M. Conversi, E. Pancini and O. Piccioni, Phys. Rev. 71 (1947) 209

[Co56]   C.L. Cowan et al., Science 124 (1956) 103

[Co96]   L. Covi, E. Roulet and F. Vissani, Phys. Lett. B 384 (1996) 169

[Co97]   L. Covi and E. Roulet, Phys. Lett. B 399 (1997) 113

[Co07]   A.G. Cocco, G. Mangano and M. Messina, JCAP 06 (2007) 015

[Cu60]   R.E. Cutkosky, J. Math. Phys. 1 (1960) 429

[Da55]   R. Davis, Phys. Rev. 97 (1955) 766

[Da62]   G. Danby et al., Phys. Rev. Lett. 9 (1962) 36

[DA03]   G. D'Ambrosio, G.F. Giudice and M. Raidal, Phys. Lett. B 575 (2003) 75

[Di78]   S. Dimopoulos and L. Susskind, Phys. Rev. D 18 (1978) 4500

[Di00]   A.S. Dighe and A.Yu. Smirnov, Phys. Rev. D 62 (2000) 033007

[Do92]   A.D. Dolgov and M. Fukugita, Phys. Rev. D 46 (1992) 5378

[Dr18]   M. Drewes et al., Int. J. Mod. Phys. A 33 (2018) 1842002

[Du10]   H. Duan, G.M. Fuller and Y-Z. Qian, Ann. Review of Nucl. and Part. Science 60 (2010) 569

[Dy12]   S.T. Dye, Reviews of Geophysics 50 (2012) RG3007

[Dz81]   A.M. Dziewonski and D.L. Anderson, Phys. Earth Plan. Int. 25 (1981) 297

[En08]   R. Enberg, M.H. Reno and I. Sarcevic, Phys. Rev. D 78 (2008) 043005

[Es20]   I. Esteban, M.C. Gonzalez-García, M. Maltoni, T. Schwetz and A. Zhou, JHEP 20 (2020) 178

[Ev13]   J.J. Evans, Advances in High Energy Physics (2013) 182537

[Fa08]   Y. Farzan and A.Yu. Smirnov, Nucl. Phys. B 805 (2008) 356

[Fe34]   E. Fermi, Z. Phys. 88 (1934) 161

[Fe58]   R. Feynman and M. Gell-Mann, Phys. Rev. 109 (1958) 193

[Fe58b] G. Feinberg, Phys. Rev. 110 (1958) 1482

[Fe19]   A. Fedynitch et al., *Hadronic interaction model Sibyll 2.3c and inclusive lepton fluxes*, Phys. Rev. D 100 (2019) 103018

[Fi07]   G. Fiorentini, M. Lissia and F. Mantovani, Phys. Reports 453 (2007) 117

[Fi19]   B.D. Fields, P. Molaro and S. Sarkar, Particle Data Group (2019)

[Fo95]   G.L. Fogli, E. Lisi and G. Scioscia, Phys. Rev. D 52 (1995) 5334

[Fo12]   J.A. Formaggio and G.P. Zeller, Rev. Mod. Phys. 84 (2012) 1307

[Fr57]   J.I. Friedman and V.L. Telegdi, Phys. Rev. 105 (1957) 1681

[Fr77]   D.Z. Freedman, D.N. Schramm and D.L. Tubbs, Annu. Rev. Nucl. Sci. 27 (1977) 167

[Fu39]   W.H. Furry, Phys. Rev. 56 (1939) 1184

[Fu86]   M. Fukugita and T. Yanagida, Phys. Lett. B174 (1986) 45

[Fu96]   Y. Fukuda et al. (Kamiokande II Collaboration), Phys. Rev. Lett. 77 (1996) 1683

[Fu98]   Y. Fukuda et al. (Super-Kamiokande Collaboration), Phys. Rev. Lett. 81 (1998) 1562

[Fu99]   T. Futagami et al. (Super-Kamiokande Collaboration), Phys. Rev. Lett.

82 (1999) 5194

[Ga36] G. Gamow and E. Teller, Phys. Rev. 49 (1936) 895

[Ga46] G. Gamow, Phys. Rev. 70 (1946) 572

[Ga57] R.L. Garwin, L.M. Lederman and M. Weinrich, Phys. Rev. 105 (1957) 1415

[Ga98] R. Gandhi, Ch. Quigg, M.H. Reno and I. Sarcevic, Phys. Rev. D 58 (1998) 093009

[Ga02] T.K. Gaisser and M. Honda, Ann. Rev. Nucl. Part. Sci. 52 (2002) 153

[Ga13] A. Gando et al. (KamLAND Collaboration), Phys. Rev. D 88 (2013) 033001

[Ga15] M.V. Garzelli, S. Moch and G. Sigl, JHEP 10 (2015) 1

[Ga16] A. Gando et al. (KamLAND-Zen Collaboration), Phys. Rev. Lett. 117 (2016) 082503

[Ga16b] R. Gauld et al., JHEP 02 (2016) 130

[Ge79] M. Gell-Mann, P. Ramond and R. Slansky, in *Supergravity*, Ed. F. van Nieuwenhuizen and D. Freedman (1979), p. 135

[Gi64] V.L. Ginzburg and S.I. Syrovatskii, *The Origin of Cosmic Rays*, New York: Macmillan (1964)

[Gi04] G.F. Giudice, A. Notari, M. Raidal, A. Riotto and A. Strumia, Nucl. Phys. B 685 (2004) 89

[Gl60] S.L. Glashow, Phys. Rev. 118 (1960) 316

[Gl61] S.L. Glashow, Nucl. Phys. 22 (1961) 579

[Go35] M. Goeppert-Mayer, Phys. Rev. 48 (1935) 512

[Go58] M. Goldhaber, L. Grodzins and A.W. Sunyar, Phys. Rev. 109 (1958) 1015

[Gr69] V. Gribov and B. Pontecorvo, Phys. Lett. B 28 (1969) 493

[Gr98] N. Grevesse and A.J. Sauval, Space Science Reviews 85 (1998) 161

[Gr03] Y. Grossman, T. Kashti, Y. Nir and E. Roulet, Phys. Rev. Lett. 91 (2003) 251801

[Ha73] F.J. Hasert et al. (Gargamelle Collaboration), Phys. Lett. 46B (1973) 38

[Ha86] W.C. Haxton, Phys. Rev. Lett. 57 (1986) 1271

[Ha90] J.A. Harvey and M.S. Turner, Phys. Rev. D 42 (1990) 3344

[Ha99] W. Hampel et al. (GALLEX Collaboration), Phys. Lett. B 447 (1999) 127

[Ha09] F. Halzen and G.G. Raffelt, Phys. Rev. D 80 (2009) 087301

[Ha17] F. Halzen, A. Kheirandish and V. Niro, Astropart. Phys. 86 (2017) 46

[Hi88] K.S. Hirata et al. (Kamiokande-II Collaboration), Phys. Rev. D 38 (1988) 448

[Ho07] M. Honda et al., Phys. Rev. D 75 (2007) 04300

[Ho09] S. Horiuchi, J.F. Beacom and E. Dwek, Phys. Rev. D 79 (2009) 083013

[Iv18] A.V. Ivanchik and V.Yu. Yurchenko, Phys. Rev. D 98 (2018) 081301

[Ja01] H.T. Janka, Astron. Astrophys. 368 (2001) 527

[Ja16] H.T. Janka, T. Melson and A. Summa, Ann. Rev. Nucl. Part. Sci. 66 (2016) 341

[Ju96] G. Jungman, M. Kamionkowski and K. Griest, Phys. Rept. 267 (1996) 195

[Ka81]   B. Kayser, Phys. Rev. D 24 (1981) 110
[Ka93]   A.G. Cohen, D.B. Kaplan and A.E. Nelson, Annu. Rev. Nucl. Part. Sci.
         43 (1993) 27
[Ka05]   T. Kashti and E. Waxman, Phys. Rev. Lett. 95 (2005) 181101
[Ka14]   E. Kafexhiu, F. Aharonian, A. Taylor and G.S. Vila, Phys. Rev. D 90
         (2014) 123014
[Ke03]   M.T. Keil, G.G. Raffelt and H.T. Janka, Astrophys. J. 590 (2003) 971
[Ke06]   S.R. Kelner, F.A. Aharonian and V.V. Bugayov, Phys. Rev. D 74 (2006)
         034018
[Ke08]   S.R. Kelner and F.A. Aharonian, Phys. Rev. D 78 (2008) 034013
[Ke16]   J. Kersten and A.Yu. Smirnov, Eur. Phys. J. C 76 (2016) 339
[Kh11]   R. Khatri and R.A. Sunyaev, Astronomy Lett. 37 (2011) 367
[Ki96]   K. Kiers, S. Nussinov and N. Weiss, Phys. Rev. D 53 (1996) 537
[Kl84]   F.R. Klinkhamer and N.S. Manton, Phys. Rev. D 30 (1984) 2212
[Kl21]   J. Klarić, M. Shaposhnikov and I. Timiryasov, Phys. Rev. Lett. 127
         (2021) 111802
[Ko80]   E.W. Kolb and S. Wolfram, Nucl. Phys. B 172 (1980) 224
[Ko08]   K. Kodama et al. (DONUT Collaboration), Phys. Rev. D 78 (2008)
         052002
[Kr84]   L.M. Krauss, S.L. Glashow and D.N. Schramm, Nature 310 (1984) 191
[Ku66]   V.A. Kuzmin, Sov. Phys. JETP 22 (1966) 1051
[Ku85]   V.A. Kuzmin, V.A. Rubakov and M.E. Shaposhnikov, Phys. Lett. B 155
         (1985) 36
[Ku86]   T.K. Kuo and J. Pantaleone, Phys. Rev. Lett. 57 (1986) 1805
[Kw99]   J. Kwiecinski, A.D. Martin and A.M. Stasto, Phys. Rev. D 59 (1999)
         093002
[La57]   L.D. Landau, Nucl. Phys. 3 (1957) 127
[La96]   K. Langanke, P. Vogel and E. Kolbe, Phys. Rev. Lett. 76 (1996) 2629
[La01]   J.M. Lattimer and M. Prakash, Astrophys. J. 550 (2001) 426
[Le56]   T.D. Lee and C.N. Yang, Phys. Rev. 104 (1956) 254
[Le57]   T.D. Lee and C.N. Yang, Phys. Rev. 105 (1957) 1671
[Le60]   T.D. Lee and C.N. Yang, Phys. Rev. Lett. 4 (1960) 307
[Le95]   J.G. Learned and S. Pakvasa, Astropart. Phys. 3 (1995) 267
[Le19]   J. Lesgourges and L. Verde, Neutrinos in Cosmology, Particle Data
         Group 2019
[Li93]   P. Lipari, Astropart. Phys. 1 (1993) 195
[Lo02]   T.J. Loredo and D.Q. Lamb, Phys. Rev. D 65 (2002) 063002
[Lo14]   A.J. Long, C. Lunardini and E. Sabancilar, JCAP 1408 (2014) 038
[Lu92]   M.A. Luty, Phys. Rev. D 45 (1992) 455
[Lu01]   C. Lunardini and A.Yu. Smirnov, Nucl. Phys. B 616 (2001) 307
[Lu14]   C. Lujan-Peschard, G. Pagliaroli and F. Vissani, JCAP 07 (2014) 051
[Ma37]   E. Majorana, Nuovo Cimento 14 (1937) 170
[Ma62]   Z. Maki, M. Nakagawa and S. Sakata, Prog. Theoret. Phys. 28 (1962)
         870
[Ma19]   C. Mascaretti and F. Vissani, JCAP 08 (2019) 004
[Me17]   P. Mészáros, Ann. Rev. Nucl. Part. Sci. 67 (2017) 45

[Mi77]   P. Minkowski, Phys. Lett. B 67 (1977) 421

[Mi85]   S.P. Mikheyev and A.Yu. Smirnov, Sov. J. Nucl. Phys. 42 (1985) 913

[Mi16]   A. Mirizzi et al., *Supernova Neutrinos: Production, Oscillations and Detection*, Riv. Nuovo Cim. 39 (2016) 1

[Mo80]   R.N. Mohapatra and G. Senjanović, Phys. Rev. Lett. 44 (1980) 912

[Mo06]   I.V. Moskalenko, T.A. Porter and A.W. Strong, Astrophys. J. 640 (2006) L155

[Mo18]   S. Mollerach and E. Roulet, Prog. Part. Nucl. Phys. 98 (2018) 85

[Mo19]   S. Mollerach and E. Roulet, JCAP 03 (2019) 017

[Mu00]   A. Mücke, R. Engel, J.P. Rachen, R.J. Protheroe and T. Stanev, Comput. Phys. Commun. 124 (2000) 290

[Mu13]   K. Murase, M. Ahlers and B.C. Lacki, Phys. Rev. D 88 (2013) 121301

[Na78]   D.K. Nadyozhin, Astrophys. Space Sci. 53 (1978) 131

[Na06]   E. Nardi, Y. Nir, J. Racker and E. Roulet, JHEP 01 (2006) 068

[Na06b] E. Nardi, Y. Nir, E. Roulet and J. Racker, JHEP 01 (2006) 164

[Ne37]   S.H. Neddermeyer and C.D. Anderson, Phys. Rev. 51 (1937) 884

[Nu76]   S. Nussinov, Phys. Lett. B 63 (1976) 201

[Od04]   A. Odrzywolek, M. Misiaszek and M. Kutschera, Acta Physica Polonica B 35 (2004) 1981

[Od11]   A. Odrzywolek and T. Plewa, Astron. & Astrophys. 529 (2011) A156

[Or21]   G.D. Orebi Gann, K. Zuber, D. Bemmerer and A. Serenelli, Annu. Rev. Nucl. Part. Sci. 71 (2021) 1

[Pa86]   S.J. Parke, Phys. Rev. Lett. 57 (1986) 1275

[Pa09]   G. Pagliaroli, F. Vissani, M.L. Costantini and A. Ianni, Astropart. Phys. 31 (2009) 163

[Pa09b] G. Pagliaroli, F. Vissani, E. Coccia and W. Fulgione, Phys. Rev. Lett. 103 (2009) 031102

[Pa10]   G. Pagliaroli, F. Rossi-Torres and F. Vissani, Astropart. Phys. 33 (2010) 287

[Pa15]   A. Palladino and F. Vissani, Eur. Phys. J. C 75 (2015) 433

[Pa17]   K.M. Patton, C. Lunardini and R.J. Farmer, Astrophys. J. 840 (2017) 2

[PDG]   P.A. Zyla et al. (Particle Data Group), Prog. Theor. Exp. Phys. (2020) 083C01

[Pe77]   M.L. Perl et al., Phys. Lett. 70B (1977) 487

[Pe88]   S.T. Petcov, Phys. Lett. B 214 (1988) 139

[Pi04]   A. Pilaftsis and T.E.J. Underwood, Nucl. Phys. B 692 (2004) 303

[Po46]   B. Pontecorvo, National Research Council of Canada Report No. P.D.-205 (1946)

[Po47]   B. Pontecorvo, Phys. Rev. 72 (1947) 246

[Po57]   B. Pontecorvo, Sov. Phys. JETP 6 (1957) 429; ibidem 7 (1958) 172

[Po68]   B. Pontecorvo, Sov. Phys. JETP 26 (1968) 984

[Pr96]   R.J. Protheroe and P.A. Johnson, Astropart. Phys. 4 (1996) 253

[Ra98]   J.P. Rachen and P. Mészáros, Phys. Rev. D 58 (1998) 123005

[Re59]   F. Reines and C.L. Cowan, Phys. Rev. 113 (1959) 273

[Re65]   F. Reines et al., Phys. Rev. Lett. 15 (1965) 429

[Ri04]   A. Ringwald and Y.Y.Y. Wong, JCAP 12 (2004) 005

[Ro93]   E. Roulet, Phys. Rev. D 47 (1993) 5247
[Ro14]   E. Roulet, G. Sigl, A. van Vliet and S. Mollerach, JCAP 01 (2013) 028
[Ro18]   E. Roulet and F. Vissani, JCAP 10 (2018) 049
[Ro21]   K. Rozwadowska, F. Vissani and E. Cappellaro, New Astron. 83 (2021)
         101498
[Ro21b] E. Roulet and F. Vissani, JCAP 03 (2021) 050
[Ro21c] E. Roulet, JCAP 08 (2021) 009
[Ru96]   V.A. Rubakov and M.E. Shaposhnikov, Phys. Usp. 39 (1996) 461
[Sa57]   A. Salam, Nuovo Cimento 5 (1957) 299
[Sa67]   A.D. Sakharov, JETP Lett. 5 (1967) 24
[Sa68]   A. Salam, Proc. Eighth Nobel Symposium, Ed. N. Svartholm (1968) 367
[Sa16]   P.F. de Salas and S. Pastor, JCAP 07 (2016) 051
[Se16]   A. Serenelli, The European Phys. J. A 52 (2016) 78
[Sm19]   O. Smirnov, Progress in Particle and Nuclear Physics 109 (2019) 103712
[St49]   J. Steinberger, Phys. Rev. 75 (1949) 1136
[St77]   G. Steigman, D.N. Schramm and J.E. Gunn, Phys. Lett. B 66 (1977)
         202
[St79]   F.W. Stecker, Astrophys. J. 228 (1979) 919
[St03]   A. Strumia and F. Vissani, Phys. Lett. B 564 (2003) 42
[Su58]   E. Sudarshan and R. Marshak, Phys. Rev. 109 (1958) 1860
[tH72]   G. 't Hooft and M. Veltman, Nucl. Phys. B 44 (1972) 189
[tH76]   G. t Hooft, Phys. Rev. Lett. 37 (1976) 8
[Ti49]   S. Tiomno and J.A. Wheeler, Rev. Mod. Phys. 21 (1949) 153
[To03]   R. Tomas, D. Semikoz, G.G. Raffelt, M. Kachelriess and A.S. Dighe,
         Phys. Rev. D 68 (2003) 093013
[Tu11]   S. Turck-Chièze and S. Couvidat, Rep. Prog. Phys. 74 (2011) 086901
[Ve16]   S. Vernetto and P. Lipari, Phys. Rev. D 94 (2016) 063009
[Ve21]   D. Vescovi et al., J. Phys. G: Nucl. Part. Phys. 48 (2021) 015201
[Vi99]   F. Vissani, JHEP 06 (1999) 022
[Vi08]   F.L. Villante and F. Vissani, Phys. Rev. D 78 (2008) 103007
[Vi11]   F. Vissani, F. Aharonian and N. Sahakyan, Astropart. Phys. 34 (2011)
         778
[Vi15]   F.L. Villante, Phys. Lett. B 742 (2015) 279
[Vi15b] F. Vissani, J. Phys. G 42 (2015) 013001
[Vi17]   N. Vinyoles et al., Astrophys. J. 835 (2017) 202
[Vi20]   E. Vitagliano, I. Tamborra and G.G. Raffelt, Rev. Mod. Phys. 92 (2020)
         45006
[Vo80]   L.V. Volkova, Sov. J. Nucl. Phys. 31 (1980) 784
[Vo99]   P. Vogel and J.F. Beacom, Phys. Rev. D 60 (1999) 053003
[Wa99]   E. Waxman and J. Bahcall, Phys. Rev. D 59 (1999) 023002
[Wa00]   E. Waxman and J. Bahcall, Astrophys. J. 541 (2000) 707
[Wa01]   E. Waxman and J. Bahcall, Phys. Rev. D 64 (2001) 023002
[Wa15]   M. Wallraff and C. Wiebusch, Comput. Phys. Commun. 197 (2015) 185
[We62]   S. Weinberg, Phys. Rev. 128 (1962) 1457
[We67]   S. Weinberg, Phys. Rev. Lett. 19 (1967) 1264
[We79]   S. Weinberg, Phys. Rev. Lett. 42 (1979) 850

[We84] T. Weiler, Astrophys. J. 285 (1984) 495
[Wo78] L. Wolfenstein, Phys. Rev. D 17 (1978) 2369
[Wr17] W.P. Wright et al., Phys. Rev. D 95 (2017) 043006
[Wu57] C.S. Wu et al., Phys. Rev. 105 (1957) 1413
[Ya79] T. Yanagida, Proc. of the *Workshop on unified theory and baryon number in the universe*, KEK, Japan (1979)
[Ya16] R. Yang, F. Aharonian and C. Evoli, Phys. Rev. D 93 (2016) 123007
[Ye17] Ch. Yèche, N. Palanque-Delabrouille, J. Baur and H. du Mas des Bourboux, JCAP 06 (2017) 047
[Yo78] M. Yoshimura, Phys. Rev. Lett. 41 (1978) 281
[Yu35] H. Yukawa, Proc. Phys. Math. Soc. Japan 17 (1935) 48
[Ze80] A. Zee, Phys. Lett. B 93 (1980) 389

CPSIA information can be obtained
at www.ICGtesting.com
Printed in the USA
JSHW030837071022
31042JS00005B/38

9 789811 260933